£6

THE DIRECTORY OF
British Engine Sheds
and Principal Locomotive Servicing Points: 2
North Midlands, Northern England, and Scotland
Roger Griffiths & Paul Smith

The date of opening of the 6TS shed at **Dundee Tay Bridge** (NO3929.3/1A) is, as yet, unclear. The design and size indicate a a building dating from the 1890-1910 era, but as it seems that the predecessor at Dundee East (NO4130.1/1A) may have been closed around 1885, there could have been an intermediate shed that has yet to be discovered. Whatever, this magnificent shot from the 1930s clearly portrays the importance of Tay Bridge depot, which was, at the end, famous for housing the last of the East Coast Pacifics, the surviving Class A2s - paradoxically, considering the supposed unpopularity of such engines. Tay Bridge shed was closed in May 1967.   *Authors' Collection*

OPC

Oxford Publishing Co

CONTENTS

This book is dedicated to
Sally Louise Prescott
beloved daughter of Shirley

Artwork and Design by **Paul Smith**

All shed maps reproduced by kind permission
of
The Syndics of Cambridge University

This picture taken from the top of the coaling tower in July 1937 clearly demonstrates the amount of space required even for a medium-sized engine shed. **Annesley** (SK5252.1/1A) was a 6TS example of the MS&LR's "London Extension" design dating from 1898.

The original coaling stage stands at the centre, with wagons of coal parked ready to be elevated to the top of the then new coaling tower. The open top water tank has received the benefit of softening apparatus, whilst, in the distance, the northlight pattern roof shed is hosting a number of engines and a steam railcar - see also the "Goliath" sheer-legs, another common provision by the MS&LR.

Annesley gained prominence in the last years of the GC main line, even housing displaced "Royal Scot" 4-6-0 locomotives for the semi-fast trains from Nottingham to London. The depot closed in 1966. *W Potter*

First published 2000

ISBN 0 86093 548 5

Published by Oxford Publishing Co

an imprint of Ian Allan Publishing Ltd, Terminal House, Shepperton, Surrey TW17 8AS.

Printed by Ian Allan Printing Ltd, Riverdene Business Park, Hersham, Surrey KT12 4RG.

Code: 0008/A

THE DIRECTORY OF
BRITISH ENGINE SHEDS
AND PRINCIPAL LOCOMOTIVE SERVICING POINTS

VOLUME TWO
PREFACE

1825

1968

Volume 2 of the *Directory of British Engine Sheds* "completes" our survey of steam engine sheds and principal stabling points by continuing from where Volume I left off, and covering the remaining Midlands area, up through the North of England and all of Scotland. Previous authors have provided shed *aficionados* with in-depth surveys of the depots of most of the large railway companies, but in the north of the area covered by this volume two have still to be so treated - the North British and Great North of Scotland Railways. One result of this is that there are many previously unpublished photographs upon which we may draw and it is our pleasure to present some of the best, or rarest, in this publication.

The use of inverted commas for the word "complete" above implies that we are not so foolish as to assume that we have produced a work that may be considered definitive! Whilst both volumes of the directory were being prepared any misplaced thoughts that we may have had about creating a comprehensive list - the result of much research over many years - were frequently dispelled as additional sheds and stabling points were incessantly uncovered, right up to publication.

So, close to "complete" perhaps? Maybe, but our experience thus far leads us to believe that a fair number of sites remain to be revealed and it is to this end that we have left a section of this book for the owner to enter what will no doubt be additional information, as it is uncovered. As those who purchased Volume I of the directory will know, *Ian Allan* will assist this exercise by producing periodic updates to our listings through the pages of *Railway World* magazine. Again, experience has shown that we shall learn much that is new from post-publication contacts with readers, whose help we actively now seek and welcome. Please write with your comments and any corrections to the publisher and we shall answer everyone as quickly and as comprehensively as possible.

A list of acknowledgements for the help and advice so unstintingly given by so many, over so many years, would fill a volume by itself, so whilst we will try to mention the most prominent of our supporters and mentors, we can only profusely apologise should we inadvertently miss out someone's name.

First, and deserving of special comment, is Shirley Smith, for her efforts in assisting our re-

search into the Ordnance Survey and for the establishment of geographic co-ordinates for each site. Then comes Jane Griffiths whose contribution came through being so tolerant and supportive over such a long time. Next, for being a publisher willing to take on a *magnum opus* such as this, we must thank Peter Waller of *Ian Allan* who, through *OPC*, has allowed us to bring our work to a wider audience. Lastly, we are indebted to Tony Rawlings and his colleagues in the Map Room at Cambridge University Library, for their always cheerful disposition and assistance in aiding our quest for copies of period maps and plans.

Roger Griffiths, Cotham, Bristol
Paul Smith, Kings Heath, Birmingham

STOBCROSS (NS5665.1/1A) **1948**   *WA Camwell*

BASIC BUILDING DESIGN

Contemporary engravings reveal that in the early days engine sheds were often built in a decorative style in keeping with the architecture employed at the railway stations, no doubt reflecting the pride with which the companies viewed the technical marvels which were housed within them. Pictorial records of these buildings are scarce but it is quite obvious that as the railways quickly grew they became more functional and the designs of all sheds were eventually based on one of three different configurations;

STRAIGHT SHED; As the name implies the building was straight (or in very rare instances slightly curved) and covered one or a multiple of tracks. It was either dead ended or the lines passed right through the shed, or a combination of both.

ROUNDHOUSE; In early days the loco was detached from the tender and "stabled" around the turntable on short spurs. In general the buildings were circular in shape with a conical (qv) self supporting roof. As the turntables and spurs became longer in order to accommodate larger engines square buildings with multi-pitched roofs were proven to be more suitable. *Barrow Hill*, a classic example of a Midland Railway square roundhouse, has been preserved.

SEMI-ROUNDHOUSE; Although popular on the continent, this style of design with a semi-circular building housing tracks radiating from an outside turntable was not utilized to a great extent in Britain. *Nine Elms* and *Kings Cross* were famous examples of this sort of building on the grand scale whilst *St.Blazey* has been preserved, albeit as industrial units.

The other major characteristic of the building was the design of the roof and to assist the reader an illustrated summary of the basic designs which are recorded in this directory are shown:

NORTHLIGHT PATTERN

This design could be found throughout Britain, varying from 2TS engine sheds to the very largest. They were usually constructed in multiple pitches with one face in slate and the other, facing north, in glass. At some locations, the disposition of the building was sometimes west-east but in both instances the objective was to give a good working light without glare from the sun. The roof was generally built with the pitches at right angles to the sides but in some instances, notably at *Stewarts Lane (TQ2976.1/1C)* the shed was rebuilt with a transverse northlight pattern roof. *(Some depots were built with a sawtooth style of roof which, in view of the similarity of design have been described in this book as having northlight pattern roofs.)*

Hugely popular amongst railways from about 1880 onwards, the northlight pattern roof was relatively easy and cheap to build, but quickly proved to be a liability as its lack of durability to soot and steam almost inevitably led to premature re-roofings. This example, at **Speke Junction** (SJ4184.2/1A) was viewed in 1931. *H Garrett Collection*

DUTCH BARN

A simple curved roof in the style, as the name would imply, of a barn. Not a common design and all, as far as we know, constructed in corrugated iron. Generally employed as a single span, a double version of a bizarre style was used at *Fackenham West (TF9129.1/1A)* and the only example found to date of a transverse structure was that at *Bourne-mouth Central (SZ0992.1/1A).*

The depot at **Saltburn** (NZ6521.1/1C) was rebuilt in this style following a roof fire on April 17th, 1907. *J Peden*

LEAN-TO

Used mainly as a simple extension to existing facilities, as at *Slough (SU9780.2/2A).* Instances of the shed itself being of a lean-to structure are not common. *Trawsfynydd (SH7135.1/1A)* is the only known example, certainly amongst those depots surviving into BR days.

A slight cheating had to be resorted to so that the scarce lean-to type of shed could be illustrated in this volume. Cheating inasmuch that the building shown here at **Selby** (SE6131.1/3A) was put up as an extension to the coal stage *(in similar fashion to Riccarton Junction [NY5497.1/1A])* at the main depot to house the petrol-electric railcar utilized on the Cawood branch. This view dates from 1963. *Authors' Collection*

CONICAL

Employed in the construction of the first generation of roundhouses, the smaller examples would have been almost self supporting but larger roofs were supported by props. A preserved example, although no longer in railway use is found at *Camden* (TQ2884.1/1B).

This example, at **Gateshead (Chaytors Bank)** (NZ2563.1/1B), which illustrates the utilization of a double conical configuration survived until 1965.
Authors' Collection

FLAT

This design was most commonly employed by British Railways during the construction of the last generation of steam sheds. Those built in the 1950s took into account that dieselization was imminent and embraced the designs of the new generation of depots under the assumption that they would house and maintain the new locomotives. They were usually constructed in concrete with glazed panels to maximize natural light.

The installation of flat roofs on small depots was thankfully, due to their uninspiring appearance, rarely employed. **Coniston** (SD3197.1/1B) was re-roofed by BR in this style and is viewed here in 1959.
J Edgington

LOUVRE

This was an LMS design and featured a series of shallow pitches supported on cross beams. Many of the depots rebuilt in BR days adopted this style, one of the features of which was a brick screen at each end. Both the SR and LMS had distinctive designs for these screens. The SR version, which was also utilized on the Southern Region during BR days, had diagonal corners (as at *Templecombe ST7022.2/1C*) whilst the LMS utilized a plain brick wall on top of a long concrete lintel (as at *Camden TQ2884.2/1B*).

An example of a louvre-style roof being employed on a roundhouse was the LMS built depot at **Leicester** (SK5904.1/4A). This view was taken in 1945 and clearly shows what was intended to be, but overtaken and usurped by the speed of change, the LMS's standard design of large shed.
Authors' Collection

TANK SHED

The basic design of these consisted of a ITS building surmounted by a water tank and they were not usually considered as sheds in themselves but as locomotive servicing areas offering covered accommodation to both locomotives and crews as required. However some sheds proper were constructed with this configuration, GWR structures at *Bath* (ST7464.1/1A) and *Glyn Neath* (SN8605.1/1A) and an LNWR 2TS depot at *Market Harborough* (SP7487.1/1A) being better known examples.

Woodhead (SK1199.1/1A) built in the manner of a castle, was intended for use as a refuge for banking engines. However, it is believed that in practice, it served little purpose other than as a reservoir for the water cranes at the lay-by sidings visible in the distance. This view was taken in 1938.   *H Garrett Collection*

ACKNOWLEDGEMENTS

Amongst the individuals who have given invaluable assistance in the accumulation of information for this volume, may we thank:

Chris Bush, Ken Fairey, Ron Fareham, Tony Foster, Eric Hannan, JW Henshaw, Charlie Herring, Rob Holden, John Hooper, Eddie Lyons, Rae Montgomery, Les Nixon, Nick Pigott, Ken Plant, Stan Robinson, Peter Rowbotham, Stuart Sellar, Ray Smith, Allan Somerfield, Bill Stubbs, Bill Taylor, MA Vanns and John Williams. Anne Taylor, Karen Amies and Karen Murkin at Cambridge University Map Library.

Grateful thanks are extended to Philip Stuart for his meticulous checking of this volume, and his numerous comments and corrections.

And, sadly no longer with us, we acknowledge the help and/or photographic artistry of Peter Winding, Ron Dyer, James Stevenson, HC Casserley and the doyen shed fan of them all, WA (Bill) Camwell. It was a privilege and pleasure to have known each of them.

PLEASE NOTE
In compiling a volume such as this, which takes in a very broad field, the authors have sometimes had to rely upon information sourced from previous publications both contemporary and of a historical nature.

This is particularly relevant with regard to the opening and closure dates of sheds. Many of these have been quoted from stock list alterations in enthusiast magazines, whilst line closure and opening dates have led to other basic assumptions regarding the provision of facilities.

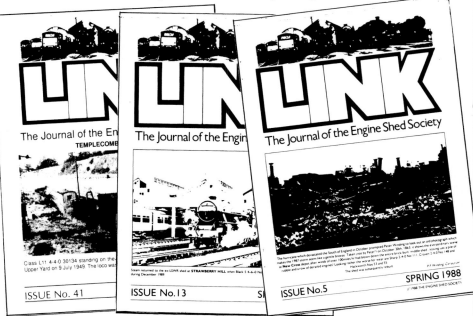

NOTES ON THE USE OF THIS BOOK

THE INDEXING SYSTEM

With any listing that is "fluid", with changes and amendments likely at any time, it is helpful that a system able to embrace them is employed. Alphabetical and numerical sequences were considered and discarded but one based on locations was found to possess the greatest flexibility.

Using the National Grid and dividing the country into 1km squares enables each site and building to be allocated a unique index number. The method of creating this number is demonstrated here;

Example: **BUSHBURY**

a) The OS square in which it is found - SJ9101

b) The general site area - *On the east side of the line, at Bushbury Junction, north of Wolverhampton High Level Station* - SJ9101.1

(Other sites within the OS square would be numbered 2,3,4 and so on)

c) The foundations of the shed building - SJ9101.1/1

(Other foundations on the site would be numbered 2,3,4 and so on)

d) The building on those foundations is given a letter, yielding a unique index number for the shed - SJ9101.1/1A

Shed extensions may, depending upon circumstances, be considered either as an additional building appended to the original (and thus given its own "foundations" number) or simply as a rebuilt building and given a new "building" letter. An anomoly in this area is where a new building has been appended, which under normal conditions would justify the allocation of a "foundations" number, and then both the "new" and "original" buildings are demolished and replaced by another building which embraces both foundations. In this instance all are considered to be on one set of foundations and allocated "building" letters

Although the letter part of the code is generally in chronological order (as the building is modified or re-roofed subsequent letters B,C etc are applied) it is not hard and fast. The situation could easily arise in which earlier buildings or rebuilds on the foundations are subsequently discovered and these would simply be allocated further letters in the sequence as they come to light. Once a code number is established then this remains unchanged.

There are, of course, situations where the details regarding a shed are very obscure, particularly with early depots and temporary sheds and these, in some instances, are given "holding codes". In locations of intense railway development the general site code of "0"; "*In the vicinity of ...*" is given. This counters the problem that one of these sheds may have occupied the same site as later buildings in which case it would have been allocated one of the specific site codes. The "holding code" is thus given until research confirms the true site.

Similarly, in other locations where the exact site is not known but it is the only known shed in the area it is quite conceivable to allocate a "final" code, eg. 1: "*In the vicinity of ...*", with the true site possibly being clarified at a later date.

Anomalies occur with this system where the grid line passes through the, shed site. *Shrewsbury Coleham* is a case in point but the basic rules, as detailed above, are still applied although the general site is given a "twin" coding (eg Coleham SJ4911.1 & SJ5011.1). In other instances the grid line passes through the shed itself (*Belle Vue* actually has two) and it is purely arbitrary as to which square the site is allocated.

MAPS AND DESCRIPTIVE ANALYSIS

As the simplest and most understandable method of dividing up the areas the country has been split into counties.

Preceding each county section is a map showing the location of each site within that county. Conurbations are dealt with similarly but Greater London with, in some areas, a great concentration of shed sites has been further sub-divided into 10km National Grid squares.

Although it is preferable it has not been possible to arrange each site in alphabetical order within each section. In order to accommodate all the sites within an economically viable set of books a "best-fit" approach has had to be undertaken in order to save space. For this reason the Index at the end of this volume should be consulted.

There are a considerable number of instances where shed sites have not appeared on OS maps. As discussed previously the very early depots predated the first surveys but there are numerous examples of 20th century sites not being mapped either. These are typically those that were opened in the early years of the century and closed prior to 1960, or only existed for a short period of time and were located in rural areas which did not require frequent surveys. In these instances track, as well as buildings, may be superimposed as a general guide to the layout.

Furthermore other rural areas were not drawn up to 25in scale and only 6in maps are available (eg. *Hawes Junction, Rosedale*). These have been enlarged to 17.5in:1mile

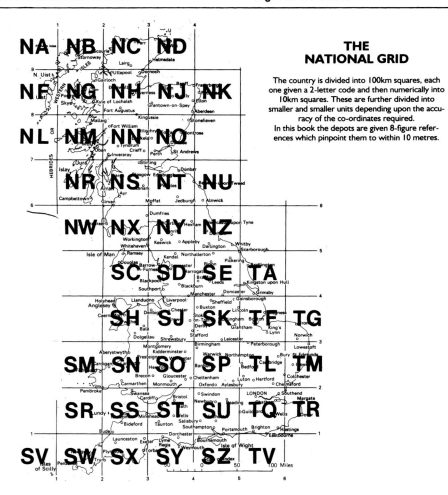

THE NATIONAL GRID

The country is divided into 100km squares, each one given a 2-letter code and then numerically into 10km squares. These are further divided into smaller and smaller units depending upon the accuracy of the co-ordinates required.
In this book the depots are given 8-figure references which pinpoint them to within 10 metres.

The basic information given for each shed is;

The code (*qv*), site location with National Grid reference to 8 figures, originating company, opening and closing dates, description of building(s) and facilities available.

Each shed with a known site is accompanied by a map. These are based upon the Ordnance Survey 25in series and are reproduced at a scale of 17.5in:1mile. Where possible the map is contemporary to the sheds existence, otherwise the site is superimposed upon it. Unfortunately the reproduction quality on some of the extracts is not as high as we would like but has nonetheless been included as too invaluable to omit.

Excessive use of abbreviations and footnotes has been avoided as it is felt that this destroys the flow of the narrative and hinders the assimiliation of information. Although it is assumed that the reader is well aware of the abbreviations of the major companies a short appendix has been added whilst those initials of the more obscure companies are expanded upon in the general information on each depot. It is only necessary, therefore, to acquaint the reader with the terms "TS" which is shorthand for track straighthouse and "RH" for roundhouse.

• THE DIRECTORY OF •
BRITISH ENGINE SHEDS
AND PRINCIPAL LOCOMOTIVE SERVICING POINTS

Track Diagrams are scaled at 17.5in/mile

0 FEET   500

VOLUME TWO
NORTH MIDLANDS, NORTHERN ENGLAND
& SCOTLAND

In gathering together the photographs for this book, the authors have tried, as far as is possible, to display old and/or obscure engine sheds, with as many pictures as possible dating from before the era of British Railways.

Readers will, perhaps, note the preponderance of illustrations covering the LNER and its antecedents. This is no accident, because parts of Britain served by the LMS and its constituents have already been covered in great detail in a number of published works. Accordingly, the authors recommend the reader to those books, which contain a wealth of interesting pictures.

The independent Wirral Railway opened for business in January 1888, but its origins were in the earlier Hoylake Railway Company. The Wirral provided itself with its sole locomotive depot at **Birkenhead North** and the 2TS shed (SJ2990.1/1A) is seen here in about 1905. It was closed by the LMS in March 1938. *Ian Allan Library*

(See Page 236)

A number of early railway companies had sheds at Derby, with most being incorporated into the Midland Railway. One of those pioneer lines was the Midland Counties which erected the 2TS **Derby (MCR)** shed (SK3635.1/1A) that opened in June 1839. The depot closed in 1863 and was incorporated into the expanding Derby Works, serving in a number of uses for no less than 125 years.

The MCR shed is seen here prior to demolition, an event which, because of the building's history, many said should not have been allowed to happen. However, with the adjacent 1840 roundhouse of the North Midland Railway (SK3635.1/2A) already having "listed" status, pleas for the MCR building fell upon the deaf ears of officialdom. *Bernard Matthews Collection*

(See Page 225)

With the August 1847 opening of the line through Wetherby to Harrogate, the Y&NMR erected a brick built 2TS shed (SE5037.1/1A) at the new junction station of **Church Fenton**. How long the building served as an engine shed is unknown, but it did stand into the 1960s at least, latterly being utilized as an engineering workshop. The shed is seen here serving that purpose in September 1962. *Authors' Collection*

(See Page 299)

Reportedly provided to house a banking engine for assisting on the climb to Buxton, the Stockport, Disley & Whaley Bridge Railway opened a small 1TS "tankshed" (SK0181.1/1A) at **Whaley Bridge**. The line passed to the L&NWR in 1866 and that company closed the shed in 1900. It continued to stand and provide shelter, however, for many years, as evidenced by this picture of 1961; when the building was finally removed is not known. *Bernard Matthews Collection*

(See Page 240)

Encouraged by the new traffic, mostly coal, created through its joint line with the GNR, the London & North Western Railway opened an 8TS northlight roof shed (SK6240.2/1A) near to the GNR's Colwick depot at **Netherfield & Colwick**.

Declining traffic following the grouping led the LMSR to close the shed in April 1932, but the building saw many more years as a wagon works and then an engineering establishment prior to demolition in the 1980s. The still largely intact building was photographed in 1946, in use by Wrigley & Sons Ltd, a wagon repairing company. *Authors' Collection*

(See Page 243)

The Garston & Liverpool Railway opened between those points in June 1864, with MR engines becoming regular denizens of the original (SJ3587.1/1A) 3TS shed at **Brunswick** in 1873. The G&L's successor, the MS&LR, provided the Midland with a 3TS shed (SJ3587.1/2A) of its own in 1874 and that building is seen here in a rare photograph dating from around 1913. 4-4-0 No.303 and a Single grace the scene outside the building which would eventually be closed in 1929. At that time the LMS engines moved across the lines to share the 5TS LNER depot (SJ3587.2/1A) put up by the MS&LR in 1879. *Bernard Matthews Collection*

(See Page 278)

Destined to become one of the biggest "white elephants" in British engine shed history, the large ten road depot at **Allerton** (SJ4184.1/1A), just outside of Liverpool, was opened by the Cheshire Lines Committee in 1882. Of the three partners in the CLC joint operation, the GNR seems never to have stationed locomotives at Allerton leaving the Midland and MS&LR to share the spacious accommodation. The former pulled out its engines in 1896 with the MS&LR leaving a year later, at which point the depot closed.

However, it saw several later uses, culminating as an electrification depot for the modernization of the West Coast Main Line. Despite its size, Allerton shed was rarely photographed; this picture dates from April 10th, 1966, some four years before demolition. *WT Stubbs*

(See Page 280)

Branching off the Darlington to Barnard Castle line, the Forcett Railway was opened in 1866 to carry stone and general goods traffic, with trains being worked by the NER. A shed (NZ1712.1/1A) was provided at **Eppleby** and that long out of use building (as NZ1712.1/1B) is seen in this picture dated August 12th, 1963. The Forcett Railway closed three years later but, against the odds, Eppleby engine shed still stood in 1999 in private use. *Authors' Collection*

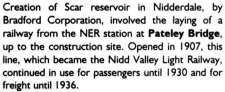

(See Page 287)

Creation of Scar reservoir in Nidderdale, by Bradford Corporation, involved the laying of a railway from the NER station at **Pateley Bridge**, up to the construction site. Opened in 1907, this line, which became the Nidd Valley Light Railway, continued in use for passengers until 1930 and for freight until 1936.

It was renowned for its eccentric collection of motive power, two examples of which can be seen in this 1928 photograph of the shed (SE1566.1/1A). The railmotor had been purchased from the Great Western Railway and was responsible for the passenger service. Note the wooden water tank. *HC Casserley*

(See Page 287)

For its opening in 1857 **Starbeck** shed was provided with a site of limited width, so after at least four extensions in the years up to 1889, the 2TS building (SE3355.1/1E) was of extraordinary length, as may be discerned from the view taken on July 24th, 1938 *(top)*.

Some years later the building required renovation and this was carried out by BR in the mid-1950s. What resulted was the truncated brick and concrete structure (SE3355.1/1F) viewed some 21 years and one month after the date of the top picture *(bottom)*.

However, despite the expense of rebuilding, the depot was only a month away from total closure, providing yet another example of wasted effort and resources brought about by the rapid "modernization" of Britain's railways.

WA Camwell & K Fairey

(See Page 287)

When the L&YR built its new works at **Horwich** in 1885 an 18in gauge system was installed for the shops' internal use. The diminutive 0-4-0 saddle tanks were kept in a 3TS shed (SD6410.1/1A), the closure date of which has yet to be established.

This photograph dates from June 21st, 1936 and the shed stood into the 1960s, having been put to other use prior to demolition. *WA Camwell*

(See Page 267)

This delightful panorama of the terminus at **Richmond** clearly indicates the age of the buildings through their style - early hipped roofs with large vents - typical of the York & Newcastle Railway of 1846. The stone built engine shed (NZ1700.1/1A) may be seen between the station and pumping house, patently in use as a goods shed, which means the photograph post-dates the depot's closure at the end of 1933. That was not the end though, as Richmond engine shed still stood in 1999, in excellent condition, in use as a health centre. *Bernard Matthews Collection*

(See Page 287)

Also known as *"Skinningrove"*, the 3TS shed at **Carlin How** (NZ7019.1/1A), seen here in about 1935, had a chequered history, very much dictated by the economies of the local area's various mines. Opened in 1866, the depot closed in 1902, only to re-open five years later. It finally closed in 1921, then saw use as a wagon shop, remaining most of the time in surprisingly good condition.

By 1954, however, the building had reached a parlous state and demolition occurred in that year. *WA Camwell*

(See Page 290)

Hipped roof and large vent again, indicating another shed from the early days - in this case the York & North Midland depot (TA0387.1/1A) constructed in **Scarborough** and dating from July 1845. The building closed to locomotives in 1882 and served in goods use until demolition in 1906/7.

This picture, from the NER official archive, dates from just prior to the shed's demise - note the enginemen's cottages at left. *K Taylor Collection*

(See Page 291)

An engine shed first appeared at **Malton** in 1853/4, the building being extended within the next two decades (as SE7871.1/1B). The depot provided locomotives for the network of cross-country lines which met at Malton and also for the summer time assistance on the increasingly heavy traffic flowing from York to the coast - predominantly Scarborough. Such duties were fulfilled until closure of the shed in April 1963; demolition soon followed. *H Garrett Collection*

(See Page 293)

The little engine shed at **Pickering** (SE7983.1/1A) is one of the oldest still in existence, with its origins in the York & North Midland Railway of 1845, followed by a service record spanning 114 years.

That was not the end though because, as indicated above, the shed still stood in 1999 in commercial use and hardly showing any of its 154 years. From this 1949 photograph note the coaling crane and ready-filled tub - what a delightful prototype this would all make for a model!

H Garrett Collection

(See Page 293)

During the late 1920s the LNER provided itself with a fleet of locomotives for "departmental", rather than line, use. Mostly these engines were of the Sentinel type, for which the LNER built separate (usually timber) sheds with the barest of facilities.

One of these obscure depots served **Doncaster Wagon Works** (SE5800.1/1A) and is depicted here on October 19th, 1937. *WA Camwell*

(See Page 295)

This magnificently posed photograph of the NER's main shed at **Hull Dairycoates** was taken in 1914, just prior to the construction, to the left of this view, of an extension comprising three in-line turntable sheds (TA0626&0726.1/4A, 5A & 6A).

The crowded aspect of Dairycoates, doubtless on a Sunday, clearly demonstrates the need for more space, even though at that time, the depot was already formed of three roundhouses - No.1 from 1863 (TA0626&0726.1/1A) is on the right, with Nos 2 & 3 of 1876 (TA0626&0726.1/2A & 3A) beyond.

The enormous shed was much rebuilt by British Railways, and later saw further conversion for use by diesels; some remnants of the structure stand today, as part of an industrial estate.

Authors' Collection

(See Page 296)

The Cawood, Wistow & Selby was a light railway opened in February 1898. The company's engine shed (SE6031.1/1A) was at **Selby**, but fell out of use after only a few years, thereafter being utilized for a number of purposes, one of which was a Mutual Improvement classroom for the men of the nearby NER double-turntable shed at Selby. The photograph is thought to date from a short time before the CW&S shed was demolished in 1963.

Authors' Collection

(See Page 301)

A perfect example of the once numerous and largely unnoticed locomotive stabling/servicing points is this pit and sleeper-built coaling platform, complete with lamp standard (SK3585.1/F1), at the Midland Railway's **Sheffield Queens Road** goods yard. Typically, engines would be stationed at such places during the working week - mostly, but not always, returning to the main shed at weekends for boiler washouts etc.

Although many of these locations came and went largely unrecorded, the date of opening of the Queens Road facility is known as 1892. This photograph of April 13th, 1958 shows the site as not having been used for some time but it was not "officially" dispensed with until 1965.   *WT Stubbs*

(See Page 310)

A relative latecomer to Britain's rail network was the Hull & Barnsley Railway, which opened to its western terminus at **Cudworth** in July 1885. It erected an 8TS shed here (SE3610.1/1A), employing the then-fashionable northlight pattern of roof.

The building is viewed here to good effect from an elevated position in June 1936, but by closure in 1951 the depot had reached a state of near ruin. In the distance, below the left-hand chimney seen on the skyline, is the LMS-built 10TS shed at Royston (SE3711.1/1A), opened some four years previously.
WA Camwell

(See Page 312)

A scarce design of engine shed for Britain was the part, or semi-, roundhouse with an open turntable. One of the lesser-known examples was the NER shed (NZ1631.1/1A) at **Wear Valley Junction**, a small building with just six roads under its curving roof. Opened in 1876, the depot was captured on film by Mr Camwell on a very gloomy day, just a few weeks before its July 8th, 1935 closure. By that time Class G5 No.408 was the sole remaining locomotive.
WA Camwell

(See Page 314)

The Darlington & Barnard Castle Railway opened in July 1856, with a 1TS shed (NZ0517.1/1A) being provided at the **Barnard Castle** terminus. This closed nine years later when a new line and station were opened, and a 1TS shed (NZ0517.2/1A) erected. That building was extended to two roads in 1875 (as NZ0517.2/1B) and, according to the authors' records, was closed by the LNER in May 1937.

However, this picture from June 1930 shows the customary allocation of two locomotives parked outside the shed with its doors firmly closed, so it may be that closure came some years earlier than thought.
Authors' Collection

(See Page 316)

When the NER saw the need for an engine shed at **Bowes Bridge**, it adopted the simple expedient of converting a former winding-engine house to a 2TS shed (NZ2057.1/1A). That structure is seen here, together with a glimpse of the former engine house chimney on the left, in about 1936, some seven years before fire partially destroyed the building.

Not until 1954 did British Railways rebuild the shed (as NZ2057.1/1B) in steel and asbestos, only to close it in 1962 and demolish it four years later. One could say that some taxpayers' money was not best used! *Authors' Collection*

(See Page 316)

Located high up on the Durham moors, **Waskerley** grew with the railway and the traffic it carried, from April 1846. The first 2TS shed was joined by a second in 1854, both buildings serving until closure in September 1940. Mr Casserley's photograph of May 31st, 1935 shows what may have been the 1845 shed (NZ0545.1/1A). The other, sited behind the camera (NZ0545.1/2A), was a 2TS through road building. *HC Casserley*

(See Page 316)

When station expansion meant the end of the 6TS Leeds Northern Railway shed (NZ4419.1/1B) at **Stockton**, the NER selected historic ground for a replacement depot - the site of the Clarence Railway's engine shed and works at Clarence Junction (NZ4420.1/1A). Opened in 1891, Stockton's new shed (NZ4420.1/2A) was of identical layout and design to the straight shed opened a year earlier at Scarborough, being of massive proportions with two gabled roofs each covering four roads.

Stockton survived until closure in June 1959, some ten years after this view was taken, following which it entered private commercial use. It was demolished in 1998. *H Garrett Collection*

(See Page 318)

In his *magnum opus* on the history of engine sheds of the NER, K. Hoole refers to the GNofER shed that stood adjacent to the famous flat crossing of the East Coast Main Line by the Stockton & Darlington Railway. Hoole could not confirm whether the GNofER depot had stood on this spot since the opening of the railway in 1841, stating that it may have been moved there in 1851, from a site beside Bank Top Station.

The authors have not been able to clarify the situation further nor find out when it ceased to be used by locomotives. However, against all the odds, **Darlington (GNofER)** shed (NZ2915.1/1A) was still standing in 1999, in private use, and, as such, was one of the oldest remaining British engine sheds. It is seen here in 1987.   *N Pigott*

(See Page 320)

Few junctions were as remote as **Reedsmouth**, which is exactly why the NBR, knowing of railwaymen's superstitions, sent there the rescued and repaired engine from the Tay Bridge disaster. Such wily men were not to be deceived though, and soon the locomotive concerned had gained the appellation *"The Dipper"*!

The sheer "toughness" of the Reedsmouth site is well captured in this photograph taken on a cold and wet August 21st, 1936, when long-term resident LNER Class J36 No.9779 was visiting the coal stage. Note the coal stack, a feature normally seen only at the largest sheds but strongly indicative of the need for the NBR (LNER) to be always ready for any emergency. Opened by the Border Counties Railway in 1862, Reedsmouth shed (NY8682.1/1B) would be closed 90 years later, but still stood in 1999, in use as a store by a farmer who commented wryly upon the stream of visitors that asked to see the old engine shed!
                                                         WA Camwell

(See Page 326)

A typically ramshackle scene from a light railway, in this case the North Sunderland Light Railway which ran four miles from the East Coast Main Line junction at Chathill, to **Seahouses**, during the period December 1898 to October 1951.

In a picture taken five months before closure, Ex-LNER Class Y7 0-4-0T No.68089, one of only two such engines to survive into BR days, rests between its, by then, not onerous duties. The iron engine shed (NU2132.1/1A) survived closure and saw other use for a number of years prior to demolition.   *K Hartley*

(See Page 326)

DERBYSHIRE

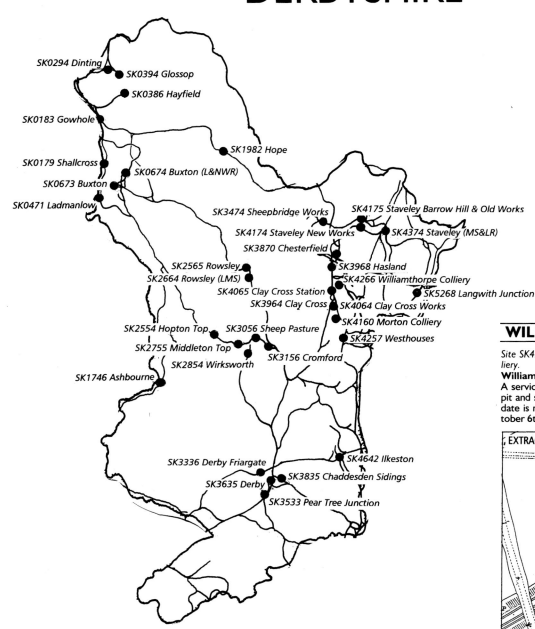

SK0294 Dinting
SK0394 Glossop
SK0386 Hayfield
SK0183 Gowhole
SK1982 Hope
SK0179 Shallcross
SK0674 Buxton (L&NWR)
SK0673 Buxton
SK0471 Ladmanlow
SK3474 Sheepbridge Works
SK4175 Staveley Barrow Hill & Old Works
SK4174 Staveley New Works
SK4374 Staveley (MS&LR)
SK3870 Chesterfield
SK2565 Rowsley
SK2664 Rowsley (LMS)
SK3968 Hasland
SK4266 Williamthorpe Colliery
SK5268 Langwith Junction
SK4065 Clay Cross Station
SK3964 Clay Cross
SK4064 Clay Cross Works
SK2554 Hopton Top
SK3056 Sheep Pasture
SK4160 Morton Colliery
SK2755 Middleton Top
SK3156 Cromford
SK4257 Westhouses
SK2854 Wirksworth
SK1746 Ashbourne
SK3336 Derby Friargate
SK4642 Ilkeston
SK3835 Chaddesden Sidings
SK3635 Derby
SK3533 Pear Tree Junction

WILLIAMTHORPE COLLIERY

Site SK4266.1; At the west end of Williamthorpe Colliery.
Williamthorpe Colliery (MR)SK4266.1/F1
A servicing area consisting of a water tank, engine pit and siding located at SK42456645. The opening date is not known but it was closed by BR on October 6th, 1967.

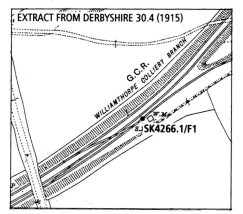

EXTRACT FROM DERBYSHIRE 30.4 (1915)

GOWHOLE

Site SK0183.1; At Gowhole Sidings on the east side of the Chinley to New Mills line.
Gowhole (MR)SK0183.1/F1
A servicing area consisting of a 60ft turntable, located at SK01518368, engine pit and water column. The opening date is not known but the facility lasted until it was abandoned by BR in c1967. (It had been regarded as a signing-on point only from 1959).

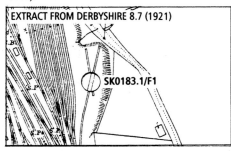

EXTRACT FROM DERBYSHIRE 8.7 (1921)

HOPE

Site SK1982.1; On the north side of the line, east of Hope Station.
Hope (MR)SK1982.1/1A
A ITS dead ended shed, it was located at SK19848293. The facilities included a coal stage. No further details are known.

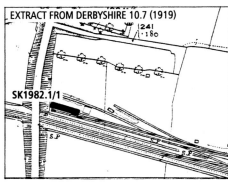

EXTRACT FROM DERBYSHIRE 10.7 (1919)

ILKESTON

Site SK4642.1; On the west side of Ilkeston (GN) Station.
Ilkeston (GNR)SK4642.1/F1
A servicing area consisting of a turntable, located at SK46284269, siding and coal stage, it was opened in 1891 and closed by the LNER in c1933.

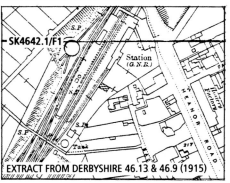

EXTRACT FROM DERBYSHIRE 46.13 & 46.9 (1915)

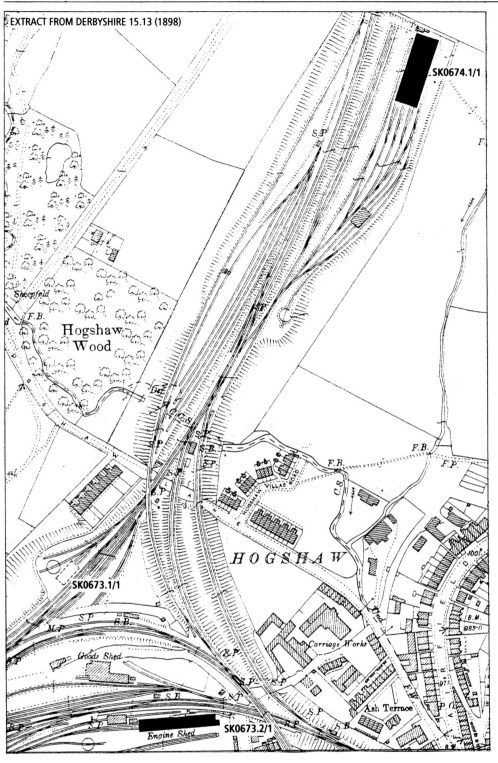

EXTRACT FROM DERBYSHIRE 15.13 (1898)

SK0674.1/1

SK0673.1/1

SK0673.2/1

Site SK0673.1; On the north side of the line, at the east end of Buxton (L&NWR) Station
Buxton (SD&WBR)SK0673.1/1A

A 2TS dead ended shed, located at SK06047389 and opened by the Stockport, Disley & Whaley Bridge Railway on June 15th, 1863. No further details are known other than that the facilities included a turntable. The line was worked from the outset by the L&NWR and absorbed by it on November 16th, 1866. The depot was closed in 1892 and demolished, the turntable being retained for further use.

Replaced by ...
Site SK0674.1; On the east side of the line, north of Buxton (L&NWR) Station.
Buxton (L&NWR)SK0674.1/1A

A brick built 6TS dead ended shed with a slated and glazed northlight pattern roof, it was located at SK06377436 and was opened in 1892. The facilities included a coal stage, later replaced with a mechanical coaler, water tank and turntable. The depot was closed by BR on March 4th, 1968 and was subsequently demolished.

Site SK0673.2; On the south side of the line, at the east end of Buxton (MR) Station.
Buxton (MR)SK0673.2/1A

A stone built 2TS dead ended shed with a slated hipped roof, it was located at SK06157375 and was opened in 1867. The facilities included a coal stage and turntable.

The shed was extended ...
Buxton (MR)SK0673.2/1B

The building was lengthened in 1884. The depot was closed by the LMS on August 19th, 1935 and was subsequently demolished.

ROWSLEY

Site SK2565.1; At the north end of Rowsley (1st) Station.
Rowsley (MB&MJR)SK2565.1/1A

A stone built 1TS dead ended shed with a slated gable style pitched roof, it was located at SK25896587 and was opened by the Manchester, Buxton & Midland Junction Railway on June 14th, 1849. The facilities included a turntable, sited outside of the shed entrance. The depot was closed in 1880.

Replaced, on the same site, by ...
Rowsley (MR)SK2565.1/1B

A stone built 4TS dead ended shed with a triple gable style pitched roof, it was opened in 1880. The pit of the original shed, SK2565.1/1A, was incorporated into the new building and other facilities included a turntable and ramped coal stage. The depot was closed by the LMS in 1924.

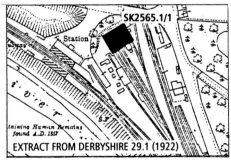

SK2565.1/1

EXTRACT FROM DERBYSHIRE 29.1 (1922)

Replaced by ...
Site SK2664.1; On the west side of the line, south of Rowsley Station.
Rowsley (LMS)SK2664.1/1A

A brick built 4TS through road shed with a slated twin gable style roof, it was located at SK26146405 and was opened in 1924 having being constructed to a MR design. The facilities included a coal plant, water tank and turntable. The depot was closed by BR on April 27th, 1964 and was subsequently demolished. In 1996 the site was excavated by Peak Rail and it was anticipated that it would be utilized as an engine servicing area when the line is re-opened.

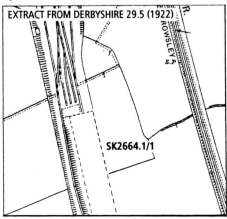

EXTRACT FROM DERBYSHIRE 29.5 (1922)

SK2664.1/1

CLAY CROSS

EXTRACT FROM DERBYSHIRE 30.7 (1938)

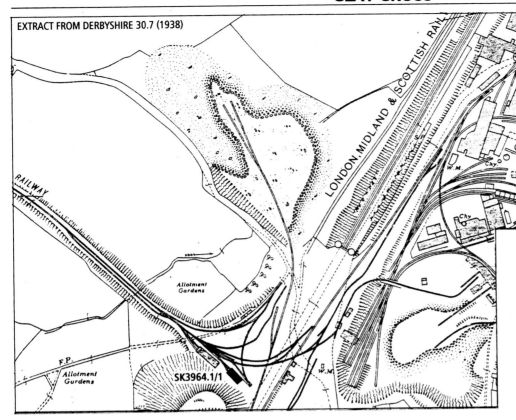

SK3964.1/1

SK4064.1/1

Site SK3964.1; On the south side of the line, at the west end of Clay Cross Works.
Clay Cross (Ashover Light)SK3964.1/1A
A 2ft 0in gauge 2TS dead ended shed with a single pitched roof, it was located at SK39616412 and was opened by the Ashover Light Railway on April 6th, 1925. No further details are known other than it was closed on March 31st, 1950 and was subsequently demolished.

Site SK4064.1; In Clay Cross Works
Clay Cross Works (MR)SK4064.1/1A
A brick built 1TS through road shed with a slated gable style pitched roof, it was located at SK40046437 and was opened in 1865 with the locomotives being hired from the MR. Details of the facilities are not known.

The building was modified ...
Clay Cross Works (LMS)SK4064.1/1B
At some time prior to 1938 the building was reduced in length and converted to a dead ended shed to accommodate track alterations within the works area.

The building was modified again ...
Clay Cross Works (LMS)SK4064.1/1C
At some stage the building was converted to a through road shed. The hiring arrangement with BR was terminated in 1954 and the depot continued to be utilized privately until it was demolished and replaced with a new building to house the two works-owned diesel shunters in the early 1970s.

Site SK4065.1; On the east side of the line, at the south end of Clay Cross Station.
Clay Cross Station (MR)SK4065.1/1A
A brick built 3TS dead ended shed with a slated gable style roof located at SK40166513. The opening date is not known but it was in existence in 1860. The facilities included a turntable.

The shed was enlarged in 1868 ...
Clay Cross Station (MR)SK4065.1/2A
A 3TS through road shed was constructed along the eastern wall of the first building (SK4065.1/1A) and on the site of the turntable.

The depot may have closed in c1905 and the buildings were then utilized as a wagon repair works and engineer's depot. After closure in the 1960s they were used for the storage of some of BR's museum artefacts including carriages and tramcars. The later shed (SK4065.1/2A), which had been rebuilt after closure, was demolished in 1987 but the first building still stood in 2000, in use as a store for the National Tramway Museum at Crich.

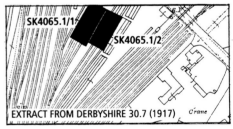

SK4065.1/1

SK4065.1/2

EXTRACT FROM DERBYSHIRE 30.7 (1917)

SHEEPBRIDGE

Site SK3474.1; In Sheepbridge Works, on the north side of the branch line.
Sheepbridge Works (MR)SK3474.1/1A
A 2TS dead ended shed, it was located at SK34727476 and was probably opened in 1870 under a locomotive loan arrangement. The facilities included a water tank. No further details are known other than it was demolished in 1948.

Replaced, on the same site, by ...
Sheepbridge Works (BR)SK3474.1/F1
A servicing area consisting of a cantilever style corrugated iron lean-to was established on the shed site. The facilities included the former sheds engine pits and water tank. It was closed in c1965.

SK3474.1/1

EXTRACT FROM DERBYSHIRE 18.14 (1919)

MORTON COLLIERY

Site SK4160.1: At Morton Colliery.
Morton Colliery (MR)SK4160.1/1A
A brick built 1TS dead ended shed with a slated gable style roof, it was located at SK41316031. The date of opening is not known but the hiring arrangement probably commenced during MR days. Details of the facilities are not known. The colliery was owned by the Clay Cross Co. Ltd until 1947 when it was vested in the NCB, East Midlands Division No.1 (Bolsover) Area. Locomotives continued to be hired from BR until June 1948 when the NCB acquired a locomotive to work the site. The shed was demolished in December 1966.

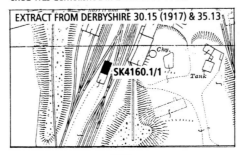

EXTRACT FROM DERBYSHIRE 30.15 (1917) & 35.13

SK4160.1/1

WIRKSWORTH

Site SK2854.1; On the west side of the line, north of Wirksworth Station.
Wirksworth (MR)SK2854.1/1A
A stone built 2TS dead ended shed with a slated gable style pitched roof, it was located at SK28945432 and opened on October 1st, 1867. The facilities included a water tank and turntable. The depot was closed in 1900, converted to a goods shed and survived in this form until 1968. It has since been demolished.

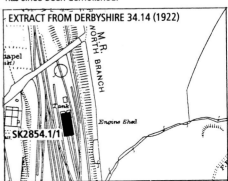

EXTRACT FROM DERBYSHIRE 34.14 (1922)

SK2854.1/1

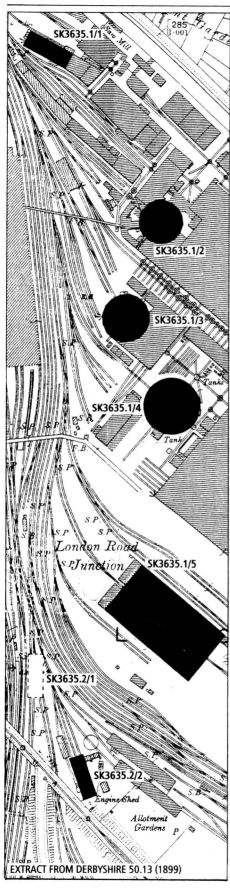

Site SK3635.3; In the L&NWR Goods Yard.
Derby Goods (L&NWR) SK3635.3/F1
Some sort of facility, approximately located at SK362350, was opened here in July 1861 and closed in 1865. No further details are known.

Site SK3635.1; In the Locomotive Works area, on the east side of Derby Station.
Derby (MCR) SK3635.1/1A
A brick built 2TS dead ended shed with a slated gable style roof, it was located at SK36253590 and was opened by the Midland Counties Railway on June 4th, 1839. Details of the facilities are not known. The depot was closed in 1863 and was incorporated into the works, finding further use as a stores building. The building was not demolished until 1990.

Derby No.1 (NMR) SK3635.1/2A
A brick built polygonal 1RH shed with a slated conical roof, it was located at SK36373576 and was opened by the North Midland Railway on May 11th, 1840. The depot probably had use of all facilities. The closure date is not known but it was absorbed into the works at some time prior to 1880, finding further use as a repair shed.

Derby No.2 (MR) SK3635.1/3A
A brick built polygonal 1RH shed with a slated conical roof, it was located at SK36343551 and was opened in 1847. The depot probably had use of all facilities. It was closed in 1888 and absorbed into the works as an engine store.

Derby No.3 (MR) SK3635.1/4A
A brick built polygonal 1RH shed with a slated conical roof, it was located at SK36383542 and was opened in 1852. The depot had use of all facilities. It was closed in 1916, having suffered air raid damage.

Derby No.4 (MR) SK3635.1/5A
A brick built square 2RH building with a triple pitched gable style slated roof, it was located at the south end of the site at SK36383521 and was opened in 1890. The facilities included a water tank, ramped coal stage and an additional external turntable. The depot was closed by BR in March 1967 and all but the offices demolished to make way for a diesel servicing shed.

Site SK3635.2; On the east side of the Birmingham line, at the south end of Derby Station.
Derby (B&DJR) SK3635.2/1A
A brick built 3TS shed, it was located at SK36273515 and was opened by the Birmingham & Derby Junction Railway on August 12th, 1839. The line was absorbed into the MR on May 10th, 1844 and the building was handed over to the NSR on July 13th, 1849. No further details are known except that the depot was closed in c1873 and demolished to make way for an access line to a new carriage and wagon works.

Replaced by ...
Derby (NSR) SK3635.2/2A
A 3TS dead ended shed with a gable style pitched roof, it was located at SK36313507 and was opened in 1873. The depot was built by the MR as part of the agreement made upon the closure of the ex-B&DJR shed (SK3635.2/1A) and the facilities included a 46ft turntable, coal stage and water tank. It was closed by the LMS on June 30th, 1923 and was subsequently demolished.

A servicing point was then established ...
Derby North Staffs (LMS) SK3635.2/F1
The turntable, water tank, coal stage and engine pits were utilized until the end of steam on the Crewe line being closed by BR in 1967.

Site SK3533.1; On the west side of the line, north of Peartree & Normanton Station.
Peartree Junction (L&NWR) SK3533.1/1A
A brick built 3TS dead ended shed with a slated hipped roof, it was located at SK35753386 and was opened in 1865. The facilities included a turntable and ramped coal stage with water tank over. The depot was closed by the LMS in 1923 and subsequently demolished.

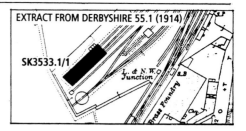

Site SK3835.1; On the north side of the line, at the east end of Chaddesden Sidings.
Chaddesden Sidings (MR) SK3835.1/F1
A servicing area consisting of a turntable, located at SK38423560, and coal stage. The opening and closing dates are not known.

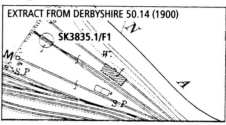

Site SK3336.1; On the north side of the line, west of Derby Friargate Station.
Derby Friargate (GNR) SK3336.1/1A
A brick built 4TS dead ended shed with a slated twin hipped roof, it was located at SK33803619 and was opened in 1876. The facilities included a 44ft 6in turntable, coal stage and water tank. The depot was closed by BR in 1955 but it was retained as a signing on point, and a store for new dmus, until 1959. Despite the dilapidated condition of the building it was let out for private use and was still standing in 1997, in use by a chemical company.

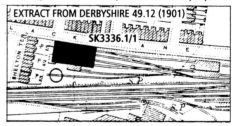

HASLAND

Site SK3968.1; On the east side of the Clay Cross line, south of Chesterfield Station.
Hasland (MR) SK3968.1/1A
A brick built square 1RH shed with a triple pitched gable style slated roof, it was located at SK39136855 and was opened in 1875. The facilities included a ramped coal stage and water tank.

The shed was re-roofed...
Hasland (LMS) SK3968.1/1B
At some stage the roof was reclad in corrugated iron sheeting. The site suffered badly from mining subsidence and by BR days the fabric of the building was such that part of the roof was demolished for safety reasons. The depot was closed on September 7th, 1964 and was subsequently demolished.

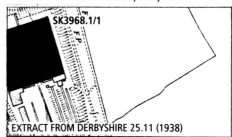

CROMFORD

Site SK3156.1; On the north side of the line, at the foot of the first incline.

Cromford (C&HPR)SK3156.1/1A

A stone built 1TS dead ended shed with a slated gable style roof and a timber built extension with a corrugated iron pitched roof, it was located at SK31275606 and was opened by the Cromford & High Peak Railway in 1860. The stone section of the shed had been built in 1831 and was originally utilized as a chain shop. There were no facilities. The depot was closed to steam by BR on July 26th, 1966 and totally shortly afterwards on April 3rd, 1967. The building was subsequently demolished.

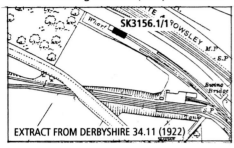

SHEEP PASTURE

Site SK3056.1; On the south side of the line, at the top of Sheep Pasture Incline.

Sheep Pasture (C&HPR)SK3056.1/1A

A timber built 1TS dead ended shed with a slated gable style pitched roof, it was located at SK30025618 and was opened by the Cromford & High Peak Railway on July 6th, 1831. The facilities included a coal stage and water tank. The line was absorbed by the L&NWR in 1877.

The shed was rebuilt ...

Sheep Pasture (L&NWR)SK3056.1/1B

At some stage the shed was enlarged and rebuilt in corrugated iron with a corrugated iron gable style pitched roof. The building was destroyed in a gale in the early 1960s and the locomotive stabled on the shed road until it was closed to steam by BR on July 26th, 1966. A diesel shunter then stabled in sidings until it was totally closed on April 3rd, 1967.

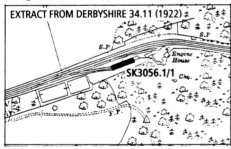

HOPTON TOP

Site SK2554.1; On the north side of the line, west of the top of Hopton Incline.

Hopton Top (C&HPR)SK2554.1/1A

A 1TS dead ended shed, it was located at SK25285464 and was opened by the Cromford & High Peak Railway on May 29th, 1830. Details of the facilities are not known. The depot was closed by the L&NWR on April 16th, 1877.

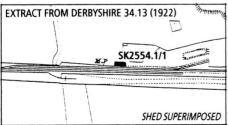

SHED SUPERIMPOSED

MIDDLETON TOP

Site SK2755.1; On the south side of the line, at the top of Middleton Incline.

Middleton Top (C&HPR)SK2755.1/1A

A timber built 1TS through road shed with a gable style pitched roof, it was located at SK27585518 and was opened by the Cromford & High Peak Railway on May 29th, 1830. The facilities included a water tank and an adjacent reservoir which was topped up by means of water tenders transported from Cromford. The line was absorbed by the L&NWR in 1877 and the shed was destroyed by a fire on July 30th, 1905.

Replaced, on the same site, by ...

Middleton Top (L&NWR)SK2755.1/1B

A corrugated iron 1TS through road shed with a corrugated iron gable style pitched roof, it was opened in 1905. The depot was closed by BR on April 30th, 1967 and was subsequently demolished.

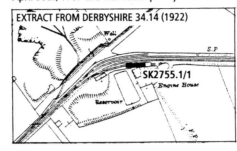

LADMANLOW

Site SK0471.1; On the east side of Ladmanlow Goods Station.

Ladmanlow (C&HPR)SK0471.1/1A

A 1TS dead ended shed, it was probably located at SK04067180 and was opened by the Cromford & High Peak Railway in 1858. The depot was closed by the L&NWR in 1897. No further details are known.

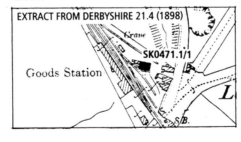

SHALLCROSS

Site SK0179.1; On the east side of the line, south of Shallcross Yard.

Shallcross (C&HPR)SK0179.1/1A

A 1TS dead ended shed it was located at SK01547959 and was opened by the Cromford & High Peak Railway in 1858. The depot was closed by the L&NWR in 1892. No further details are known.

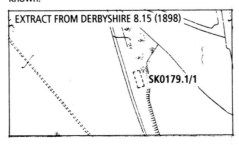

The Cromford & High Peak Railway was leased to the L&NWR in 1862 and was absorbed by them in 1877. Sometime after the line was closed by BR in 1967 it was converted to the *High Peak Nature Trail*.

WESTHOUSES

Site SK4257.1; On the south side of Blackwell East Junction, south of Westhouses & Blackwell Station.

Westhouses (MR)SK4257.1/1A

A brick built 6TS dead ended shed with a triple pitched gable slated roof, it was located at SK42705764 and was opened in 1890. The facilities included a ramped coal stage, water tank and a 50ft turntable. The depot was closed to steam by BR on October 3rd, 1966 and a diesel stabling point established. It has since been demolished.

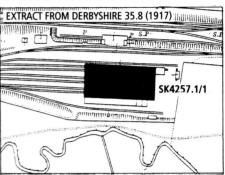

ASHBOURNE

Site SK1746.1; On the south side of the line, west of Ashbourne Station.

Ashbourne (NSR)SK1746.1/1A

A stone built 2TS dead ended shed with a slated hipped roof, it was located at SK17454612 and was opened in 1878. The facilities included a water tank and a coal stage sited outside of the shed entrance. The depot was closed by the LMS in November 1932 and, after a brief use as a servicing area, it was later demolished.

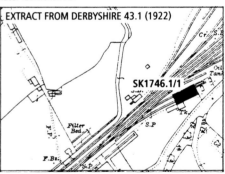

HAYFIELD

Site SK0386.1; On the south side of Hayfield Station.

Hayfield (MS&LR)SK0386.1/1A

A stone built 1TS dead ended shed with a slated gable style pitched roof, it was located at SK03628688 and was opened on March 1st, 1868. The facilities included a water tank. Although the depot was closed by BR in 1956 it was retained for servicing locomotives until the end of steam on the branch in c1959. The shed was subsequently demolished.

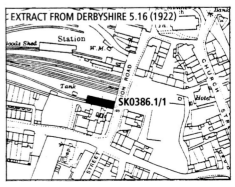

Site SK4374.1; On the east side of the line, south of Staveley Town Station.
Staveley (MS&LR)^{SK4374.1/1A}
A brick built 12TS shed with three through roads and a northlight pattern roof, it was located at SK43637443 and was opened on June 1st, 1892. The facilities included a ramped coal stage, water tank and turntable.

The shed was rebuilt ...
Staveley (BR)^{SK4374.1/1B}
Due to the poor condition of the roof the covered accommodation was reduced to five roads by the Eastern Region in 1951. The depot closed on June 14th, 1965 and was demolished in c1967.

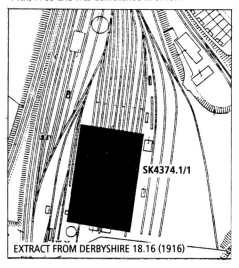

EXTRACT FROM DERBYSHIRE 18.16 (1916)

Site SK4175.2; In Staveley Devonshire Works.
Staveley Old Works (LMS)^{SK4175.2/1A}
A brick built 2TS through road shed with a shallow curved dutch barn roof, it was located at SK41877506 and was opened at some time after 1921. Details of the facilities are not known. The depot was closed by BR on October 4th, 1965 and subsequently demolished.

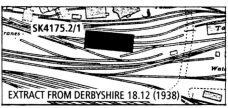

EXTRACT FROM DERBYSHIRE 18.12 (1938)

Site SK4174.1; In Staveley Iron Works.
Staveley New Works (MR)^{SK4174.1/1A}
A brick built 2TS dead ended shed with a slated gable style pitched roof, it was located at SK41337479. The opening date and details of the facilities are not known. The depot was closed by BR on October 4th, 1965 and found further use, as a garage for an industrial tractor, prior to demolition in c1995.

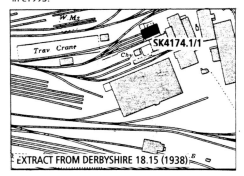

EXTRACT FROM DERBYSHIRE 18.15 (1938)

Locomotives for Staveley New and Old Works were hired from the MR from 1864 onwards.

Site SK4175.3; On the south side of Barrow Hill Station.
Barrow Hill (Staveley)^{SK4175.3/1A}
A stone built 4TS dead ended shed with a twin slated gable style roof, located at SK41707528 and opened in 1865. It was probably constructed by the Staveley Railway for the MR under the local locomotive operating agreement. Details of the facilities are not known. The depot closed in 1870 and found further use as the Devonshire Works Electrical Department and, later, as a steel fabrication works. It was finally demolished in 1987.

EXTRACT FROM DERBYSHIRE 18.12 (1938)

Replaced by ...
Site SK4175.1; On the east side of the Springwell Branch, west of Barrow Hill Station.
Barrow Hill (MR)^{SK4175.1/1A}
A brick built square 1RH shed with a slated multi-pitched roof, it was located at SK41337545 and was opened in 1870. The facilities included a water tank and a ramped coal stage.

The shed was re-roofed ...
Barrow Hill (LMS)^{SK4175.1/1B}
A new roof was installed in 1938.

The shed was re-roofed again ...
Barrow Hill (BR)^{SK4175.1/1C}
The roof was renewed with corrugated asbestos sheeting by the Eastern Region in 1958. Although the depot was closed to steam by BR on October 4th, 1965 it was then utilized as a diesel depot and, during this period, became the last operational roundhouse in the country. It was downgraded to a stabling point in 1987 and totally closed on February 11th, 1991. Following a successful campaign the shed was granted a listed building status and sold to Chesterfield Council which leased it out to the *Barrow Hill Engine Shed Society* in 1997.

The shed was renovated ...
Barrow Hill (BHESS)^{SK4175.1/1D}
A new roof in corrugated asbestos was installed by the Barrow Hill Engine Shed Society in 1997 and the building was restored to its former state, re-opening on July 18th, 1998.

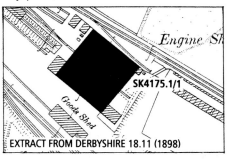

EXTRACT FROM DERBYSHIRE 18.11 (1898)

Site SK5268.1; On the west side of the Sutton in Ashfield line, south of Shirebrook North Station.
Langwith Junction (LD&ECR)^{SK5268.1/1A}
A 2TS dead ended shed, it was located at SK52956844 and was opened by the Lancashire, Derbyshire & East Coast Railway at an unknown date. The facilities included a turntable and coal stage. No further details are known except that it was demolished in c1896.

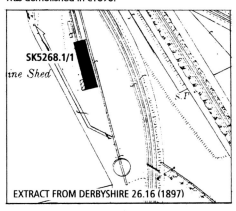

EXTRACT FROM DERBYSHIRE 26.16 (1897)

Replaced by ...
Langwith Junction (LD&ECR)^{SK5268.1/2A}
A brick built 2TS through road shed with a slated northlight pattern roof, it was sited slightly east of its predecessor at SK52966840 and was opened on November 16th, 1896. The facilities included the original turntable, later re-sited and enlarged, coal stage and water columns. The line was absorbed by the GCR in 1907.

Langwith Junction (GCR)^{SK5268.1/3A}
A timber built 3TS dead ended shed with a gable style pitched roof, it was located alongside of SK5268.1/2A at SK52986840 and was opened in c1910. The building had originally been employed as a carriage shed and was open sided up to a height of 4ft from the ground.

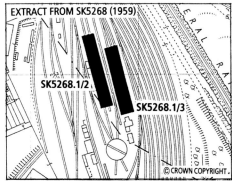

EXTRACT FROM SK5268 (1959)
© CROWN COPYRIGHT.

The depot was closed by BR on February 6th, 1966 and the site taken over by Davis's Wagon Works. The 3TS building was demolished but SK5268.1/2A was retained and utilized, remaining standing until 1993 at least.

Site SK0294.1; On the south side of Dinting Station
Dinting (MS&LR)^{SK0294.1/1A}
A brick built 1TS through road shed with a slated gable style pitched roof, located at SK02189460 and opened in 1894. The facilities included a coal stage and water tank. The depot was closed by the LNER in 1935, re-opened in 1942 and was finally closed by BR in 1954. The building was not demolished but was leased to *The Dinting Railway Centre* railway preservation group in 1968 which utilized the building until 1990 when it was abandoned. The shed was still standing in 1996.

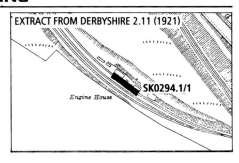

EXTRACT FROM DERBYSHIRE 2.11 (1921)

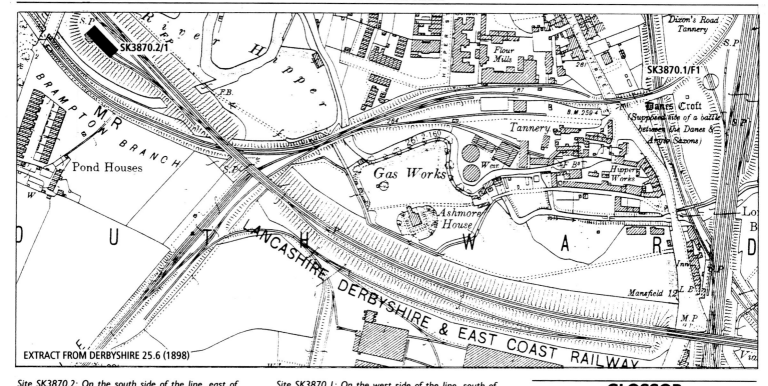

EXTRACT FROM DERBYSHIRE 25.6 (1898)

Site SK3870.2; On the south side of the line, east of Chesterfield Market Place Station.
Chesterfield Market Place (LD&ECR)^{SK3870.2/1A}
A timber built 2TS dead ended shed with a gable style roof, it was located at SK38137078 and was opened by the Lancashire, Derbyshire & East Coast Railway. The facilities included a water tank and turntable. The building was destroyed by a fire on April 19th, 1903.

Site SK3870.1; On the west side of the line, south of Chesterfield (MR) Station.
Chesterfield (MR)^{SK3870.1/F1}
A servicing area consisting of a turntable, located at SK38717077, engine pit, siding and water column, it was opened in c1900 and was closed by BR in 1967.

GLOSSOP

Site SK0394.1; In the vicinity of Glossop Station.
Glossop (Duke of Norfolk)^{SK0394.1/F1}
A servicing area consisting of an engine pit, it was approximately located at SK034942 and was opened by the Duke of Norfolk's Railway on June 9th, 1845. The line was worked from the outset by the Sheffield, Ashton-under-Lyme & Manchester Railway and was absorbed by them in 1846. No further details are known.

RUTLAND

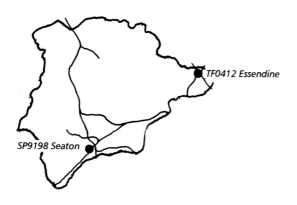

ESSENDINE

Site TF0412.1; On the east side of Essendine Station.
Essendine (GNR)^{TF0412.1/F1}
Some sort of facility, approximately located at TF047124, was provided here for the Bourne branch engine. No further details are available.

SEATON

Site SP9198.1; In the fork of the Stamford and Wansford lines, north of Seaton Station.
Seaton (L&NWR)^{SP9198.1/1A}
A timber built 1TS dead ended shed with a slated gable style pitched roof, it was located at SP91179823 and was opened on October 1st, 1894. There were no facilities. Although the building was severely damaged by fire on April 29th, 1957 the depot was not dispensed with by BR until the Uppingham branch was closed on June 1st, 1964.

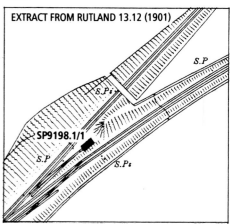

EXTRACT FROM RUTLAND 13.12 (1901)

LEICESTERSHIRE

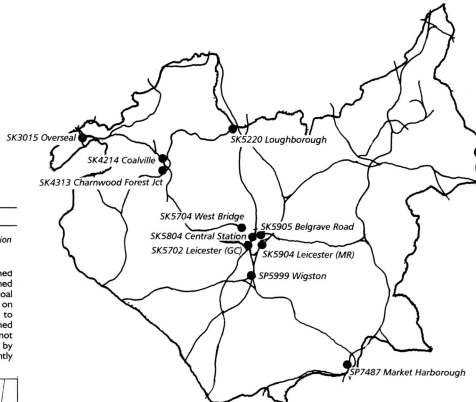

SK3015 Overseal
SK5220 Loughborough
SK4214 Coalville
SK4313 Charnwood Forest Jct
SK5704 West Bridge
SK5905 Belgrave Road
SK5804 Central Station
SK5702 Leicester (GC)
SK5904 Leicester (MR)
SP5999 Wigston
SP7487 Market Harborough

WIGSTON

Site SP5999.1; On the east side of Wigston Junction North, north of Wigston Station.
Wigston (MR)SP5999.1/1A

A brick built IRH with a triple gable style pitched roof, it was located at SP59409905 and was opened in 1873. The facilities included a water tank and coal stage. The depot was closed by the LMS on November 5th, 1934 and re-opened in 1944 to relieve the congestion at Leicester shed (SK5904.1/1) during its rebuilding. The shed was not totally dispensed with until it was finally closed by BR in April 1955. The building was subsequently demolished.

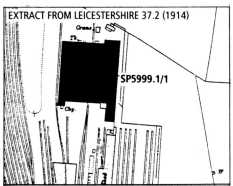

EXTRACT FROM LEICESTERSHIRE 37.2 (1914)

SP5999.1/1

MARKET HARBOROUGH

Site SP7487.1; On the west side of the line, at the north end of Market Harborough Station.
Market Harborough (L&NWR) SP7487.1/1A

A brick built 2TS through road tank shed, it was opened in 1864 and was located at SP74138765. The facilities also included a turntable, resited and enlarged in c1920, and a coal ramp. The depot was closed by BR on October 4th, 1965 and demolished in August 1966.

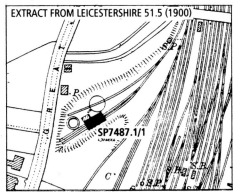

EXTRACT FROM LEICESTERSHIRE 51.5 (1900)

SP7487.1/1

OVERSEAL

Site SK3015.1; In the fork of the lines at Moira Junction South, south of Overseal Station.
Overseal (L&NW/MR) SK3015.1/1A

A brick built 2TS dead ended shed with a slated gable style roof, it was located at SK30621585 and was opened on September 1st, 1873. The facilities included a coal stage, with water tank over, and a turntable. The depot was closed by BR in August 1964 and was later demolished.

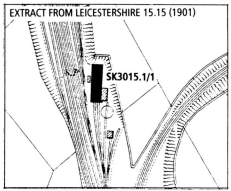

EXTRACT FROM LEICESTERSHIRE 15.15 (1901)

SK3015.1/1

LOUGHBOROUGH

Site SK5220.1; On the south side of the line, west of Loughborough (L&NWR) Station.
Loughborough (L&NWR) SK5220.1/1A

A brick built 4TS dead ended shed with a northlight pattern roof, it was located at SK52612002 and was opened on April 16th, 1883. The facilities included a water tank, coal stage and turntable. The depot was closed by the LMS in 1931, with the building being let out for private use. It was still standing in 1997.

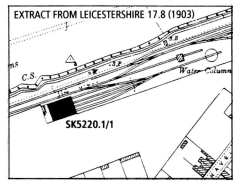

EXTRACT FROM LEICESTERSHIRE 17.8 (1903)

SK5220.1/1

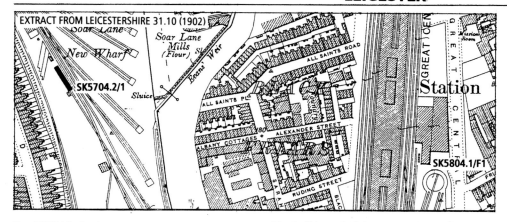

EXTRACT FROM LEICESTERSHIRE 31.10 (1902)

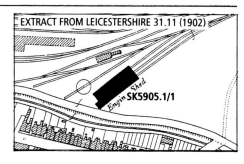

EXTRACT FROM LEICESTERSHIRE 31.11 (1902)

Site SK5804.1; On the east side of Leicester Central Station.
Leicester Central (GCR) SK5804.1/F1
A servicing area consisting of a turntable, located at SK58190465, coal stage, water column and sidings, it was opened on March 9th, 1899. The facility was still utilized in BR days and probably lasted until c1964.

Site SK5704.1; In the vicinity of West Bridge Station.
West Bridge (L&SR) SK5704.1/1A
A 1TS shed was opened here by the Leicester & Swannington Railway on July 17th, 1832. No further details are known.

Replaced by ...
Site SK5704.2; On the west side of the line, at the north end of West Bridge Station.
West Bridge (MR) SK5704.2/1A
A brick built 1TS dead ended shed with a slated gable style roof incorporating a water tank, it was located at SK57840475. No further details are known except that it was closed by the LMS on June 26th, 1926. The depot was not demolished immediately and locomotives continued to utilize the facilities into the 1930s at least. It was subsequently demolished.

Site SK5904.1; On the east side of the line, north of Leicester Midland Station.
Leicester No.1 (MCR) SK5904.1/1A
A brick built shed with a slated conical roof, it was located at SK59670451 and was opened by the Midland Counties Railway on July 5th, 1840.

The building was modified ...
Leicester No.1 (MR) SK5904.1/1B
At some stage the west side of the building was removed to facilitate widening of the main line.

Leicester No.2 (MR) SK5904.1/2A
A brick built 1RH with a slated conical roof, it was located at SK59700448 and was opened in 1855.

Leicester (MR) SK5904.1/3A
A brick built 3TS dead ended shed with a slated gable style roof, it was located at SK5968044 and was opened in 1893.

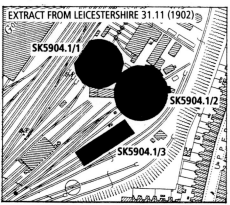

EXTRACT FROM LEICESTERSHIRE 31.11 (1902)

The facilities, which were steadily improved over the years, included a repair shop, coke/coal shed, water tank and additional turntable. The LMS commenced modernization of the depot in 1944 and the buildings were progressively demolished.

Replaced by ...
Leicester (LMS) SK5904.1/4A
A concrete built 1RH polygonal shed with a flat roof, it was located at SK59730453 and opened in 1945. The shed was closed to steam by BR on June 13th, 1965 and the former repair shop converted to a diesel servicing depot (as SK5904.1/5A). The roundhouse was demolished in 1970 and the site utilized for stabling and sidings.

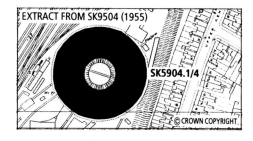

EXTRACT FROM SK9504 (1955)

© CROWN COPYRIGHT.

Site SK5702.1; On the east side of the line, south of Leicester Central Station.
Leicester (GCR) SK5702.1/1A
A brick built 4TS dead ended shed with a northlight pattern roof, it was located at SK57880294 and was opened in 1897. The facilities included a coal stage, water tank and turntable. The depot was closed by BR on July 6th, 1964 and was subsequently demolished.

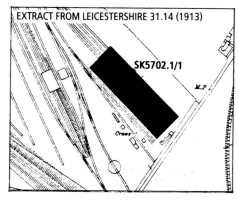

EXTRACT FROM LEICESTERSHIRE 31.14 (1913)

Site SK5905.1; On the south side of the line, east of Leicester Belgrave Road Station.
Belgrave Road (GNR) SK5905.1/1A
A brick built 3TS dead ended shed with a northlight pattern roof, it was located at SK59870547 and was opened in 1882. The facilities included a water tank, coal stage and turntable. By the time the depot was closed by BR on June 11th, 1955, the building had become totally derelict and was immediately demolished.

Site SK4313.1; On the east side of the Nuneaton line, south of Coalville (MR) Station.
Charnwood Forest Jct (L&NW/MR) SK4313.1/1A
A timber built 1TS dead ended shed with a gable style roof, it was located at SK43411333 and was opened on September 1st, 1873. The facilities included a water tank and turntable. The depot was closed by the LMS on July 23rd, 1928 and was subsequently demolished.

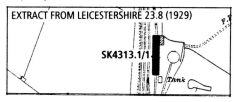

EXTRACT FROM LEICESTERSHIRE 23.8 (1929)

Site SK4314.1; In the vicinity of Coalville (L&NWR) Station.
Coalville (L&NWR) SK4314.1/F1
Some sort of facility was provided here. No further details are available.

Site SK4214.1; On the east side of Coalville (MR) Station
Coalville (L&SR) SK4214.1/1A
A brick built 1TS dead ended shed with a slated gable style roof, it was located at SK42551437 and was opened by the Leicester & Swannington Railway on April 22nd, 1833. The facilities included a turntable. At some stage, possibly in LMS days, the building was demolished with the shed road and engine pit being utilized right up until the depot was closed.

Coalville (MR) SK4214.1/2A
A brick built 3TS shed with one through road and a slated gable style roof, it was located at SK42631438 and was opened in 1890. As well as the existing turntable the facilities also included a ramped coal stage and water tank.

The shed was re-roofed ...
Coalville (BR) SK4214.1/2B
The roof was re-clad with corrugated asbestos sheeting by the London Midland Region and the depot was closed on October 4th, 1965. The building stood in a derelict condition until demolition in 1969.

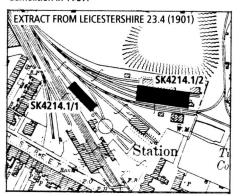

EXTRACT FROM LEICESTERSHIRE 23.4 (1901)

STAFFORDSHIRE

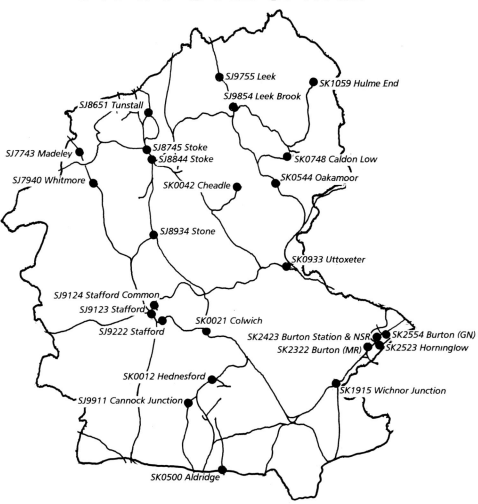

SJ9755 Leek

SK1059 Hulme End

SJ9854 Leek Brook

SJ8651 Tunstall

SJ7743 Madeley

SJ8745 Stoke
SJ8844 Stoke

SK0748 Caldon Low

SJ7940 Whitmore

SK0544 Oakamoor

SK0042 Cheadle

SJ8934 Stone

SK0933 Uttoxeter

SJ9124 Stafford Common
SJ9123 Stafford
SK0021 Colwich
SJ9222 Stafford

SK2423 Burton Station & NSR
SK2554 Burton (GN)
SK2322 Burton (MR)
SK2523 Horninglow

SK0012 Hednesford

SJ9911 Cannock Junction

SK1915 Wichnor Junction

SK0500 Aldridge

In an attempt to open up the scenic Manifold Valley in cost-effective manner, the North Staffordshire Railway used the Light Railways Act, and a 2ft 6in gauge, for the Leek & Manifold Light Railway, which opened in June 1904. Alas the coming of the motor bus and car ensured the railway a short life, and it closed in 1934.

The line's engine shed (SK1059.1/1A) was at the **Hulme End** terminus - seen here about 1925. After closure the entire terminus site was put to other use and the engine shed itself still stood in 1999, in service as a council depot.

Authors' Collection

BURTON

Site SK2523.0; At the end of the Horninglow Goods Spur, on the east side of the line, north of Burton Station.
Horninglow (L&NWR) SK2523.0/1A
A 2TS shed, approximately located at SK251238, was opened here in 1868. The depot was closed in 1882. No further details are known.

Replaced by ...
Site SK2523.1; On the east side of Horninglow Goods Spur, on the east side of the main line, north of Burton Station.
Horninglow (L&NWR) SK2523.1/1A
A brick built 6TS dead ended shed with a northlight pattern roof, it was located at SK25152375 and was opened in 1882. The facilities included a water tank, coal stage and turntable.

The shed was re-roofed ...
Horninglow (LMS) SK2523.1/1B
A louvre style roof with brick screen was installed in 1946 and the depot was closed by BR on September 12th, 1960. The building was let out for private use and was still standing in 1997, being utilized as a keg and barrel depot for a local brewery.

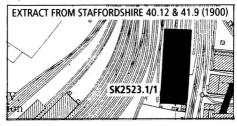
EXTRACT FROM STAFFORDSHIRE 40.12 & 41.9 (1900)
SK2523.1/1

Site SK2423.1; In the vicinity of Burton Station.
Burton (MR) SK2423.1/F1
A servicing area consisting of a coke stage and engine pit, it was approximately located at SK241231 and was opened in 1849.

Replaced by ...
Site SK2322.0; South of Burton Station.
Burton (MR) SK2322.0/1A
A 2TS shed was opened here in June 1859 and was closed in 1870. No further details are known.

Replaced by ...
Site SK2322.1; On the west side of the line, south of Burton Station.
Burton No.1 (MR) SK2322.1/1A
A brick built 1RH shed with a slated triple gable style roof, it was located at SK23692267 and was opened in 1870. The facilities included a ramped coal stage and water tank.

The shed was enlarged in 1892 ....
Burton No.2 (MR) SK2322.1/2A
A brick built 1RH shed with a slated triple gable style roof was constructed adjacently to the east wall of No.1 shed (SK2322.1/1A) at SK23722264.

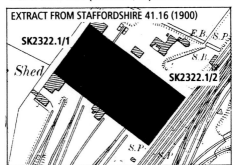
EXTRACT FROM STAFFORDSHIRE 41.16 (1900)
SK2322.1/1
Shed
SK2322.1/2

The depot was closed by BR in September 1966 and although No.2 shed was partially demolished to accommodate an access line to the diesel depot built in the shed yard (SK2322.1/3A) the buildings were let out for private use. They remained standing until demolition in 1995/6.

Site SK2554.1; On the east side of Wetmoor Sidings, east of the line, north of Burton Station.
Burton (GNR) SK2554.1/F1
A servicing area consisting of a turntable, located at SK25255432, water tank and siding, it was opened in August 1878. The facility lasted into BR days.

EXTRACT FROM STAFFORDSHIRE 41.9 (1884)
SK2554.1/F1
Gravel Pit

Site SK2423.1; On the west side of the line, north of Burton Station.
Burton (NSR) SK2423.1/1A
A 4TS shed with one through road, it was located at SK24342345 and was opened in 1865. The facilities included a turntable. The depot was closed by the LMS on July 6th, 1923 and the buildings demolished in 1930.

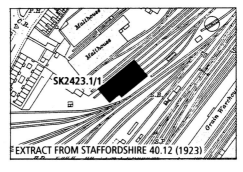
SK2423.1/1
EXTRACT FROM STAFFORDSHIRE 40.12 (1923)

HEDNESFORD

Site SK0012.1; In the vicinity of Hednesford Station.
Hednesford (CCR) SK0012.1/F1
A servicing area, composed of sidings, was established here by the Cannock Chase Railway in 1863. No further details are known.

CANNOCK JUNCTION

Site SJ9911.1; In the vicinity of Cannock Junction.
Cannock Junction (SSR) SJ9911.1/F1
Some sort of facility was established here on February 1st, 1858 by the South Staffs Railway. No further details are known.

ALDRIDGE

Site SK0500.1; In the vicinity of Aldridge Station.
Aldridge (MR) SK0500.1/F1
Some form of facility, approximately located at SK052006, was established here on July 1st, 1884. No further details are known.

STONE

Site SJ8934.1; In the vicinity of Stone Station.
Stone (NSR) SJ8934.1/1A
A 1TS shed, approximately located at SJ896346 was opened here on April 3rd, 1848. No further details are known.

MADELEY

Site SJ7743.1; On the east side of the line, at the south end of Madeley Station.
Madeley (GJR) SJ7743.1/1A
A 1TS dead ended shed, it was located at SJ77474371 and was opened by the Grand Junction Railway in 1839. No further details are known except that it was still standing, possibly in use, in 1898.

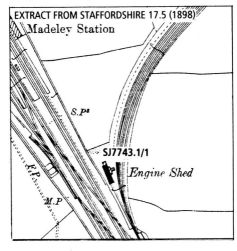
EXTRACT FROM STAFFORDSHIRE 17.5 (1898)
Madeley Station
S.P.
SJ7743.1/1
Engine Shed
M.P

CHEADLE

Site SK0042.1; At the east end of Cheadle Station.
Cheadle (NSR) SK0042.1/F1
A servicing area, located at SK00674274 and consisting of a water tank, coal stage and siding. No further details are known.

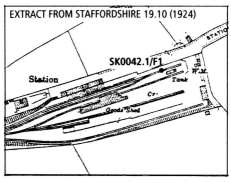
EXTRACT FROM STAFFORDSHIRE 19.10 (1924)
SK0042.1/F1
Station
Tank

TUNSTALL

Site SJ8651.1; In the vicinity of Tunstall Station.
Tunstall (NSR) SJ8651.1/F1
A servicing area consisting of a coke/coal stage and engine pit, approximately located at SJ866512, was opened here in 1882. No further details are known.

WHITMORE

Site SJ7940.1; In the vicinity of Whitmore Station.
Whitmore (GJR) SJ7940.1/1A
A 1TS shed, approximately located at SJ795404, was opened here by the Grand Junction Railway in 1837. The facilities included a coke stage and water column on each platform of the station. No further details are known.

STAFFORD

Site SJ9222.1; On the east side of the line, south of Stafford Station.
Stafford (GJR)SJ9222.1/1A
A 2TS dead ended shed, located at SJ92262231, was opened here by the Grand Junction Railway*. No further details are known except that it remained standing until BR days.

Stafford (GJR)SJ9222.1/2A
A 1TS dead ended shed, located at SJ92362219, was opened here by the Grand Junction Railway*. No further details are known except that it found further use as a stores and remained standing until BR days.

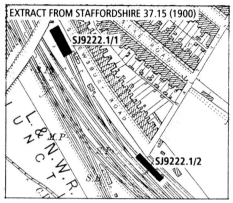

*Either one or both of these sheds may have opened on July 4th, 1837.

Site SJ9123.1; On the west side of the line, at the north end of Stafford Station.
Stafford No.1 (L&NWR)SJ9123.1/1A
A brick built 4TS dead ended shed with a twin slated hipped roof, it was located at SJ91622312 and was opened in 1852. After the construction of No.2 shed (SJ9123.1/2) this was designated as No.1 and was utilized by the "Northern Division". The building was demolished by the LMS in 1937.

Stafford No.2 (L&NWR)SJ9123.1/2A
A brick built 6TS dead ended shed with a triple slated hipped roof, it was located at SJ91602309 and was opened in 1861 for use by the "Southern Division".

The shed was re-roofed ...
Stafford No.2 (LMS)SJ9123.1/2B
A louvre-style roof with brick screen was installed in 1947. The depot was closed by BR on July 19th, 1965 and stood semi-derelict for many years before being leased out for industrial use. It was still standing in 1997.

The facilities included a turntable, coal stage and water tank.

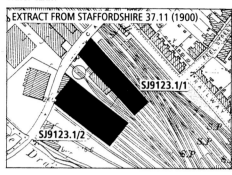

Site SJ9124.1; On the south side of the line, at the west end of Stafford Common Station.
Stafford Common (S&UR)SJ9124.1/1A
A timber built 1TS through road shed with a slated gable style roof, it was located at SJ91982475 and was opened by the Stafford & Uttoxeter Railway on December 23rd, 1867. The line was absorbed by the GNR on August 1st, 1881 and the building was destroyed by a fire just shortly afterwards, on November 22nd of the same year. After this locomotives were serviced at the nearby L&NWR sheds (SJ9123.1/1&2).

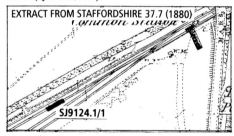

CALDON LOW

Site SK0748.1; On the east side of the line, south of Caldon Low Quarries.
Caldon Low (NSR)SK0748.1/1A
A 3ft 6in gauge timber built 2TS dead ended shed with a slated gable style roof, it was located at SK07484822. Details of the facilities are not known. The depot was closed, along with the line, on April 1st, 1932.

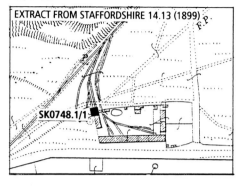

HULME END

Site SK1059.1; At the east end of Hulme End Station.
Hulme End (L&MVLR)SK1059.1/1A
A 2ft 6in gauge timber built 2TS dead ended shed with a dutch barn style roof, it was located at SK10355932 and was opened by the Leek & Manifold Valley Light Railway on June 27th, 1904. The facilities included a water tank. The line was worked by the NSR and the depot was closed by the LMS on March 12th, 1934. The building was let out for private use and was still standing in 1999, in use as a council depot.

WICHNOR JUNCTION

Site SK1915.1; In the fork of the Tamworth and Lichfield lines, south of Barton & Walton Station.
Wichnor Junction (SSR)SK1915.1/1A
A 3TS shed with two through roads, it was located at SK19141534 and was opened by the South Staffs Railway in 1854. The facilities included a coal stage and turntable. The line was absorbed by the L&NWR on February 1st, 1861 and the depot was closed in 1896.

A servicing point was then established ...
Wichnor Junction (L&NWR)SK1915.1/F1
The engine pits and sidings were utilized until c1967.

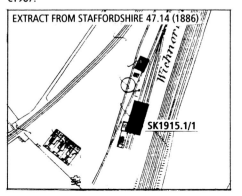

OAKAMOOR

Site SK0544.1; On the east side of a spur line at the north end of Oakamoor Station.
Oakamoor (NSR)SK0544.1/1A
A timber built 1TS dead ended shed with a lean-to style roof, it was located at SK05424474 and was opened in 1917. The shed was built solely for the use of the battery locomotive BEL2, which shunted the adjacent copper works sidings and the facilities included a battery charger. The depot was closed upon the withdrawal of the locomotive by BR in 1963.

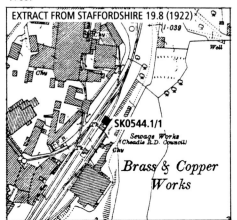

COLWICH

Site SK0021.1; On the north side of the line, at the west end of Colwich Station.
Colwich (NSR)SK0021.1/1A
A brick built 1TS dead ended shed with a gable style slated roof and a water tank surmounting the entrance, it was located at SK00792122 and was opened on May 1st, 1849. Additional facilities included a turntable. Although the depot was officially closed in 1896 it was, for some years, utilized as a servicing point for locomotives "running in" from Stoke Works. The building was demolished in c1936.

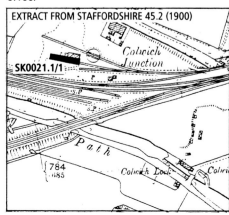

UTTOXETER

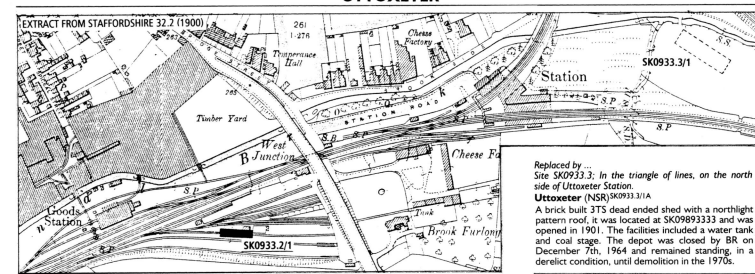

EXTRACT FROM STAFFORDSHIRE 32.2 (1900)

SK0933.2/1

Site SK0933.1; West of Uttoxeter Station.
Uttoxeter (NSR)[SK0933.1/1A]
A shed was opened here, *"west of Pinfold Crossing"* on August 7th, 1848. It was closed in 1850 and converted to a cheese warehouse. No further details are known.

Replaced by ...
Site SK0933.2; On the south side of the line, west of Uttoxeter Station.
Uttoxeter (NSR)[SK0933.2/1A]
A 1TS through road shed, it was opened in 1850 and was located at SK09443316. The facilities included a coal stage. The depot was closed in 1901 and was subsequently demolished.

Replaced by ...
Site SK0933.3; In the triangle of lines, on the north side of Uttoxeter Station.
Uttoxeter (NSR)[SK0933.3/1A]
A brick built 3TS dead ended shed with a northlight pattern roof, it was located at SK09893333 and was opened in 1901. The facilities included a water tank and coal stage. The depot was closed by BR on December 7th, 1964 and remained standing, in a derelict condition, until demolition in the 1970s.

EXTRACT FROM STAFFORDSHIRE 32.2 (1920)

SK0933.3/1

STOKE

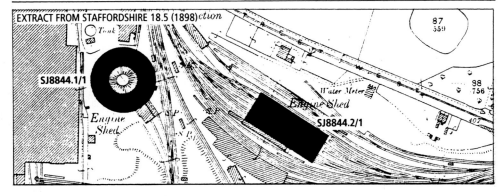

EXTRACT FROM STAFFORDSHIRE 18.5 (1898)

SJ8844.1/1

SJ8844.2/1

Site SJ8745.1; In the vicinity of Stoke Station.
Stoke (NSR)[SJ8745.1/1A]
A shed was opened here on April 17th, 1848 and closed in 1852. No further details are known

Replaced by ...
Site SJ8844.1; On the west side of the line, south of Stoke Station.
Stoke (NSR)[SJ8844.1/1A]
A brick built 1RH shed with a continous pitched roof, it was located at SJ88234489 and was opened in 1852. The facilities included a water tank and coal stage.

The shed was re-roofed ...
Stoke (LMS)[SJ8844.1/1B]
A new roof, of the continuous pitched variety was installed in 1935. This construction only covered about half of the stalls, with the remainder being left open to the elements. The shed was closed by BR on August 7th, 1967 and the building lasted until the 1970s before being demolished.

Site SJ8844.2; On the east side of the line, south of Stoke Station.
Stoke (NSR)[SJ8844.2/1A]
A brick built 6TS dead ended shed with twin slated hipped roofs, it was known as the *"new"* shed and was located across the main line from SJ8844.1/1, at SJ88384485. The building was opened in 1872.

It was enlarged ...
Stoke (NSR)[SJ8844.2/1B]
A timber built 1TS dead ended extension with a slated hipped roof, known as *"the Parlour"* was built along the northern wall in 1888. It was removed in 1934 to accommodate coaling and ash disposal improvements.

It was enlarged again ...
Stoke (NSR)[SJ8844.2/1C]
A brick built 2TS extension with a slated gable style roof with built along the southern wall in 1905. It was constructed to house railmotor units and became known as *"the motor shed"*. It was possibly at this time that the original building SJ8842.2/1A was modified to a through road structure.

It was rebuilt ...
Stoke (LMS)[SJ8844.2/1D]
The northern three tracks were re-roofed in a single pitch style with a brick screen in 1939. The outbreak of war precluded the completion of the improvements and the southern section remained covered with the original hipped roof until it was removed by BR, the tracks then remaining uncovered until the whole depot was closed on August 7th, 1967.

The facilities on the eastern side of the line, which were steadily upgraded, included a water tank and coal stage (later replaced with a coaling plant).

LEEK

Site SJ9755.1; On the west side of the line, south of Leek Station.
Leek (NSR)[SJ9755.1/1A]
A 1TS dead ended shed, it was opened on July 1st, 1867 and was located at SJ97985570. No further details are known except that it was closed in c1912 and was replaced by Leek Brook shed (SJ9854.1/1).

EXTRACT FROM STAFFORDSHIRE 8.9 (1898)

SJ9755.1/1

LEEK BROOK

Site SJ9854.1; In the triangle of the Waterhouses and Churnet lines, at Cheddleton Junction, south of Leek Station.
Leek Brook (NSR)[SJ9854.1/1A]
A timber built 1TS dead ended shed with a slated gable style roof, it was located at SJ98235415 and was opened on June 5th, 1905. The facilities included a water tank and coal stage. The depot was closed by the LMS on January 4th, 1932 and was subsequently demolished.

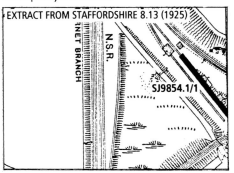

EXTRACT FROM STAFFORDSHIRE 8.13 (1925)

SJ9854.1/1

CHESHIRE

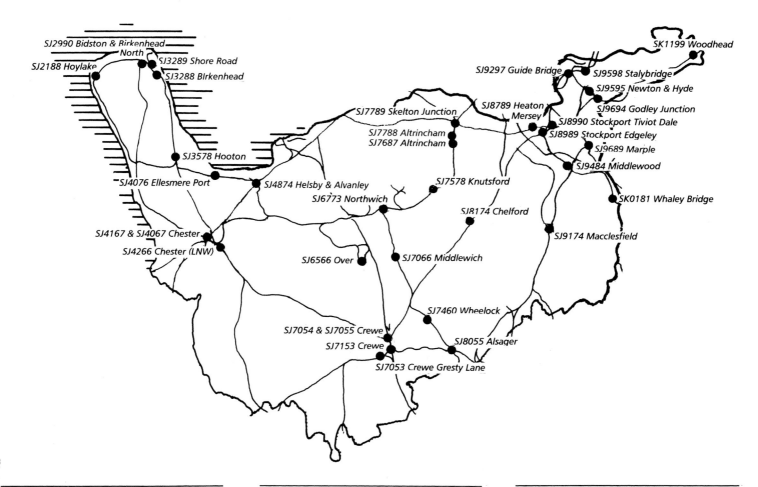

SK1199 Woodhead
SJ2990 Bidston & Birkenhead North
SJ3289 Shore Road
SJ2188 Hoylake
SJ3288 Birkenhead
SJ9297 Guide Bridge
SJ9598 Stalybridge
SJ9595 Newton & Hyde
SJ7789 Skelton Junction
SJ8789 Heaton Mersey
SJ9694 Godley Junction
SJ7788 Altrincham
SJ8990 Stockport Tiviot Dale
SJ7687 Altrincham
SJ8989 Stockport Edgeley
SJ3578 Hooton
SJ9689 Marple
SJ4076 Ellesmere Port
SJ9484 Middlewood
SJ4874 Helsby & Alvanley
SJ7578 Knutsford
SK0181 Whaley Bridge
SJ6773 Northwich
SJ4167 & SJ4067 Chester
SJ8174 Chelford
SJ4266 Chester (LNW)
SJ9174 Macclesfield
SJ6566 Over
SJ7066 Middlewich
SJ7460 Wheelock
SJ7054 & SJ7055 Crewe
SJ8055 Alsager
SJ7153 Crewe
SJ7053 Crewe Gresty Lane

HEATON MERSEY

Site SJ8789.1; On the south side of the fork of the Cheadle and Didsbury lines, west of Tiviot Dale Station.
Heaton Mersey (CLC) SJ8789.1/1A
A brick built 8TS dead ended shed with a northlight pattern roof, it was located at SJ87778997 and was opened in January 1889. The facilities included a water tank, coal stage and 50ft turntable.

The shed was re-roofed ...
Heaton Mersey (BR) SJ8789.1/1B
A corrugated iron louvre style multi-pitched roof was installed by the London Midland Region in 1952. At the same time the turntable was increased in size to 70ft and re-sited. The depot was closed on May 6th, 1968 and was subsequently demolished.

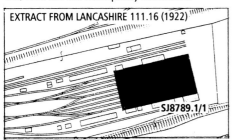

EXTRACT FROM LANCASHIRE 111.16 (1922)
SJ8789.1/1

WHEELOCK

Site SJ7460.1; In the vicinity of Wheelock Station.
Wheelock (NSR) SJ7460.1/1A
A shed was built here at some time prior to 1871. No further details are known.

MARPLE

Site SJ9689.1; On the east side of the line, at the south end of Marple Station.
Marple (GC/MR) SJ9689.1/F1
A stabling point consisting of a 50ft turntable, located at SJ96358923 and sidings. It opened in 1898 and closed in 1915. No further details are known.

EXTRACT FROM CHESHIRE 20.2 (1898)
Tennis Ground
SJ9689.1/F1

CHELFORD

Site SJ8174.1; On the west side of the line, at the south end of Chelford Station.
Chelford (L&NWR) SJ8174.1/1A
A 1TS dead ended shed located at SJ81377485 and opened in 1860. The facilities included a water tank. It was closed and demolished in 1880 to accommodate enlargements to the cattle dock.

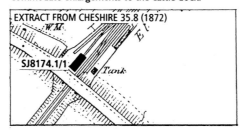

EXTRACT FROM CHESHIRE 35.8 (1872)
W.M.
SJ8174.1/1
Tank

GUIDE BRIDGE

Site SJ9297.1; In the vicinity of Guide Bridge Station.
Guide Bridge (MS&LR) SJ9297.1/F1
Some form of facility, approximately located at SJ928976, was established here. No further details are known.

HELSBY & ALVANLEY

Site SJ4874.1; On the east side of the line, north of Helsby & Alvanley Station.
Helsby & Alvanley (West Cheshire) SJ4874.1/F1
A servicing area consisting of a turntable, located at SJ48617483, and siding was opened here by the West Cheshire Railway on September 1st, 1869.

The facility was improved ...
Helsby & Alvanley (West Cheshire) SJ4874.1/1A
A 2TS dead ended shed with a northlight pattern roof was constructed adjacently to the turntable at SJ48617484 and was opened in 1893. The facilities also included a coal stage. The line was absorbed by the CLC which closed the depot in 1929. The shed was subsequently demolished.

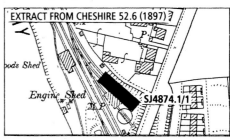

EXTRACT FROM CHESHIRE 52.6 (1897)
...ods Shed
Engine Shed
SJ4874.1/1

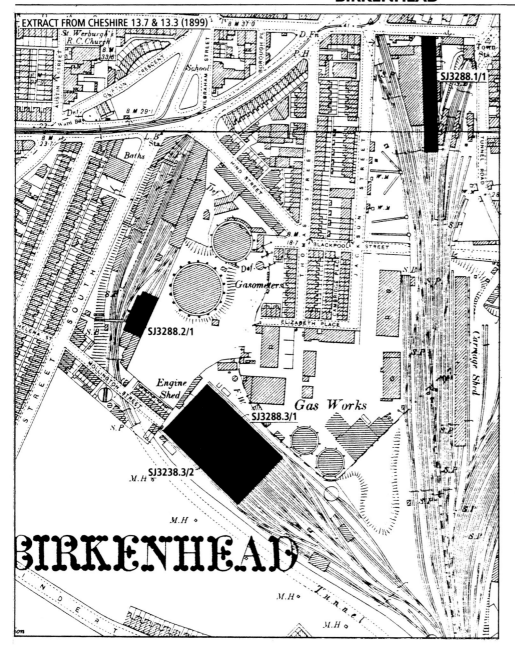

EXTRACT FROM CHESHIRE 13.7 & 13.3 (1899)

SJ3288.1/1

SJ3288.2/1

SJ3288.3/1

SJ3238.3/2

BIRKENHEAD

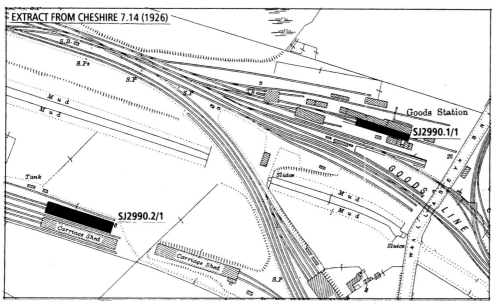

EXTRACT FROM CHESHIRE 7.14 (1926)

Goods Station

SJ2990.1/1

SJ2990.2/1

Site SJ3288.1; On the west side of Birkenhead Town Station.

Birkenhead Town (C&BR) SJ3288.1/1A
A brick built 3TS dead ended shed with a slated northlight roof, it was located at SJ32478848 and was opened by the Chester & Birkenhead Railway on September 23rd, 1840. Details of the facilities are not known.

The building was enlarged ...
Birkenhead Town (GWR/L&NWR) SJ3288.1/1B
At some stage the shed was extended. The depot closed in 1878.

Replaced by ...
Site SJ3288.3; On the west side of the line, south of Birkenhead Town Station.
Mollington Street (GWR) SJ3288.3/1A
A brick built 8TS dead ended shed with a northlight pattern roof, it was located at SJ32288821 and was opened in 1878.

The shed was re-roofed ...
Mollington Street (BR) SJ3288.3/1B
A multi-pitched roof was installed by the London Midland Region in 1961.

Adjoined on the southern wall by ...
Mollington Street (L&NWR) SJ3288.3/2A
A brick built 8TS dead ended shed with a northlight pattern roof, located at SJ32268819 and opened in 1878.

The shed was rebuilt ...
Mollington Street (LMS) SJ3288.3/2B
The length of the building was reduced and a multi-pitched roof installed in 1936.

The shed was re-roofed ...
Mollington Street (BR) SJ3288.3/2C
The roof was refurbished by the London Midland Region in 1961.

The facilities included a coal stage and turntable for the use of each company. The shed was closed to steam by BR on November 6th, 1967 and found further use as a diesel depot until November 24th, 1985. It was demolished in July 1987.

Site SJ3288.2; On the east side of the line, at the south end of Birkenhead Central Station.
Central (Mersey) SJ3288.2/1A
A 3TS dead ended shed located at SJ32198831 and opened by the Mersey Railway on January 20th, 1886. The facilities included a turntable. The depot closed on May 3rd, 1903 and was utilized as a carriage shed, surviving until at least 1967.

Site SJ2990.2; On the west side of the line, north of Birkenhead North Station.
Bidston (MS&LR) SJ2990.2/1A
A brick built 2TS dead ended shed with a northlight pattern roof, it was located at SJ29429049 and was opened in 1897. The facilities included a water tank and coal stage.

The shed was re-roofed ...
Bidston (LNER) SJ2990.2/1B
At some date, probably during LNER days, a new roof with brick screen was installed. The depot was closed by BR on February 11th, 1963 and was subsequently demolished.

Site SJ2990.1; In the Goods Station on the east side of the line, north of Birkenhead North Station.
Birkenhead North (Wirral) SJ2990.1/1A
A corrugated iron 2TS shed with one through road and a pitched corrugated iron roof, it was located at SJ29719057 and was opened by the Wirral Railway on January 2nd, 1888. The facilities included a water tank and coaling shed.

Continued ...

The shed was re-roofed ...

Birkenhead North (LMS) SJ2990.1/1B

A corrugated iron dutch barn style roof was installed in c1934 and the depot was closed on March 13th, 1938 and was subsequently demolished.

Site SJ3289.1; On the south side of the line, west of Shore Road Goods Station.

Shore Road (CLC) SJ3289.1/1A

A timber built 1TS dead ended shed with a gable style roof, it was located at SJ32308946 and was opened in 1888. There were no facilities. The depot was closed by BR on June 5th, 1961 and it was then utilized for private shunters. It has since been demolished.

EXTRACT FROM CHESHIRE 13.3 (1899)

SJ3289.1/1

MACCLESFIELD

Site SJ9174.1; In the goods yard on the east side of Hibel Road Station.

Macclesfield (MS&LR) SJ9174.1/1A

A brick built 2TS through road shed with a slated hipped roof, located at SJ91837421 and opened on August 2nd, 1869. The facilities included a coal stage, water tank and turntable. The depot was closed by the LNER in 1933 and was utilized as a stabling point until demolition in the 1950s.

Macclesfield (NSR) SJ9174.1/2A

A brick built 3TS through road shed, it was located at SJ91837421 and opened in 1864. The facilities included a coal stage, water tank and a 40ft turntable which was enlarged to 50ft in 1914.

The shed was re-roofed ...

Macclesfield (LMS) SJ9174.1/2B

By 1936 the original roof, which had deteriorated badly, was replaced by one of a shallow louvre style multi-pitched variety. The depot was closed by BR on June 12th, 1961, but was retained as a signing-on point until 1965 when the shed buildings were demolished.

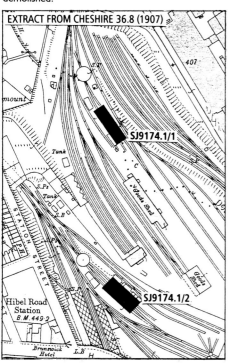

EXTRACT FROM CHESHIRE 36.8 (1907)

SJ9174.1/1

SJ9174.1/2

OVER

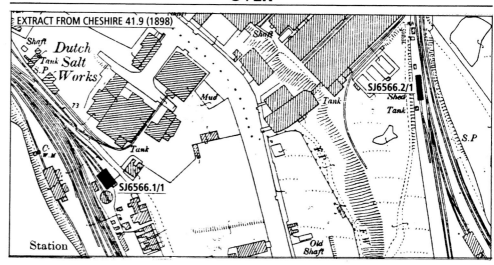

EXTRACT FROM CHESHIRE 41.9 (1898)

SJ6566.1/1

SJ6566.2/1

Site SJ6566.1; On the east side of the line, north of Winsford & Over Station.

Winsford & Over (West Cheshire) SJ6566.1/1A

A 1TS dead ended shed, it was located at SJ65346657 and was opened by the West Cheshire Railway on June 1st, 1870. The facilities included a water tank and turntable.

The shed was enlarged ...

Winsford & Over (CLC) SJ6566.1/1B

The building was increased in size to a 2TS dead ended shed in 1892 and it was closed by the LNER in July 1929.

Site SJ6566.2; On the west side of the line, north of Over & Wharton Station.

Over & Wharton (L&NWR) SJ6566.2/1A

A brick built 1TS dead ended shed with a slated gable style roof, it was located at SJ65646665 and was opened on June 1st, 1882. The facilities included a water tank. The depot was closed by the LMS on August 30th, 1947.

A stabling point was then established ...

Over & Wharton (LMS) SJ6566.2/F1

The building was demolished and locomotives were then, until about 1964, serviced on the shed road.

NORTHWICH

Site SJ6773.1; On the east side of Northwich Station.

Northwich (West Cheshire) SJ6773.1/1A

A brick built 2TS shed, it was located at SJ67007388 and was opened by the West Cheshire Railway on September 1st, 1869. The facilities included a turntable.

The shed was enlarged ...

Northwich (West Cheshire) SJ6773.1/1B

The building was increased to a 4TS dead ended shed in December 1876 and a larger turntable was installed.

The shed was re-roofed ...

Northwich (BR) SJ6773.1/1C

An LMS style louvre roof with brick screen was installed by the Eastern Region in 1948. The depot closed to steam on March 4th, 1968 and was utilized for diesel servicing until 1987. It was demolished in February 1991.

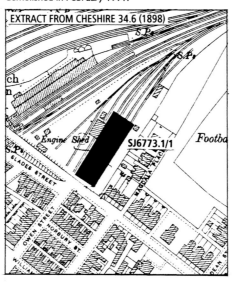

EXTRACT FROM CHESHIRE 34.6 (1898)

SJ6773.1/1

ALSAGER

Site SJ8055.1; On the south side of the line, east of Alsager Station.

Alsager (NSR) SJ8055.1/F1

A servicing area consisting of a coal stage, water tank and siding was opened here in 1866 and closed in 1890. No further details are known.

Replaced by ....

Alsager (NSR) SJ8055.1/1A

A brick built 4TS dead ended shed with a northlight pattern roof, it was located at SJ80635517 and opened in 1890. The facilities included a water tank, coal stage and turntable.

The shed was re-roofed ....

Alsager (LMS) SJ8055.1/1B

The shed was rebuilt with a louvre-style roof in 1945 and the depot was closed by BR on June 19th, 1962.

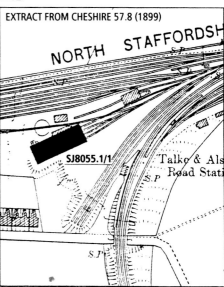

EXTRACT FROM CHESHIRE 57.8 (1899)

SJ8055.1/1

CHESTER

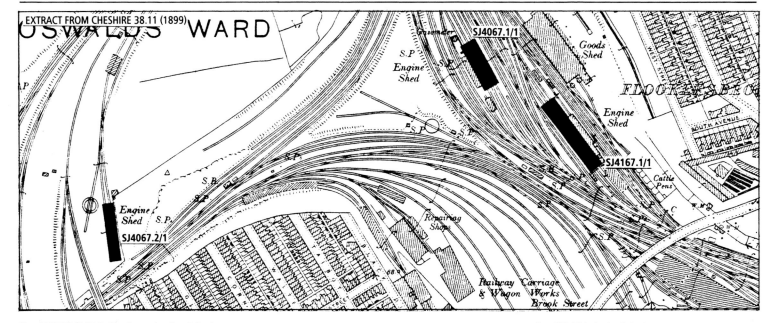

EXTRACT FROM CHESHIRE 38.11 (1899)

Site SJ4067&4167.1; On the east side of the line, at the north end of Chester General Station.

Chester (C&BR)SJ4167.1/1A

A brick built 3TS through road shed with a slated gable style roof, it was located at SJ41066702 and was opened by the Chester & Birkenhead Railway in 1856. The facilities included a coal stage and water tank.

The shed was re-roofed ...

Chester (GWR)SJ4167.1/1B

The building was re-roofed in 1928 and, at the same time, new messrooms were added and the coal stage improved.

Chester (C&CR)SJ4067.1/1A

A brick built 3TS through road shed with a slated gable style roof, it was located at SJ40976739 and was opened by the Chester & Crewe Railway on October 1st, 1840. The facilities included a water tank and coal stage. The L&NWR opened a new depot (SJ4266.1/1) in 1870 and the building was handed over to the GWR.

The shed was rebuilt ...

Chester (BR)SJ4067.1/1B

The shed was rebuilt with a northlight pattern roof and brick screen by the London Midland Region in 1957 with further improvements being made to the portals in 1960.

The depot was closed to steam by BR in April 1960 and both buildings were utilized for dmu and locomotive servicing until demolition in 1998.

Site SJ4067.2; On the east side of the line, at the north end of Northgate Station.

Northgate (CLC)SJ4067.2/1A

A brick built 2TS dead ended shed with a slated gable style roof, it was located at SJ40616713 and was opened on November 2nd, 1874. The facilities included a coal stage and turntable.

The shed was re-roofed ...

Northgate (BR)SJ4067.2/1B

The shed was rebuilt with a northlight pattern roof by the Eastern Region in 1950. The depot was closed in January 1960 and was subsequently demolished.

Site SJ4266.1; In the fork of the Warrington and Crewe lines, east of Chester General Station.

Chester (L&NWR)SJ4266.1/1A

A brick built 8TS dead ended shed with a twin slated hipped roof, it was located at SJ42306670 and was opened in 1870. The facilities included a ramped coal stage, with water tank over, and a 42ft turntable.

The shed was re-roofed...

Chester (LMS)SJ4266.1/1B

The shed was rebuilt with a louvre-style roof and brick screen in 1944. The depot was closed by BR on June 5th, 1967 and was subsequently demolished.

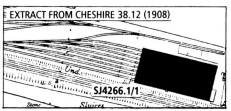

EXTRACT FROM CHESHIRE 38.12 (1908)

GODLEY JUNCTION

Site SJ9694.1; On the south side of Godley Junction Station.

Godley Junction (GCR)SJ9694.1/F1

A servicing area consisting of a turntable, located at SJ96939453, coal stage and engine pits. No further details are known.

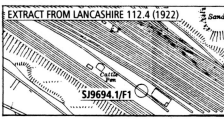

EXTRACT FROM LANCASHIRE 112.4 (1922)

SKELTON JUNCTION

Site SJ7789.1; In the fork of the Timperley and Warrington lines, south of Timperley Station.

Skelton Junction (CLC)SJ7789.1/F1

A servicing area consisting of a turntable, located at SJ77688935, and siding was established here.

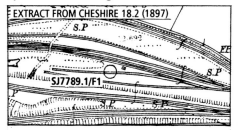

EXTRACT FROM CHESHIRE 18.2 (1897)

WOODHEAD

Site SK1199.1; On the north side of Woodhead Station.

Woodhead (SA&MR)SK1199.1/1A

A brick built 1TS dead ended tank shed, it was located at SK11279988 and was opened by the Sheffield, Ashton under Lyne & Manchester Railway on August 7th, 1844. No further details are known.

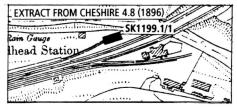

EXTRACT FROM CHESHIRE 4.8 (1896)

KNUTSFORD

Site SJ7578.1; On the east side of Knutsford Station.

Knutsford (Cheshire Midland) SJ7578.1/1A

A 2TS shed, approximately located at SJ754784, was opened here by the Cheshire Midland Railway on January 1st, 1863. In 1865 the line was absorbed by the CLC which closed the depot in 1869. No further details are known.

NEWTON & HYDE

Site SJ9595.1; In the vicinity of Newton Station.

Newton & Hyde (SA&MR)SJ9595.1/1A

A 2TS shed was opened here by the Sheffield, Ashton under Lyne & Manchester Railway on November 17th, 1841. No further details are known except that after closure the building was further utilized as a wagon works.

HOYLAKE

Site SJ2188.1; In the vicinity of Hoylake Station.

Hoylake (Hoylake)SJ2188.1/F1

Some sort of facility, approximately located at SJ217887, was opened here by the Hoylake Railway on July 2nd, 1866. No further details are known.

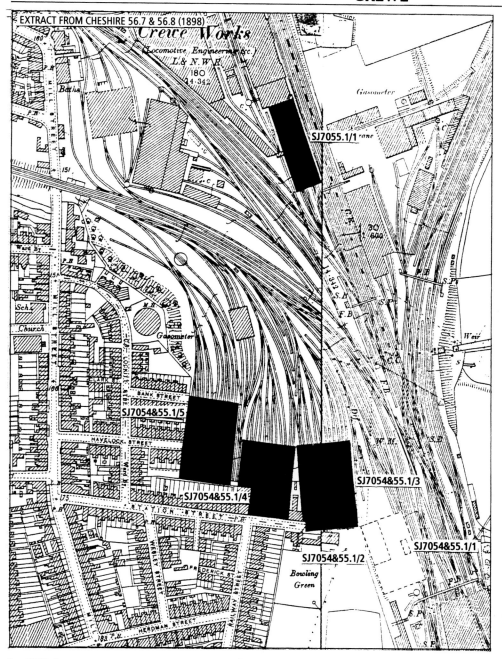

EXTRACT FROM CHESHIRE 56.7 & 56.8 (1898)

Crewe Works
(Locomotive, Engineering, &c.)
L. & N.W.R.

SJ7055.1/1

SJ7054&55.1/5

SJ7054&55.1/4

SJ7054&55.1/3

SJ7054&55.1/2

SJ7054&55.1/1

Adjoined by ...
Crewe Stock Shed (L&NWR) SJ7054&55.1/5A
A brick built 12TS dead ended shed with a north-light pattern roof, it was located at SJ70835506 and was opened in 1891. It was not considered as part of the Running Department but housed locomotives entering and leaving the works. The building was closed by BR in 1950 and demolished.

Replaced by ...
Crewe North (BR) SJ7054&55.1/5B
A brick built 12 track semi-roundhouse with a corrugated asbestos continuous pitched roof, it was completed by the London Midland Region in 1950.

Following the opening of Crewe South (SJ7153.2/1) in 1891 the site became known as "Crewe North".

Over the years the facilities were gradually improved and new mechanical coalers were installed by BR in 1953. The depot was closed by BR on May 24th, 1965 and the whole site was cleared.

Site SJ7055.1; In the fork of the Chester and Preston lines north of Crewe Station.
Crewe (GJR) SJ7055.1/1A
A brick built 4TS dead ended shed with a twin slated hipped roof, it was located at SJ70905542 and was opened by the Grand Junction Railway in December 1843. Details of the facilities are not known. The shed was closed in 1853 and the building was then utilized as an erecting shop within Crewe Works complex until 1927 when it found further use as a boiler plate store. It was demolished by BR during the 1970s.

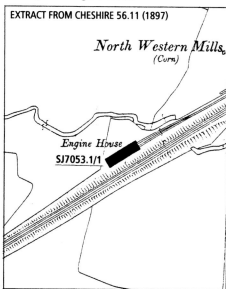

EXTRACT FROM CHESHIRE 56.11 (1897)

North Western Mills
(Corn)

Engine House
SJ7053.1/1

Site SJ7053.1; On the north side of the Nantwich line, south of Crewe Station.
Crewe Gresty Lane (GWR/L&NWR) SJ7053.1/1A
A brick built 2TS dead ended shed with a slated gable style pitched roof, it was located at SJ70675365 and was opened in 1870. The facilities included a coal stage and water tank.

The building was enlarged ...
Crewe Gresty Lane (GWR/L&NWR) SJ7053.1/1B
The shed was extended to double its length in 1913 and was closed by BR on June 17th, 1963.

Site SJ7153.1; On the west side of the Stoke line, south of Crewe Station.
Crewe (NSR) SJ7153.1/1A
A 1TS dead ended shed with a gable style pitched roof, it was located at SJ71545390 and was opened in 1872. The facilities included a water column. The depot was closed by the LMS on March 30th, 1923 and was subsequently demolished.

Site SJ7054&55.1; On the west side of the line, at the north end of Crewe Station.
Crewe (GJR) SJ7054&55.1/1A
A timber built 1TS through road shed, it was located at SJ70995495 and was opened by the Grand Junction Railway in 1839. The facilities included a coke/coal stage and a 40ft turntable added in 1843. The depot was closed in 1851 and immediately demolished.

Crewe (C&CR) SJ7054&55.1/2A
Probably a 4TS shed, it was located at SJ70975496 and was opened by the Chester & Crewe Railway in 1847. Although the building was only of a temporary nature it suffered a premature demise when it was destroyed by a hurricane in September 1848.

Replaced by ...
Crewe No.1 (L&NWR) SJ7054&55.1/2B
A stone built 8TS dead ended shed with four slated hipped roofs, it was opened in 1851 and occupied the sites of both SJ7054&55.1/2A and SJ7054&55.1/1A. The facilities included a coal stage. The shed was closed in 1897 and demolished to accommodate the construction of the station avoiding line.

Crewe (L&NWR) SJ7054&55.1/3A
A brick built 12TS dead ended shed with three slated hipped roofs, it was located at SJ70925501 and was opened in 1865. The building was originally known as the *"middle shed"* and later, following the demolition of SJ7054&55.1/2B, *"No.1"*.

Adjoined by ...
Crewe (L&NWR) SJ7054&55.1/4A
A brick built 12TS dead ended shed with three slated hipped roofs, it was located at SJ70875501 and was opened in 1868. The building was composed of two sections, an eight road portion which stretched the full length and was known as the *"Abyssinnia, or Abba, shed"* and, on the western side a truncated 4TS shed known as *"The Cage".* *(These later became known as Nos 2 & 3 respectively).* At the same time as this was constructed a double-sided coal stage and 45ft turntable were installed in the yard.

The shed was rebuilt ...
Crewe (BR) SJ7054&55.1/4B
The building was reduced by the London Midland Region to a 4TS shed in 1950 to accommodate the construction of a turntable for SJ7054&55.1/5B.

Continued ...

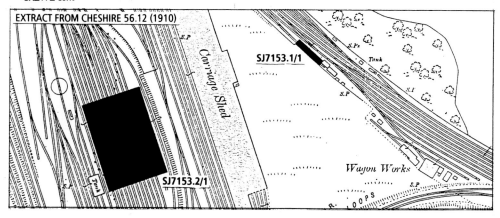

EXTRACT FROM CHESHIRE 56.12 (1910)

Site SJ7153.2; On the west side of the Stafford line, south of Crewe Station.
Crewe South (L&NWR) SJ7153.2/1A
A brick built 12TS through road shed with a north-light pattern roof, it was located at SJ71365383 and was opened on October 1st, 1897. The facilities included a coal stage, with water tank over, and a 50ft turntable.

WHALEY BRIDGE

Site SK0181; On the east side of the line, at the north end of Whaley Bridge Station.
Whaley Bridge (SD&WBR) SK0181.1/1A
A 1TS dead ended shed with a water tank surmounted over the entrance, it was located at SK01138164 and was opened by the Stockport, Disley & Whaley Bridge Railway on June 9th, 1857. The facilities included a coal stage. The line was absorbed by the L&NWR on November 16th, 1866 and although the depot was closed in 1900 it remained standing into the 1960s.

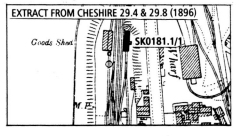

EXTRACT FROM CHESHIRE 29.4 & 29.8 (1896)

HOOTON

Site SJ3578.1; On the east side of the line, at the south end of Hooton Station.
Hooton (Birkenhead) SJ3578.1/1A
A brick built 1TS through road shed with a slated gable style roof, it was located at SJ35017801 and was opened by the Birkenhead Railway in 1869. Details of the facilities are not known. The line became GWR/L&NWR joint in 1860 and the depot was closed in 1929. It saw further use as a goods shed before being demolished.

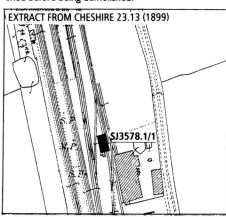

EXTRACT FROM CHESHIRE 23.13 (1899)

The shed was rebuilt ...
Crewe South (BR) SJ7153.2/1B
The depot was rebuilt with a corrugated iron LMS louvre style multi pitched roof by the London Midland Region in 1959. At the same time the number of covered roads were reduced to 8. The shed was closed on November 6th, 1967 and subsequently demolished.

STALYBRIDGE

Site SJ9598.1; On the south side of Stalybridge (SA&MR) Station.
Stalybridge (SA&MR) SJ9598.1/1A
A 1TS shed, located at SJ95859862, it was opened by the Sheffield, Ashton under Lyne & Manchester Railway on December 23rd, 1845. The depot was closed on July 1st, 1849 and the site was later utilized for station enlargements. No further details are known.

Site SJ9598.2; On the south side of Stalybridge (AS&LJR) Station.
Stalybridge (AS&LJR) SJ9598.2/1A
A 1TS shed, located at SJ95889866, it was opened by the Ashton, Stalybridge & Liverpool Junction Railway on October 5th, 1846. The line was absorbed by the Manchester & Leeds Railway on July 9th, 1847 and the depot was closed on July 1st, 1849. No further details are known.

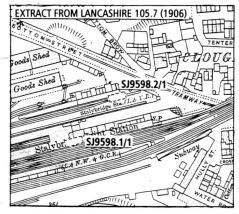

EXTRACT FROM LANCASHIRE 105.7 (1906)

MIDDLEWOOD

Site SJ9484.1; In the vicinity of Middlewood Low Level Junction, east of Middlewood Lower Station.
Middlewood Lower (L&NWR) SJ9484.1/1A
A 1TS shed, approximately located at SJ9468465, was opened here. No further details are known.

MIDDLEWICH

Site SJ7066.1; In the vicinity of Middlewich Station.
Middlewich (L&NWR) SJ7066.1/F1
Some sort of facility, approximately located at SJ707664, was established here. No further details are known.

STOCKPORT

Site SJ8989.1; On the west side of the line, south of Stockport (L&NWR) Station.
Stockport Edgeley (L&NWR) SJ8989.1/1A
A brick built 8TS dead ended shed with a northlight pattern roof, it was located at SJ89158915 and was opened on May 24th, 1883. The facilities included a ramped coal stage, with water tank over, and a turntable which was enlarged to 60ft in 1927.

The shed was re-roofed ...
Stockport Edgeley (LMS) SJ8989.1/1B
A multi-pitched roof was installed in 1932. The depot was closed by BR on May 6th, 1968 and was subsequently demolished.

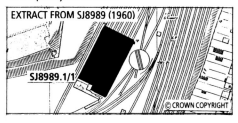

EXTRACT FROM SJ8989 (1960)
© CROWN COPYRIGHT

Site SJ8990.1; On the north side of Teviot Dale Station.*
Stockport Tiviot Dale* (ST&AJR) SJ8990.1/1A
A 2TS dead ended shed, it was located at SJ89569093 and was opened by the Stockport, Timperley & Altrincham Junction Railway on February 1st, 1866. The facilities included a water tank and turntable. The depot was closed by the CLC upon the opening of Heaton Mersey shed (SJ8789.1/1) in March 1889.

A servicing area was then established ...
Stockport Tiviot Dale* (CLC) SJ8990.1/F1
The shed building was demolished and the water tank, shed roads and turntable were utilized for locomotive servicing until BR days.

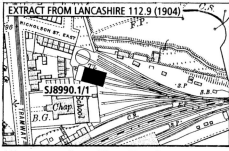

EXTRACT FROM LANCASHIRE 112.9 (1904)

*Alternative spellings of Teviot/Tiviot Dale were in use.

ELLESMERE PORT

Site SJ4076.1; On the north side of the line, at the west end of Ellesmere Port Station.
Ellesmere Port (L&NWR) SJ4076.1/1A
A timber built 2TS dead ended shed with a northlight pattern roof, located at SJ40277652 and opened in 1885. The facilities included a water reservoir supplying the columns. The depot was closed in 1921 and rented out to the Manchester Ship Canal Company which utilized it into the 1960s. The building was demolished in 1972.

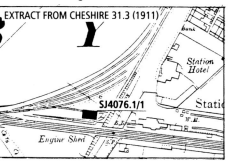

EXTRACT FROM CHESHIRE 31.3 (1911)

ALTRINCHAM

Site SJ7687.1; On the east side of the line, at the north end of Bowdon Station.

Altrincham (MSJ&AR) SJ7687.1/1A

A 1TS dead ended building located at SJ76858767 may have been utilized as an engine shed by the Manchester South Junction & Altrincham Railway.

Site SJ7788.1; On the east side of the line, north of Altrincham & Bowdon Station.

Altrincham (MSJ&AR) SJ7788.1/1A

A brick built 2TS dead ended shed, located at SJ77158831 and opened by the Manchester South Junction & Altrincham Railway on July 20th, 1849. The facilities included a coal stage and turntable, sited outside of the shed entrance.

The shed was enlarged in 1865 ...

Altrincham (MSJ&AR) SJ7788.1/1B

The shed was extended at the rear to give a rhomboidal shaped building and the turntable was removed.

The shed was rebuilt ...

Altrincham (MSJ&AR) SJ7788.1/1C

At some stage it was extended and converted to a brick built 2TS through road shed with a slated gable style roof. No further details are known other than it was closed by the LMS in February 1931.

EXTRACT FROM CHESHIRE 18.2 & 18.6 (1910)

SJ7788.1/1

SJ7687.1/1

NOTTINGHAMSHIRE

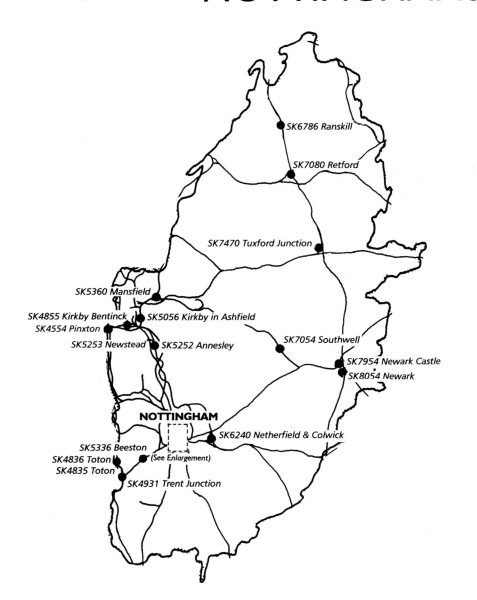

NOTTINGHAM

SK5740 Victoria

SK5739 Nottingham (MR)

SK5839 London Rd. Low Level

SK5739 Nottingham (MCR)

SK5839 London Road Junction

SK5638 Nottingham (MR)

SK5738 Arkwright St

RANSKILL

Site SK6786.1; In Ranskill Wagon Works.
Ranskill Wagon Works (LNER) SK6786.1/1A
A 1TS shed, approximately located at SK672867, was opened here in 1946 and closed by BR in 1959. No further details are known.

NEWARK

Site SK8054.1; In the fork of the Wharf branch and Newark Curve, north of Newark Castle Station.
Newark Castle (MR) SK8054.1/F1
A servicing area consisting of a turntable, located at SK80155479, and siding. Other facilities were dispersed along the Newark Curve with coaling expedited on a siding at SK79945474, and it is believed that there was an engine pit alongside the goods shed at SK79695447. The opening date is not known but the facility was officially closed by the LMS on September 14th, 1931.

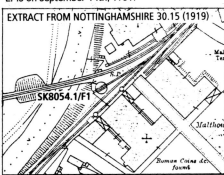

EXTRACT FROM NOTTINGHAMSHIRE 30.15 (1919)

SK8054.1/F1

Site SK8054.2; On the west side of the line, south of Newark Northgate Station.
Newark Northgate (GNR) SK8054.2/1A
A brick built 2TS dead ended shed with a slated hipped roof, it was located at SK80585402 and was opened in June 1880. The facilities included a water tank, coal stage and 45ft turntable. The depot was closed by BR on January 5th, 1959 and demolished in the same year.

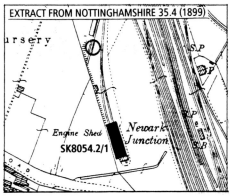

EXTRACT FROM NOTTINGHAMSHIRE 35.4 (1899)

Engine Shed
SK8054.2/1
Newark Junction

ANNESLEY

Site SK5252.1; On the west side of the GCR line, south of Hollinwell & Annesley Station.
Annesley (MS&LR) SK5252.1/1A
A brick built 6TS dead ended shed with a slated northlight pattern roof and brick screen, it was located at SK52495289 and was opened in 1898. The facilities included a coal stage, turntable and water tank. The depot was closed by BR on January 3rd, 1966 and demolished in the same year.

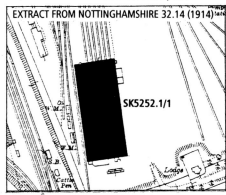

EXTRACT FROM NOTTINGHAMSHIRE 32.14 (1914)

SK5252.1/1

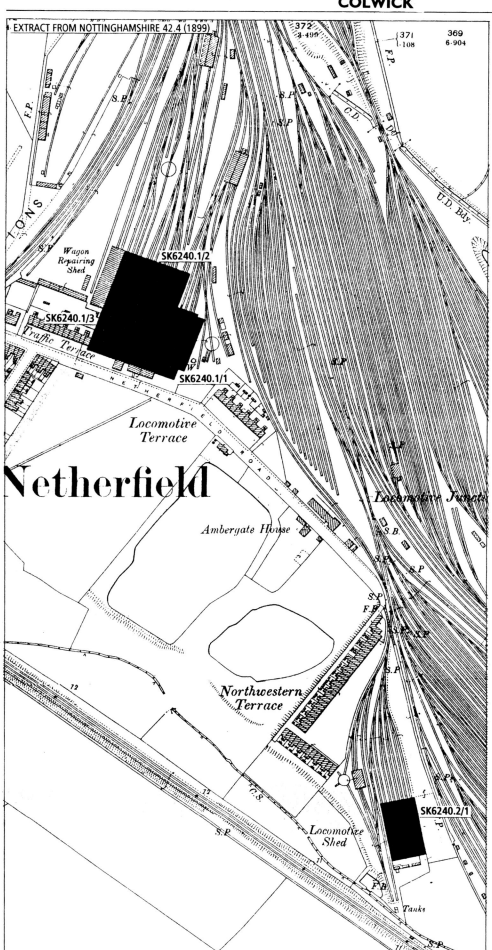

EXTRACT FROM NOTTINGHAMSHIRE 42.4 (1899)

Site SK6240.1; In the fork of the Colwick North Junction to Colwick East and Netherfield & Colwick Station lines.

Colwick (GNR)SK6240.1/1A
A brick built 4TS dead ended shed with a slated twin hipped roof, it was located at SK62654092 and was opened in 1876. The facilities included a repair shop, 45ft turntable, water tank and coal stage. After the completion of SK6240.1/2A it was known as the "old" shed.

The shed was extended in 1897...
Colwick (GNR)SK6240.1/1B
The building was extended at the rear by 50ft.

The shed was re-roofed ...
Colwick (BR)SK6240.1/1C
The building was re-roofed by the Eastern Region with asbestos sheeting and a brick screen in c1960.

Adjoined by ...
Colwick (GNR)SK6240.1/2A
A brick built 8TS dead ended shed with a northlight roof, it was built alongside of the repair shop at SK62624095 and was opened in June 1882. At this time the facilities were improved with the provision of a larger coal stage. This building was known as the "big" shed.

The shed was enlarged in 1897...
Colwick (GNR)SK6240.1/2B
The building was extended at the rear by 55ft.

The shed was re-roofed ...
Colwick (BR)SK6240.1/2C
The building was re-roofed by the Eastern Region with aluminium sheeting in c1950.

The shed was re-roofed again...
Colwick (BR)SK6240.1/2D
The building was re-roofed by the Eastern Region with asbestos sheeting and a brick screen in c1960.

Adjoined by ...
Colwick (GNR)SK6240.1/3A
A brick built 4TS dead ended shed with a northlight pattern roof, it was located at SK62594097 and was constructed along the western wall of SK6240.1/2B. At the same time an additional coaling stage was provided. This building was known as the "new" shed.

The shed was re-roofed ...
Colwick (BR)SK6240.1/3B
The building was re-roofed by the Eastern Region with aluminium sheeting in c1950.

The shed was re-roofed again...
Colwick (BR)SK6240.1/3C
The building was re-roofed by the Eastern Region with asbestos sheeting and a brick screen in c1960.

The depot was closed to steam by BR on December 12th, 1966 and to diesels on April 13th, 1970. It was totally demolished during 1971.

Site SK6240.2; On the north side of Colwick East Junction.
Netherfield & Colwick (L&NWR)SK6240.2/1A
A brick built 8TS dead ended shed with a northlight pattern roof, it was located at SK62874045 and was opened in 1880. The facilities included a water tank, coal stage and turntable. The depot was closed by the LMS on December 4th, 1932 and it was converted into a wagon works. The building lasted into BR days when, amongst other things, it was utilized for light engineering, but was eventually demolished during the 1980s.

MANSFIELD

Site SK5360.1; On the south side of the line, at the west end of Mansfield Station.
Mansfield (MR) SK5360.1/1A
A 1TS through road shed, it was located at SK53676075 and was opened on October 9th, 1849. The facilities included a water column and coal stage sited outside of the shed entrance. The depot was closed in 1882 but the building remained in existence until at least 1958 before being demolished.

Replaced by ...
Site SK5360.2; In the triangle of lines, west of Mansfield Station.
Mansfield (MR) SK5360.2/1A
A brick built 4TS dead ended shed with a twin gable style slated pitched roof, it was located at SK53096023 and was opened in 1882. The facilities included a ramped coal stage, water tank and a turntable. The depot was closed by BR on April 1st, 1960 and the building was leased out for private use. It was still standing in 1997.

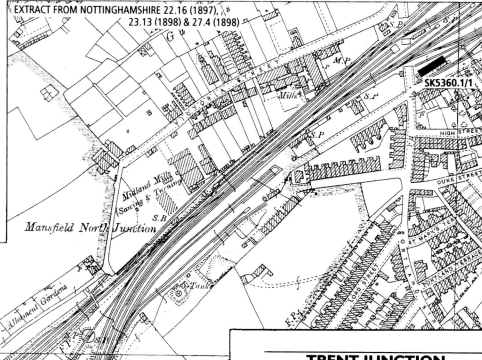

EXTRACT FROM NOTTINGHAMSHIRE 22.16 (1897), 23.13 (1898) & 27.4 (1898)

SK5360.1/1

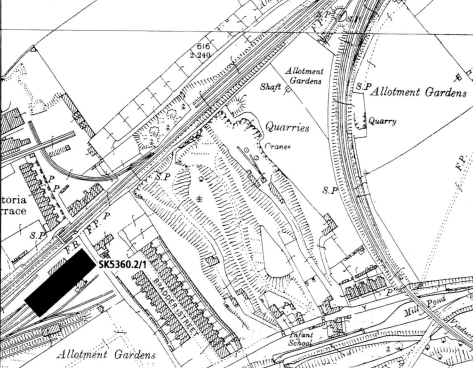

SK5360.2/1

TRENT JUNCTION

Site SK4931.1; In the fork of the lines, at the north end of Trent Junction.
Trent Junction (MR) SK4931.1/1A
A 2TS dead ended building, assumed to be an engine shed, located at SK49363141 and with a small turntable was in existence in 1848. No further details are known.

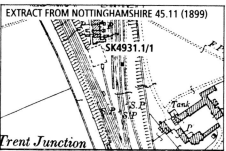

EXTRACT FROM NOTTINGHAMSHIRE 45.11 (1899)

SK4931.1/1

Trent Junction

SOUTHWELL

Site SK7054.1; On the west side of the line, at the south end of Southwell Station.
Southwell (MR) SK7054.1/1A
A brick built 1TS dead ended shed with a slated hipped roof, it was located at SK70875419 and was opened in July 1847. The facilities included a water tank and coal stage sited outside of the shed entrance. The depot was closed by BR on January 10th, 1955 and was subsequently demolished.

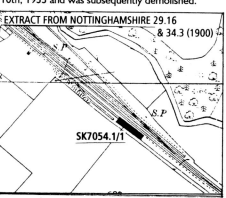

EXTRACT FROM NOTTINGHAMSHIRE 29.16 & 34.3 (1900)

SK7054.1/1

TUXFORD

Site SK7470.1; On the west side of the Newark to Doncaster line, at Dukeries Junction, south of Tuxford Station.
Tuxford (LD&ECR) SK7470.1/1A
A brick built 2TS through road shed, located at SK74897051 and opened by the Lancashire, Derbyshire & East Coast Railway on November 16th, 1896.

The shed was enlarged prior to 1912 ...
Tuxford (GCR) SK7470.1/1B
The building was increased in size to a brick built 3TS shed with one through road and a slated transverse multi-pitched roof. The facilities included a water tank and coal stage. By BR days the building was partially roofless and was closed on February 2nd, 1959.

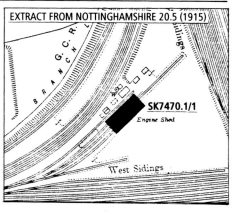

EXTRACT FROM NOTTINGHAMSHIRE 20.5 (1915)

SK7470.1/1
Engine Shed

West Sidings

Site SK5739.1; On the north side of the line, at the west end of Nottingham (Midland Counties) Station.
Nottingham (MCR)^{SK5739.1/1A}
A brick built 2TS shed, it was located at SK57233918 and was opened by the Midland Counties Railway on June 4th, 1839. Details of the facilities are not known. The depot was closed by the MR in 1850.

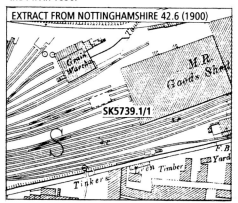

SK5739.1/1

Replaced by ...
Site SK5739.2; On the north side of the line, at the east end of Nottingham Midland Station.
Nottingham (MR)^{SK5739.2/1A}
A brick built semi-roundhouse shed with 11 roads, it was located at SK57803928 and was opened in 1850. Details of the facilities are not known. The depot was closed in 1868 and demolished.

Replaced by ...
Site SK5638.1; On the south side of the line, west of Nottingham Midland Station.
Nottingham No.1 (MR)^{SK5638.1/1A}
A brick built square roundhouse shed with a slated multi pitched roof, it was located at SK56823885 and was opened in 1868.

Adjoined by ...
Nottingham No.2 (MR)^{SK5638.1/2A}
A brick built square roundhouse shed with a slated multi pitched roof, it was located at the north west corner of SK5638.1/1A at SK56753887 and was opened in 1877. The facilities included a coal stage and a repair shop added at the rear of No.1 shed at the same time as No.2 was constructed.

Adjoined by ...
Nottingham No.3 (MR)^{SK5638.1/3A}
A brick built square roundhouse shed with a slated multi pitched roof, it was built adjacent to the north east corner of No.2 shed and was located at SK56793893 and was opened in 1893.

A further fitting shop was added at the rear of No.1 shed in 1899. The depot was closed by BR on April 4th, 1965 and was subsequently demolished.

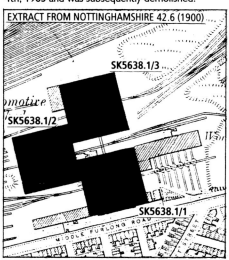

SK5638.1/3
SK5638.1/2
SK5638.1/1

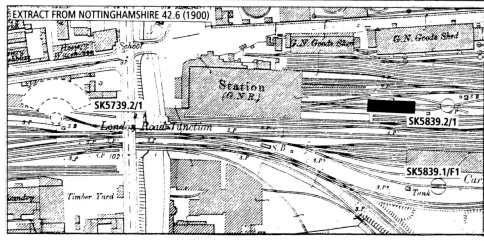

SK5739.2/1
SK5839.2/1
SK5839.1/F1

Site SK5740.1; On the west side of the line, at the north end of Nottingham Victoria Station.
Nottingham (GCR)^{SK5740.1/F1}
A servicing area consisting of a turntable, located at SK57394057, siding and water column. The facility was opened on May 24th, 1900 and closed by BR on September 2nd, 1967.

Site SK5740.2; On the east side of the line, at the south end of Nottingham Victoria Station.
Nottingham (GCR)^{SK5740.2/F1}
A servicing area consisting of a turntable, located at SK57454024, siding and water columns. The facility was opened on May 24th, 1900 and closed by BR on September 2nd, 1967.

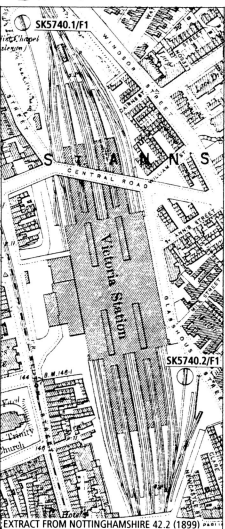

SK5740.1/F1
SK5740.2/F1

Site SK5839.2; On the south side of the line, at the east end of London Road (Low Level) Station
Nottingham (Ambergate)^{SK5839.2/1A}
A brick built 2TS through road shed with a slated gable style roof, it was located at SK58133926 and was opened by the Ambergate Railway in March 1858. The facilities included a water tank, coal stage and 38ft turntable. The depot was closed by the GNR in 1906.

Site SK5839.1; In the fork of the Lincoln and Melton Mowbray lines, east of Nottingham Midland Station.
London Road Junction (MR)^{SK5839.1/F1}
A servicing area consisting of a turntable, located at SK58163918, water tank and siding. The opening and closure dates are not known but the facility was still being utilized during BR days.

Site SK5738.1; On the east side of the line, south of Arkwright Street Station.
Arkwright Street (GCR)^{SK5738.1/1A}
A brick built 4TS dead ended shed with a northlight pattern roof, it was located at SK57193821and was opened in 1898. The facilities included a turntable, water tank and ramped coal stage. Although the depot was officially closed in 1907 it saw further use for locomotive servicing for many years afterwards and was still standing in 1953.

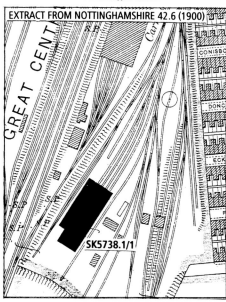

SK5738.1/1

BEESTON

Site SK5336.1; In Beeston Sidings.
Beeston (MR)^{SK5336.1/F1}
A servicing area consisting of a coal stage approximately located at SK539369. No further details are known.

TOTON

Site SK4836.1; In the vicinity of Stapleford & Sandiacre Station.
Toton (MR)^{SK4836.1/1A}
A shed, approximately located at SK483363, was opened here in 1857 and closed in 1870. No further details are known.

Replaced by ...
Site SK4835.1; On the west side of the line, south of Stapleford & Sandiacre Station.
Toton No.1 (MR)^{SK4835.1/1A}
A brick built square 1RH building with a triple gable style pitched roof, it was located at SK48613525 and was opened in 1870.

The shed was re-roofed ...
Toton No.1 (BR)^{SK4835.1/1B}
The building was re-roofed by the London Midland Region in 1948.

Adjoined by ...
Toton No.2 (MR)^{SK4835.1/2A}
A brick built square 1RH building with a triple gable style pitched roof, it was located at SK48643519 and was opened in 1873.

The shed was re-roofed ...
Toton No.2 (BR)^{SK4835.1/2B}
The building was re-roofed by the London Midland Region in 1948.

Adjoined by ...
Toton No.3 (MR)^{SK4835.1/3A}
A brick built square 1RH building with a triple gable style pitched roof, it was located at SK48633513 and was opened in 1901.

The depot possessed all facilities and these were steadily improved during the shed's existence. At some stage a single track was added along the eastern wall of Nos 2 & 3 roundhouses to accommodate the Beyer Garratt locomotives. The depot was closed by BR in December 1965 and demolished, being replaced by a diesel depot constructed on an adjacent site.

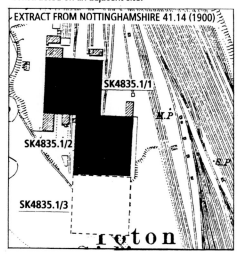
EXTRACT FROM NOTTINGHAMSHIRE 41.14 (1900)
SK4835.1/1
SK4835.1/2
SK4835.1/3

NEWSTEAD

Site SK5253.1; On the west side of Newstead (GNR) Station.
Newstead (GNR)^{SK5253.1/F1}
A servicing area consisting of a turntable, located at SK52315309 and siding. It opened in 1882 and closed in 1899.

EXTRACT FROM NOTTINGHAMSHIRE 32.14 (1914)
SK5253.1/F1

RETFORD

Site SK7080.1; On the west side of Retford (GN) Station.
Retford (GNR)^{SK7080.1/1A}
A brick built 2TS dead ended shed with a gable style slated pitched roof, it was located at SK70998039 and was opened in 1850. The facilities included a coke/coal stage, water pump & column and, provided later, a 40ft turntable.

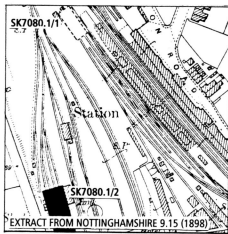
SK7080.1/1
Station
SK7080.1/2
EXTRACT FROM NOTTINGHAMSHIRE 9.15 (1898)

The shed was modified ...
Retford (GNR)^{SK7080.1/1B}
To facilitate track alterations the building was altered to a through road shed. The depot was closed in March 1875.

Replaced by ...
Retford (GNR)^{SK7080.1/2A}
A brick built 4TS dead ended shed with a twin hipped slated roof, it was located to the west of its predecessor at SK70088020 and was opened in March 1875. The facilities included a coaling shed, water tank and 44ft 8in turntable.

The shed was re-roofed ...
Retford (BR)^{SK7080.1/2B}
A new flat concrete and steel roof with brick screen was installed by the Eastern Region in c1951 and the depot was closed on June 14th, 1965. The building was let out for private use and was still standing in 1997.

Site SK7080.2; On the south side of the Gainsborough line, east of Retford Station.
Retford Thrumpton (MS&LR)^{SK7080.2/1A}
A brick built 3TS shed with two through roads and a gable style slated pitched roof, it was located at SK70788033 and was opened on July 16th, 1849. The facilities included a turntable. water tank and coal stage.

The shed was re-roofed ...
Retford Thrumpton (BR)^{SK7080.2/1B}
A northlight pattern roof was installed by the Eastern Region in the early 1950s and the depot closed in January 1965. The building was demolished in the same year.

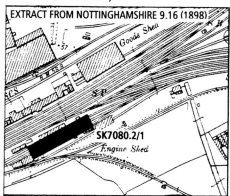
EXTRACT FROM NOTTINGHAMSHIRE 9.16 (1898)
Goods Shed
SK7080.2/1
Engine Shed

KIRKBY IN ASHFIELD

Site SK4855.1; In the fork of the Langton Colliery and Tibshelf lines, at the west end of Kirkby Bentinck Station.
Kirkby Bentinck (GCR)^{SK4855.1/F1}
A servicing area consisting of sidings, it was located at SK48355575 and was opened at some time after 1900. The facilities included water columns at the nearby station. It was closed by BR in 1966.

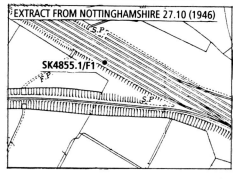
EXTRACT FROM NOTTINGHAMSHIRE 27.10 (1946)
SK4855.1/F1

Site SK5056.1; On the east side of the line, north of Kirkby in Ashfield Station.
Kirkby in Ashfield (MR)^{SK5056.1/1A}
A brick built 3TS dead ended shed with a slated gable style pitched roof, it was located at SK50565642 and was opened in 1890. The facilities included a water tank, ramped coal stage and 60ft turntable.

Adjoined by ...
Kirkby in Ashfield (BR)^{SK5056.1/2A}
A brick built 2TS dead ended shed with a corrugated asbestos roof, it was erected by the London Midland Region in 1958 and adjoined the west wall of SK5056.1/1A, being located at SK50555642.

The depot was closed to steam on October 3rd, 1966 and the later addition, SK5056.1/2A, utilized for diesel servicing for a short while until it was totally closed and subsequently demolished.

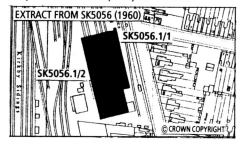
EXTRACT FROM SK5056 (1960)
SK5056.1/1
SK5056.1/2
© CROWN COPYRIGHT

PINXTON

Site SK4554.1; On the north side of the line, at the west end of Pinxton Station.
Pinxton (GNR)^{SK4554.1/1A}
A brick built 2TS dead ended shed with a slated hipped roof, it was located at SK45255426 and was opened in 1875. The facilities included a coaling shed, water pump and column and a 45ft turntable. It is believed that the depot was closed in c1906 and subsequently demolished.

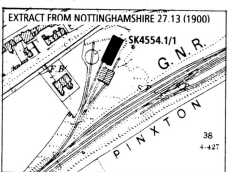
EXTRACT FROM NOTTINGHAMSHIRE 27.13 (1900)
SK4554.1/1
G.N.R.
PINXTON
38
4-427

LINCOLNSHIRE

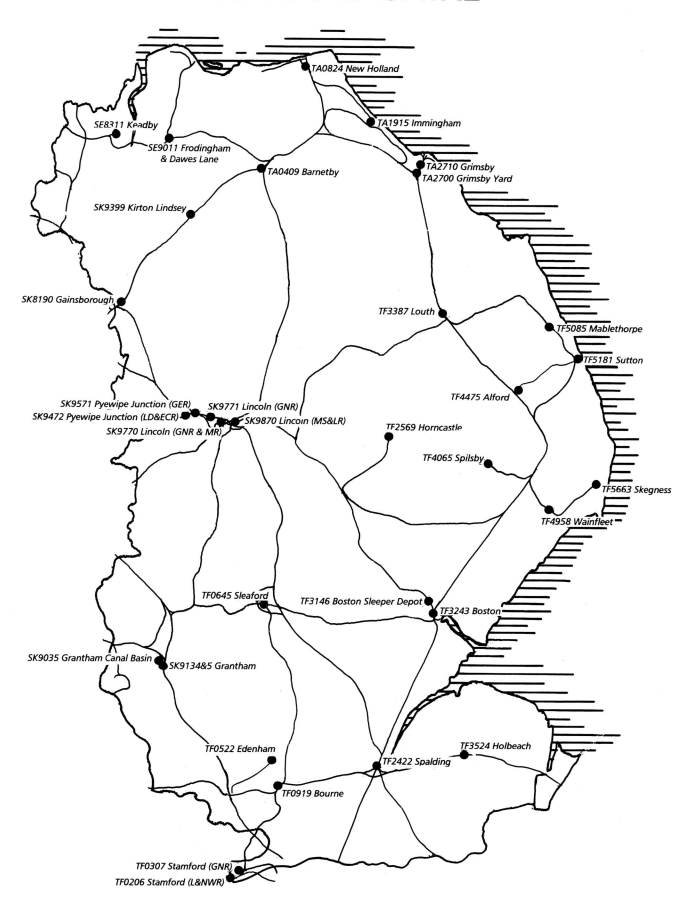

TA0824 New Holland

TA1915 Immingham

SE8311 Keadby

SE9011 Frodingham
& Dawes Lane

TA0409 Barnetby

TA2710 Grimsby
TA2700 Grimsby Yard

SK9399 Kirton Lindsey

SK8190 Gainsborough

TF3387 Louth

TF5085 Mablethorpe

TF5181 Sutton

SK9571 Pyewipe Junction (GER)
SK9472 Pyewipe Junction (LD&ECR)
SK9770 Lincoln (GNR & MR)

SK9771 Lincoln (GNR)
SK9870 Lincoln (MS&LR)

TF4475 Alford

TF2569 Horncastle

TF4065 Spilsby

TF5663 Skegness

TF4958 Wainfleet

TF0645 Sleaford

TF3146 Boston Sleeper Depot

TF3243 Boston

SK9035 Grantham Canal Basin

SK9134&5 Grantham

TF0522 Edenham

TF3524 Holbeach

TF2422 Spalding

TF0919 Bourne

TF0307 Stamford (GNR)

TF0206 Stamford (L&NWR)

BOSTON

Site TF3243.1; In the vicinity of West Street Terminus.

Boston (GNR) TF3243.1/1A
A temporary shed was opened here in 1849. No further details are known.

Site TF3243.2; On the west side of the line, south of Boston Station.

Boston (GNR) TF3243.2/1A
A brick built 9TS dead ended shed with a slated triple gable style roof, it was located at TF32254340 and was probably opened in 1851.

The shed was re-roofed in the 1930s ...

Boston (LNER) TF3243.2/1B
The roof was re-clad with corrugated asbestos sheeting and by this time the original arches had been removed and these were replaced with corrugated asbestos gable ends.

The shed was rebuilt ...

Boston (BR) TF3243.2/1C
The side walls were refurbished by the Eastern Region in 1956 and the rear wall was totally rebuilt with a large glazed area. A new, higher, roof was installed on a steel frame and clad in corrugated asbestos.

Boston (GNR) TF3243.2/2A
A brick built 4TS dead ended shed with a twin slated gable style roof, it was located at TF32264361 and became part of the running shed in 1900. The building had originally been employed as an erecting shop and smithy/turnery in Boston Works.

The building was modified ...

Boston (LNER) TF3243.2/2B
At an unknown date the entrance to the former smithy/turnery section on the west side of the building was bricked up and the building was reduced to a 2TS shed.

Boston (GNR) TF3243.2/3A
A brick built 3TS dead ended shed with a slated gable style roof, it was located at TF32224359 and became part of the running shed in 1900. The building had been partially used as a stores in Boston Works.

As the site formed part of the works the engine shed had use of all facilities. The depot was closed to steam by BR on January 5th, 1964 but only the remaining 2TS portion of TF3243.2/2, the old erecting shop of Boston Works, was utilized for diesel servicing, the remaining shed buildings being demolished.

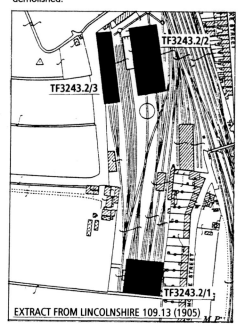

EXTRACT FROM LINCOLNSHIRE 109.13 (1905)

BOSTON SLEEPER DEPOT

Site TF3146.1; In Boston Sleeper Depot, on the east side of the Lincoln line, north of Boston Station.

Boston Sleeper Depot (LNER) TF3146.1/1A
A brick built 1TS dead ended shed with a slated gable style roof, it was located at TF31194610. The facilities included the works water tank. Neither the opening nor closing dates are known but it is probable that it was opened during the 1940s and closed in the early 1950s, the Sentinel locomotive thereafter standing in the open until withdrawal in May 1964.

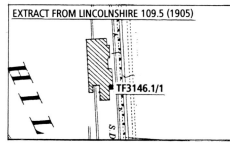

EXTRACT FROM LINCOLNSHIRE 109.5 (1905)

STAMFORD

Site TF0206.1; On the west side of the line, south of Stamford (L&NWR) Station.

Stamford (L&NWR*) TF0206.1/1A
A brick built 1TS through road shed, it was located at TF02620641 and was opened on June 2nd, 1851. The facilities included a turntable. The depot was closed by the LMS on September 20th, 1926 and was subsequently demolished.

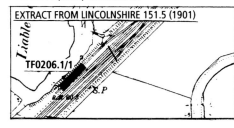

EXTRACT FROM LINCOLNSHIRE 151.5 (1901)

An L&NWR "Statement showing distribution of Engine Stock & Shed accommodation" issued on April 12th, 1855 shows three locomotives at "Stamford MR Shed". This indicates the existence of another depot [TF0206.0/1A], that this shed was of MR origin or the entry was an administrative error.

Site TF0307.1; On the west side of the line, north of Stamford (S&ER) Station.

Stamford (S&ER) TF0307.1/1A
A brick built 1TS through road shed with a slated gable style roof incorporating a water tank, it was located at TF03830713 and was opened by the Stamford & Essendine Railway on November 1st, 1856.

The shed was extended ...

Stamford (S&ER) TF0307.1/1B
A timber extension with a slated gable style roof was added to the rear of the shed in c1867. At the same time a coal stage was installed on the shed road. The depot was closed by BR on June 15th, 1959 and was subsequently demolished.

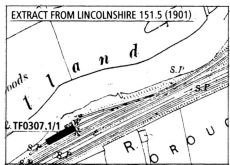

EXTRACT FROM LINCOLNSHIRE 151.5 (1901)

BARNETBY

Site TA0409.1; In the fork of the lines, west of Barnetby Station.

Barnetby (MS&LR) TA0409.1/1A
A brick built 2TS dead ended shed with a slated gable style roof, it was located at TA04550917 and was opened in 1874. The facilities included a turntable and coal stage. The depot was closed by the LNER in June 1932 and was subsequently demolished.

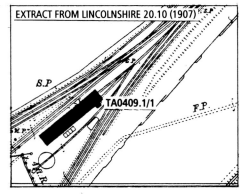

EXTRACT FROM LINCOLNSHIRE 20.10 (1907)

HORNCASTLE

Site TF2569.1; On the east side of the line, at the south end of Horncastle Station.

Horncastle (H&KJR) TF2569.1/1A
A brick built 1TS dead ended shed with a slated gable style roof, it was located at TF25416932 and was opened on August 11th, 1855 by the Horncastle & Kirkstead Junction Railway. The facilities included a water tank. The line was worked by the GNR and the depot was closed by the LNER in c1924 and demolished by 1930.

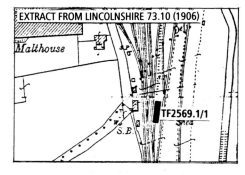

EXTRACT FROM LINCOLNSHIRE 73.10 (1906)

KEADBY

Site SE8311.1; On the north side of the line, at the west end of Keadby Goods.

Keadby (SYR) SE8311.1/1A
A brick built 1TS through road shed with a slated gable style roof, it was located at SE83321148 and was opened by the South Yorkshire Railway on September 10th, 1859. The facilities included a water column. The depot was closed by the LNER on June 12th, 1932.

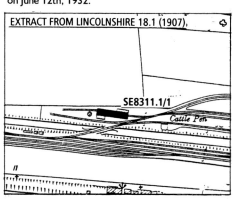

EXTRACT FROM LINCOLNSHIRE 18.1 (1907)

GRANTHAM

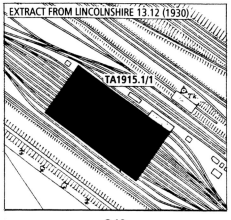

EXTRACT FROM LINCOLNSHIRE 113.4 (1903)

SK9134&5.1/1

97
10·040

LEGATE

llotment Gardens

Engine Shed
SK9134&5.1/2

Site SK9035.1; At the end of the Canal Branch, on the west side of the Nottingham line, north of Grantham Station.
Grantham Canal Basin (Ambergate)SK9035.1/1A
A 1TS shed, approximately located at SK908355, was opened here by the Ambergate Railway on July 15th, 1850. No further details are known except that it was closed in 1855.

Site SK9134&5.1; On the west side of Grantham Station.
Grantham (GNR)SK9134&5.1/1A
A brick built 2TS dead ended shed with a slated gable style roof, it was located at SK91383512 and was opened in 1855. The facilities included a coal stage, water column and, added in 1862, a turntable.

The shed was enlarged ...
Grantham (GNR)SK9134&5.1/1B
The adjacent carriage shed along the east wall, a brick built 2TS dead ended shed with a slated gable style roof was adapted as a running shed in 1863.

The shed was modified ...
Grantham (GNR)SK9134&5.1/1C
The original engine shed portion was extended by 10 feet and made into a through road building. At the same time the roof was refurbished and the turntable was re-sited at the top end of the yard. Following the construction of SK9134&5.1/2A it was known as the "old" shed. By 1960 the building had become derelict and BR abandoned and demolished it shortly after.

Grantham (GNR)SK9134&5.1/2A
A brick built 4TS dead ended shed with a northlight pattern roof, it was known as the "new" shed and was located at the south end of the yard, at SK91503487. It was opened in 1897 and a new ramped coal stage and additional turntable were provided at the same time. This turntable was removed by the LNER in 1947 and, due to problems with establishing foundations in the clay soil, a turning triangle was provided by BR on the west side of the yard in 1951. A unique feature of the triangle was the installation of a scissor crossing to reduce the space required.

The shed was re-roofed ...
Grantham (BR)SK9134&5.1/2B
An asbestos clad steel framed roof with corrugated asbestos screen was installed by the Eastern Region in 1955. The depot was closed on September 9th, 1963 and the remaining buildings were demolished in the following year.

IMMINGHAM

Site TA1915.1; On the south west side of Immingham Docks.
Immingham (GCR)TA1915.1/1A
A brick built 12TS through road shed with a multi-transverse pitched roof, it was opened on May 15th, 1912 and was located at TA19841513. The facilities included a ramped coal stage, repair shop, water tank and turntable.

The shed was re-roofed ...
Immingham (BR)TA1915.1/1B
A twin pitched corrugated asbestos clad roof on a steel frame was installed by the Eastern Region at some time prior to 1960. The shed was closed to steam in February 1966 and most of the building was progressively demolished as a new purpose-built diesel depot (TA1915.1/1C) was constructed on the same site. Part of the steam shed, including the coaling tower, was still standing in 1999.

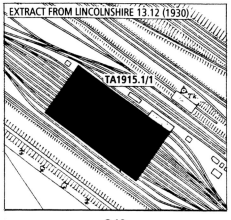

EXTRACT FROM LINCOLNSHIRE 13.12 (1930)

TA1915.1/1

SPILSBY

Site TF4065.1; On the south side of Spilsby Station.
Spilsby (S&FR)TF4065.1/1A
A brick built 1TS dead ended shed with a slated gable style roof incorporating a water tank, it was located at TF40096577 and was opened on May 1st, 1868 by the Spilsby & Firsby Railway. The depot was closed by the LNER, probably in 1941, but was not demolished until after the line was closed in 1958.

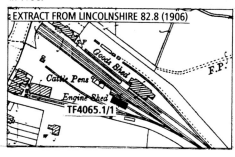

EXTRACT FROM LINCOLNSHIRE 82.8 (1906)

Goods Shed
Cattle Pens
Engine Shed
TF4065.1/1

SLEAFORD

Site TF0645.1; In the vicinity of Sleaford Station.
Sleaford (BS&MCR)TF0645.1/F1
Some sort of facility, approximately located at TF067454, was opened here by the Boston, Sleaford & Midland Counties Railway on June 16th, 1857. It was closed on April 18th, 1859

Site TF0645.2; On the south side of Sleaford Station.
Sleaford (GNR)TF0645.2/1A
A brick built 2TS dead ended shed with a slated gable style roof, it was located at TF06554538 and was opened in 1883. The facilities included a 45ft turntable, water tank and coal stage. The depot was closed to steam by BR in October 1958 and totally in November 1964 being subsequently demolished.

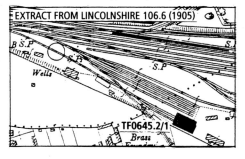

EXTRACT FROM LINCOLNSHIRE 106.6 (1905)

B S.P
Wells
TF0645.2/1
Brass

SPALDING

Site TF2422.1; On the west side of the line, south of Spalding Station.
Spalding (M&ER)TF2422.1/1A
A brick built 2TS through road shed with arched entrances and a slated gable style roof, it was located at TF24022213 and was opened on August 1st, 1866 by the Midland & Eastern Railway. The facilities included a water tank and coal stage. The line became part of the Eastern & Midlands Railway on July 1st, 1883 and was incorporated into the Midland & Great Northern Railway on July 1st, 1893. The depot was closed by BR on March 7th, 1960 and was subsequently demolished.

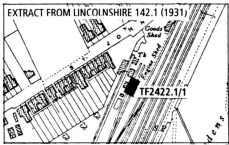

EXTRACT FROM LINCOLNSHIRE 142.1 (1931)

Goods Shed
Engine Shed
TF2422.1/1

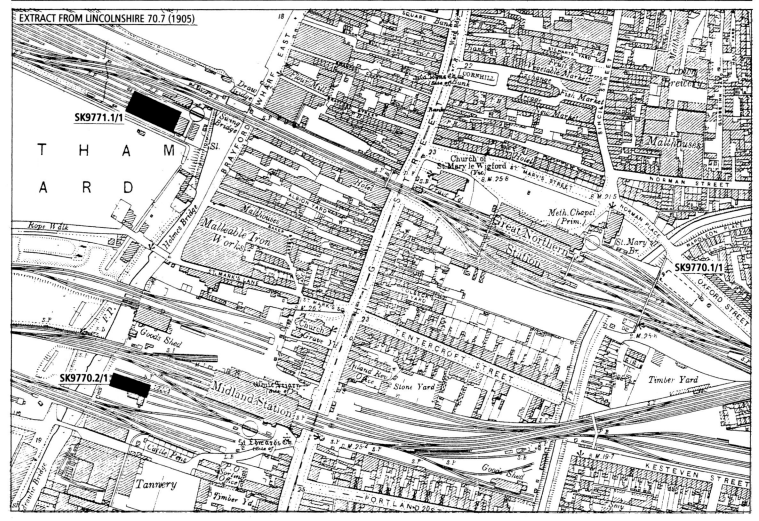

EXTRACT FROM LINCOLNSHIRE 70.7 (1905)

SK9771.1/1

THAM ARD

SK9770.1/1

SK9770.2/1

Site SK9770.0: In the vicinity of Lincoln (GNR) Station.

Lincoln (GNR)SK9770.0/1A

A temporary shed, probably built in timber, was opened here on October 17th, 1848 and closed on April 9th, 1849. The facilities included a 16ft turntable. No further details are known except that the structure was removed and re-erected elsewhere for use as a carriage shed.

Site SK9770.1; On the north side of the line, at the east end of Lincoln (GNR) Station.

Lincoln Station (GNR)SK9770.1/1A

A brick built 2TS shed with a slated gable style roof, it was located at SK97727086 and was opened in 1851. The facilities included a 40ft turntable, coke/coal stage and water tank.

The shed was enlarged ...

Lincoln Station (GNR)SK9770.1/1B

The building was lengthened to accommodate four engines in 1857. The siting of the depot meant that adjacent level crossing gates had to be closed to road traffic whenever locomotives manoeuvred in the shed yard. As a result, in 1873 it was finally decided to close the depot and relocate to a new site. Although the new shed, SK9771.1/1, was ready in 1875 it was not closed immediately and may have lasted until 1881 before being closed and demolished.

Replaced by ...
Site SK9771.1; On the south side of the line, west of Lincoln (GNR) Station.

Lincoln (GNR)SK9771.1/1A

A brick built 4TS dead ended shed with a twin slated hipped roof, it was located at SK97227101 and was opened in 1875. The facilities included a coal stage, water tank and 45ft turntable.

The shed was re-roofed ...

Lincoln (BR)SK9771.1/1B

An asbestos clad twin gable style roof was installed by the Eastern Region in 1956. Although the depot was closed in October 1964 the building remained standing, with tracks removed, until at least 1999.

Site SK9770.2; On the south side of Lincoln (MR) Station.

St. Marks (MR)SK9770.2/1A

A 2TS dead ended shed, it was opened on August 3rd, 1846 and was located at SK97207076. The facilities included a 42ft turntable and coke/coal stage. The depot was closed in 1867.

Replaced, on the same site, by ...

St. Marks (MR)SK9770.2/1B

A brick built 2TS through road shed with a slated hipped roof, it was opened in 1867. At the same time the coal stage was renewed and the turntable was replaced with a 50ft unit in 1893.

The shed was rebuilt ...

St. Marks (LMS)SK9770.2/1C

A louvre style roof with brick screen was installed in 1944. The depot was closed by BR in January 1959 and was later demolished.

Site SK9870.1; On the south side of the line, east of Lincoln (GNR) Station.

Lincoln (MS&LR)SK9870.1/1A

A 1TS shed, it was opened on December 18th, 1848 and was probably built on this site, approximately located at SK981708. No further details are known.

Replaced by ...

Lincoln (MS&LR)SK9870.1/2A

A brick built 4TS shed with one through road and a twin slated gable style roof, it was located at SK98127080 and was opened at an unknown date. The facilities included a water tank, coal stage and turntable. The depot was roofless by the time it was closed by the LNER on May 20th, 1939 and the building was subsequently utilized for locomotive stabling until 1946. It found further use for carriage servicing before demolition and a diesel servicing depot (SK9870.1/3A) was erected on the site in 1956 at SK98187089.

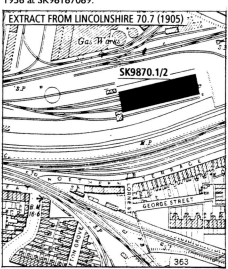

EXTRACT FROM LINCOLNSHIRE 70.7 (1905)

SK9870.1/2

363

Continued ...

SK9472.1/1

Pyewipe
Sidings

SK9472.1/F1

EXTRACT FROM LINCOLNSHIRE 70.6 (1932)

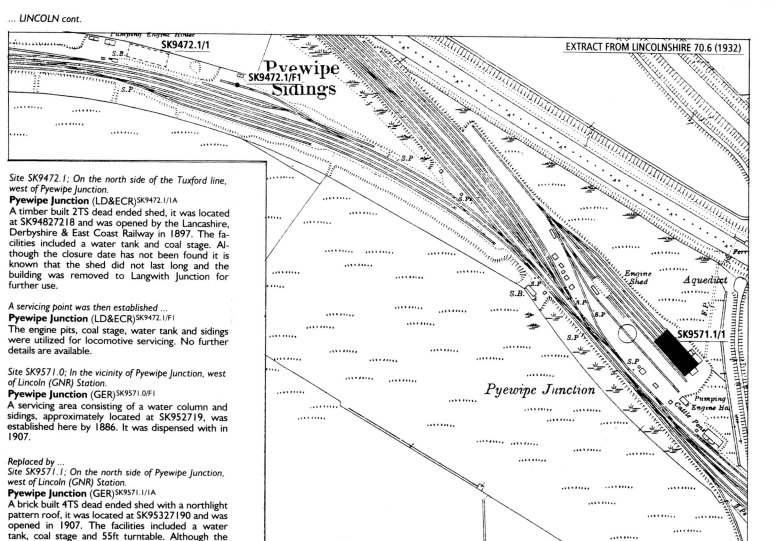

SK9571.1/1

Pyewipe Junction

Site SK9472.1; On the north side of the Tuxford line, west of Pyewipe Junction.

Pyewipe Junction (LD&ECR)SK9472.1/1A

A timber built 2TS dead ended shed, it was located at SK94827218 and was opened by the Lancashire, Derbyshire & East Coast Railway in 1897. The facilities included a water tank and coal stage. Although the closure date has not been found it is known that the shed did not last long and the building was removed to Langwith Junction for further use.

A servicing point was then established ...

Pyewipe Junction (LD&ECR)SK9472.1/F1

The engine pits, coal stage, water tank and sidings were utilized for locomotive servicing. No further details are available.

Site SK9571.0; In the vicinity of Pyewipe Junction, west of Lincoln (GNR) Station.

Pyewipe Junction (GER)SK9571.0/F1

A servicing area consisting of a water column and sidings, approximately located at SK952719, was established here by 1886. It was dispensed with in 1907.

Replaced by ...
Site SK9571.1; On the north side of Pyewipe Junction, west of Lincoln (GNR) Station.

Pyewipe Junction (GER)SK9571.1/1A

A brick built 4TS dead ended shed with a northlight pattern roof, it was located at SK95327190 and was opened in 1907. The facilities included a water tank, coal stage and 55ft turntable. Although the depot was closed by the LNER in August 1925 it was still utilized for locomotive servicing until at least 1947. The building was later demolished.

GAINSBOROUGH

Site SK8190.1; On the east side of the line, north of Gainsborough Station.

Gainsborough (MS&LR)SK8190.1/1A

A 2TS dead ended shed, it was opened on April 2nd, 1849 and was located at SK81899005. No further details are known.

Replaced, on the same site, by ...

Gainsborough (MS&LR)SK8190.1/1B

A brick built 1TS dead ended shed with a slated gable style roof incorporating a water tank. No further details are known except that it was out of use by 1899 and still stood in 1999.

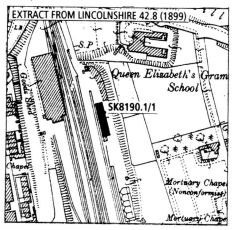

EXTRACT FROM LINCOLNSHIRE 42.8 (1899)

SK8190.1/1

Queen Elizabeth's Gram School

SKEGNESS

Site TF5663.1; On the north side of the line, at the west end of Skegness Station.

Skegness (GNR)TF5663.1/F1

A servicing area consisting of a 45ft 6in turntable, sited at TF56016306, coal stage, water tank and siding, it was opened in 1873.

The facility was improved ...

Skegness (LNER)TF5663.1/F2

A coal hoist was installed in 1936. The servicing area was closed by BR on April 27th, 1966

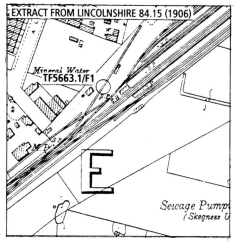

EXTRACT FROM LINCOLNSHIRE 84.15 (1906)

Mineral Water

TF5663.1/F1

Sewage Pump
(Skegness U

WAINFLEET

Site TF4958.1: On the north side of Wainfleet Station.

Wainfleet (W&FR)TF4958.1/1A

A brick built 1TS dead ended shed with a slated gable style roof, it was located at TF49655882 and was opened on September 11th, 1871 by the Wainfleet & Firsby Railway. The facilities included a water tank and a coal stage. The line was worked by the GNR which absorbed the W&FR on July 1st, 1896.

The shed was modified in c1912 ...

Wainfleet (GNR)TF4958.1/1B

To counteract subsidence, two buttresses were installed at the rear of the shed. At the same time the building was made into a through road shed and was re-roofed. Although the depot was closed by the LNER in c1940 it was utilized as a servicing facility and signing-on point until dieselization of the line in 1955. The shed was later demolished.

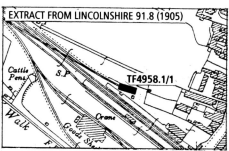

EXTRACT FROM LINCOLNSHIRE 91.8 (1905)

Cattle Pens

TF4958.1/1

LOUTH

Site TF3387.1; On the east side of Louth Station.
Louth (GNR) TF3387.1/1A
A brick built 2TS shed with one through road and a slated gable style roof, it was located at TF33358792 and was opened on March 1st, 1848. The facilities included a 40ft turntable (upgraded to 50ft in 1938), coal stage and water tank.

The shed was partially rebuilt ....
Louth (LNER) TF3387.1/1B
As a result of war damage in 1941 the north end of the building was rebuilt, the roof reclad in corrugated asbestos and the coal stage removed. The depot was closed by BR in December 1956 and was subsequently demolished.

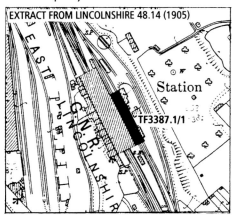
EXTRACT FROM LINCOLNSHIRE 48.14 (1905)

NEW HOLLAND

Site TA0824.1: On the south side of the New Holland to New Holland Town to Barton on Humber triangle of lines, at the south end of New Holland Town Station.
New Holland (MS&LR) TA0824.1/1A
A brick built 4TS through road shed with a twin gable style roof, it was located at TA08172413 and was opened on March 1st, 1848. The facilities included a water tank.

At some stage the shed was re-roofed ...
New Holland (LNER) TA0824.1/1B
A twin dutch barn style roof was installed and two of the original archway entrances replaced with a single steel lintel. Although the depot was closed on April 20th, 1941 it was utilized for locomotive servicing until c1960.

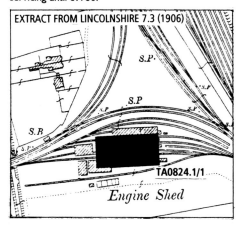
EXTRACT FROM LINCOLNSHIRE 7.3 (1906)

HOLBEACH

Site TF3524.1; In the vicinity of Holbeach Station.
Holbeach (N&SR) TF3524.1/1A
A timber built 1TS shed, approximately located at TF358243, it was opened by the Norwich & Spalding Railway on November 15th, 1858. No further details are known except that it was closed in December 1866.

MABLETHORPE

Site TF5085.1; On the west side of the line, at the north end of Mablethorpe Station.
Mablethorpe (GNR) TF5085.1/1A
A brick built 1TS dead ended shed with a slated gable style roof, it was located at TF50348517 and was opened on October 17th, 1877. The facilities included a 44ft 8in turntable (increased to 52ft by BR in 1954), coal stage and water tower, the water later being pumped from a well by means of a windmill. Although the depot was closed by the LNER in June 1924 and the shed building demolished, visiting locomotives continued to utilize the facilities until the end of steam in 1964.

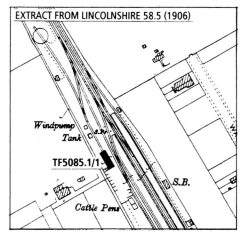
EXTRACT FROM LINCOLNSHIRE 58.5 (1906)

KIRTON LINDSEY

Site SK9399.1; On the west side of the line, south of Kirton Lindsey Station.
Kirton Lindsey (MS&LR) SK9399.1/F1
A facility consisting of a coal stage and siding, it was located at SK93289951. No further details are known.

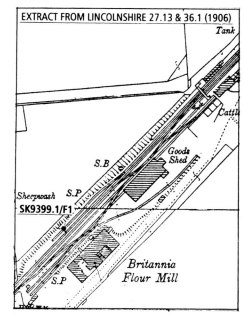
EXTRACT FROM LINCOLNSHIRE 27.13 & 36.1 (1906)

Gainsborough was an early meeting place for the MS&LR and GNR, and both companies shared a 2TS MS&LR shed (SK8190.1/1A) between April 1849 and May 1851, before the GN moved its locomotives back to Lincoln. At a time yet to be discovered the MS&LR or, possibly, the GCR replaced the shed with a 1TS brick building that had a roof-mounted water tank at the rear (SK8190.1/1B).

When this depot closed is not known, but it passed into goods use and still stood in 1999, though seemingly serving little purpose. This view was taken in August 1970. *Authors' Collection*

SCUNTHORPE

EXTRACT FROM LINCOLNSHIRE 18.4 (1907)

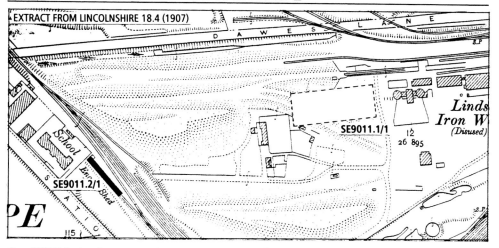

Site SE9011.0; *In the vicinity of Scunthorpe &*
Frodingham Station.
Frodingham (LNER) SE9011.0/F1
A servicing facility consisting of a coal stage and
siding, it was approximately located at SE904112.
No further details are known except that it was
dispensed with on June 12th, 1932.

EXTRACT FROM SE9011 (1965)

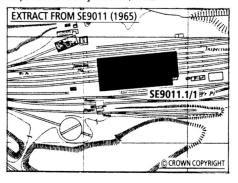

© CROWN COPYRIGHT

Replaced by ...
Site SE9011.1; *On the west side of the line, north of*
Scunthorpe & Frodingham Station.
Frodingham (LNER) SE9011.1/1A
A concrete built 5TS through road shed with a
westernlight pattern roof, it was located at
SE9045 l 146 and was opened on June 12th, 1932.
The facilities included a water tank, coal stage and
turntable. The shed was closed to steam by BR on
February 26th, 1966 and was demolished to make
way for a purpose-built diesel depot (SE9011.1/2A).

Site SE9011.2; *On the west side of the line, at the*
north end of Scunthorpe Dawes Lane Station.
Dawes Lane (NLLR) SE9011.2/1A
A 1TS dead ended shed, it was opened by the
North Lindsey Light Railway on September 3rd,
1906 and was located at SE90241140. Details of
the facilities are not known. The line was worked by
the GCR and the depot was probably closed and
demolished by the LNER in 1925 to facilitate construction of a direct line into Scunthorpe & Frodingham Station.

BOURNE

Site TF0919.1; *On the west side of Bourne Station.*
Bourne (B&ER) TF0919.1/1A
A 1TS dead ended shed, it was opened by the
Bourne & Essendine Railway on May 16th, 1860
and was located at TF09561975. The facilities included a water tank and turntable. The line was absorbed by the GNR on June 29th, 1864.

The building was modified ...
Bourne (GNR) TF0919.1/1B
The building was altered to a 1TS through road
shed in c1872. The depot was closed in c1893 and
demolished to make way for station alterations.

Replaced by ...
Bourne (GNR) TF0919.1/2A
A brick built 2TS dead ended shed with a northlight
pattern roof, it was located at TF09511974 and
was opened in 1893. The facilities included a water
tank, turntable and coal stage. The line was absorbed by the M&GNR in 1897 and the depot was
closed by BR in 1953. It was later demolished.

EXTRACT FROM LINCOLNSHIRE 140.7 (1903)

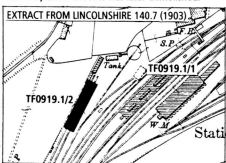

GRIMSBY

Site TA2710.1; *On the east side of the line, north of*
Grimsby Town Station.
Grimsby (MS&LR) TA2710.1/1A
A brick built 6TS dead ended shed with a slated
twin gable roof, it was located at TA27491017 and
was opened at some time prior to 1889. The
facilities included a coal stage, turntable and water
tank. The building became progressively roofless
over the years, the westernlight gable had gone by
1932, and by BR days locomotives stabled in the
open. The official closure date is not known; it was
possibly as early as 1912, but it is known that it
finally fell out of use in 1961. The remains of the
building were demolished by 1962.

Site TA2700.1; *In the vicinity of Grimsby GNR Goods.*
Grimsby (GNR) TA2700.1/F1
A facility comprising a siding and engine pit,
approximately located at TA274009, was
established in 1919. No further details are known.

EXTRACT FROM LINCOLNSHIRE 22.7 (1932)

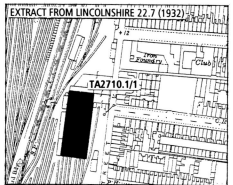

ALFORD

Site TF4475.1; *On the west side of Station Road, at*
the north end of Alford Town Station.
Alford (A&ST) TF4475.1/1A
A 2ft 6in gauge brick built 2TS dead ended shed
with a slated gable style roof, it was located at
TF44557562 and was opened by the Sutton & Alford Tramway on April 2nd, 1884. The facilities included a repair shop in the adjacent headquarters
works. Although the depot, along with the line, was
closed on December 6th, 1889 it passed into private ownership and remained standing, as part of a
garage, until at least 1971.

EXTRACT FROM LINCOLNSHIRE 66.14 (1905)

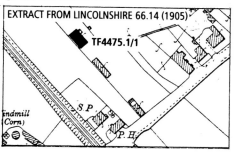

SUTTON

Site TF5181.1; *On the east side of the High Street,*
north of Sutton on Sea Station.
Sutton (A&ST) TF5181.1/1A
A 2ft 6in gauge brick built 1TS dead ended shed
with a slated gable style roof, it was located at
TF51948178 and was opened by the Alford & Sutton Tramway on April 2nd, 1884. Details of the
facilities are not known. Although the depot, along
with the line, was closed on December 6th, 1889 it
passed into private ownership and remained
standing until at least 1947.

EXTRACT FROM LINCOLNSHIRE 58.13 (1905)

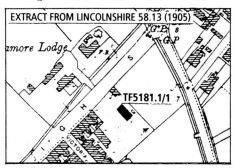

EDENHAM

Site TF0522.1; *On the east side of the line, at the*
south end of Edenham Station.
Edenham (E&LBR) TF0522.1/1A
A 1TS shed, it was located at TF05832206 and was
opened by the Edenham & Little Bytham Railway in
March 1856. It was closed in 1872. No further details are known.

EXTRACT FROM LINCOLNSHIRE 140.2 (1904)

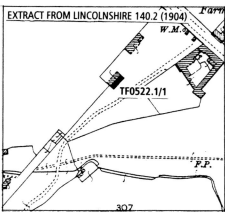

LANCASHIRE

For ease of reference the county has been split into 3 sections;

LANCASHIRE (NORTH)

BARROW

LANCASTER

BLACKBURN

LANCASHIRE (SE)

LANCASHIRE (SW)

BOLTON

MANCHESTER

LIVERPOOL

Serving a (then) sparsely populated area between Southport and Preston, the West Lancashire Railway opened its line into **Southport** in February 1878, erecting a ITS shed (SD3518.1/1A) at Hesketh Park. That was replaced in September 1882 by a two road depot (SD3416.2/1) at Windsor Road, which was closed as soon as the L&YR took over the WLR in 1897.

Following this, Windsor Road shed served in other uses, the main one being as an electricity sub-station for the electrification of the L&YR line from Liverpool. When that ceased is not known but the shed still stood in 1977, when this view was taken; it has since been demolished.

Authors' Collection

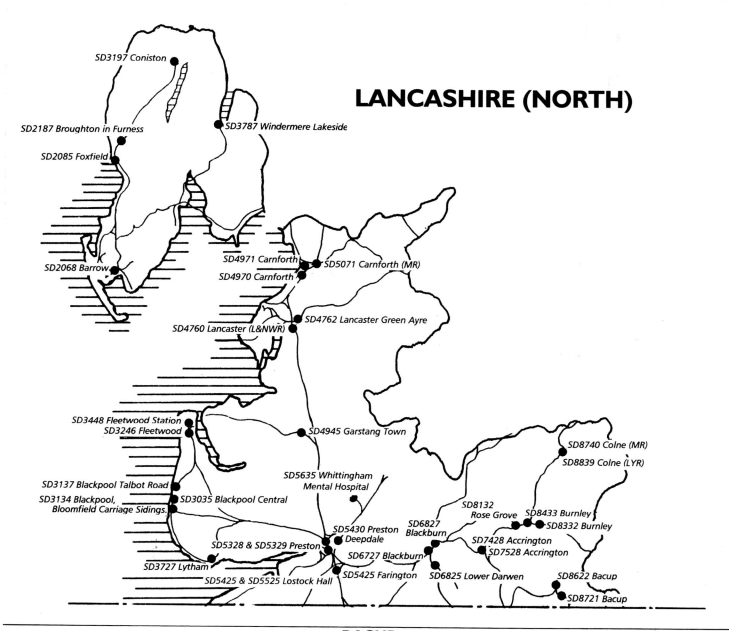

LANCASHIRE (NORTH)

SD3197 Coniston

SD2187 Broughton in Furness

SD3787 Windermere Lakeside

SD2085 Foxfield

SD2068 Barrow

SD4971 Carnforth

SD5071 Carnforth (MR)

SD4970 Carnforth

SD4762 Lancaster Green Ayre

SD4760 Lancaster (L&NWR)

SD3448 Fleetwood Station
SD3246 Fleetwood

SD4945 Garstang Town

SD8740 Colne (MR)

SD8839 Colne (LYR)

SD3137 Blackpool Talbot Road

SD5635 Whittingham
Mental Hospital

SD3134 Blackpool,
Bloomfield Carriage Sidings.

SD3035 Blackpool Central

SD8132
Rose Grove

SD8433 Burnley

SD8332 Burnley

SD6827
Blackburn

SD5430 Preston
Deepdale

SD7428 Accrington

SD7528 Accrington

SD5328 & SD5329 Preston

SD6727 Blackburn

SD3727 Lytham

SD8622 Bacup

SD5425 Faringon

SD6825 Lower Darwen

SD5425 & SD5525 Lostock Hall

SD8721 Bacup

BACUP

Site SD8622.1; On the east side of Bacup Station.
Bacup (ELR) SD8622.1/1A
A stone built 2TS dead ended shed, located at SD86892241 and opened on October 1st, 1852 by the East Lancashire Railway. The facilities included a coal stage and 40ft turntable. The depot closed in 1882 to accommodate station enlargements following construction of the Rochdale line.

Replaced by ...
Site SD8721.1; On the north side of the Rochdale line, east of Bacup Station.
Bacup (L&YR) SD8721.1/1A
A stone built 4TS through road shed with a north-light pattern roof, located at SD87332188 and opened in 1882. The facilities included a coal stage, with water tank over, and turntable.

The shed was re-roofed ...
Bacup (LMS) SD8721.1/1B
A multi-pitched roof was installed in 1934 and the depot was closed by BR on October 9th, 1954. The building was subsequently demolished.

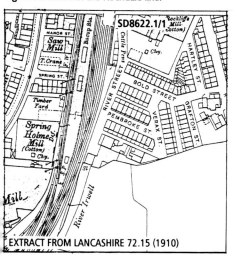

EXTRACT FROM LANCASHIRE 72.15 (1910)

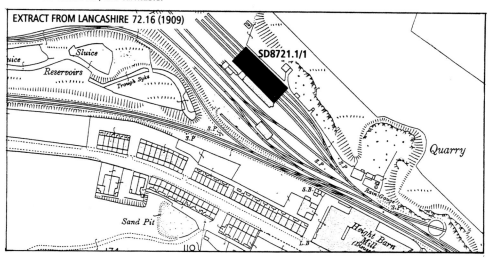

EXTRACT FROM LANCASHIRE 72.16 (1909)

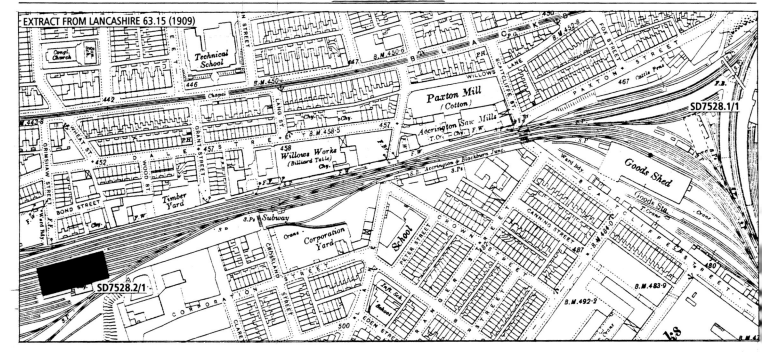

EXTRACT FROM LANCASHIRE 63.15 (1909)

SD7528.1/1

SD7528.2/1

Site SD7528.1; In the triangle of lines at Accrington Station.
Accrington (ELR) SD7528.1/1A
A 2TS through road shed, probably built in brick, it was located at SD75122853 and was opened by the East Lancashire Railway on June 17th, 1848. The facilities included a turntable. The line was absorbed by the L&YR in 1859 and the depot closed in 1873.

Replaced by ...
Site SD7528.2; On the south side of the Blackburn line, west of Accrington Station.
Accrington (L&YR) SD7528.2/1A
A brick built 6TS through road shed with a twin gable style roof, it was located at SD75122840 and was opened in 1873. Details of the facilities are not known. The depot closed in 1899, being converted into a carriage shed in 1904.

Replaced by ...
Site SD7428.1; On the south side of the Blackburn line, west of Accrington Station.
Accrington (L&YR) SD7428.1/1A
A brick built 8TS dead ended shed with a slated transverse pitched roof, located at SD74762826 and opened in 1899. The facilities included a turntable and coal stage with water tank over.

The shed was modified ...
Accrington (LMS) SD7428.1/1B
In 1937 the accommodation was reduced to six tracks and a multi-pitched roof was installed. At about the same time a mechanical coaling plant was provided. The depot was closed to steam by BR on March 6th, 1961.

Both sheds (SD7528.2/1A and SD7428.1/1B) were then utilized for dmu servicing until October 1st, 1972 and were demolished in the 1970s.

EXTRACT FROM LANCASHIRE 63.14 (1931)

SD7428.1/1

Goods Shed

BURNLEY

Site SD8332.1; On the west side of the line, south of Burnley Thorneybank Station.
Burnley Thorneybank (M&LR) SD8332.1/1A
A 1TS through road shed, located at SD83763202 and opened by the Manchester & Leeds Railway on November 12th, 1849. No further details are known other than it closed in 1866.

Replaced, on the same site, by ...
Burnley Manchester Road (L&YR) SD8332.1/1B
A stone built 1TS through road tankshed, it opened in 1866. No further details are known except that the depot closed in 1899 upon the opening of Rose Grove Shed (SD8132.1/1A), with the water tank being retained for use into BR days.

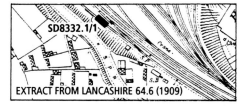

SD8332.1/1

EXTRACT FROM LANCASHIRE 64.6 (1909)

Site SD8433.1; In the vicinity of Burnley Bank Top Station.
Burnley Bank Top (L&YR) SD8433.1/F1
A servicing area consisting of a coal stage and siding, approximately located at SD840333, was in use here. No further details are known.

BROUGHTON IN FURNESS

Site SD2187.1; On the west side of the line, at the south end of Broughton in Furness (1st) Station.
Broughton in Furness (FR) SD2187.1/1A
A 1TS through road shed located at SD21198734 and opened on February 24th, 1848. No further details are known other than it closed on August 1st, 1858 and was demolished to make way for track realignments.

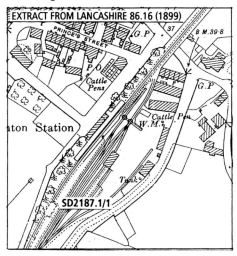

EXTRACT FROM LANCASHIRE 86.16 (1899)

SD2187.1/1

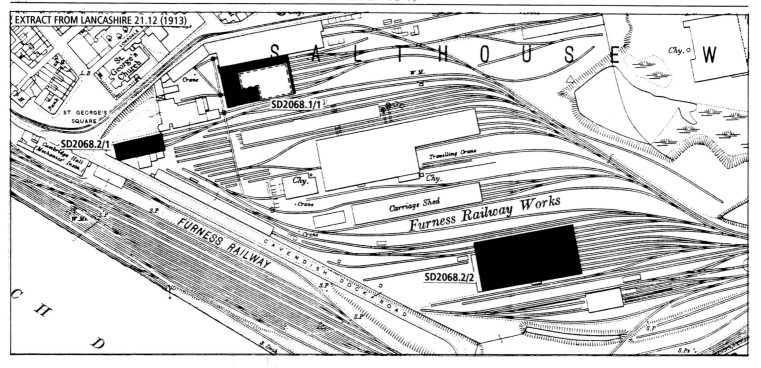

EXTRACT FROM LANCASHIRE 21.12 (1913)

FARINGTON & LOSTOCK HALL

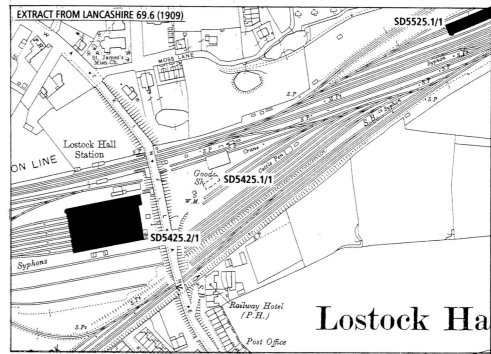

EXTRACT FROM LANCASHIRE 69.6 (1909)

Site SD2068.1; On the north side of the line, east of Barrow 1st Station*.

Barrow (FR) SD2068.1/1A

A 1TS through road *"engine house"* it was located at SD20426874 and was opened on June 3rd, 1846. No further details are known other than it closed in 1863. The building was demolished and the whole area became absorbed within Barrow Works with the site being subsequently used for the later engine shed, SD2068.1/1B.

*This whole site, including the station, subsequent to the rapid and extensive expansion of Barrow Docks and Works became part of the Works complex.

Replaced by ...
Site SD2068.2; Within Barrow Works.

Barrow (FR) SD2068.2/1A

A brick built 3TS dead ended shed with a slated triple pitched roof, it was located at SD20296867 and was opened in 1863. The facilities included a turntable and coal stage. The depot was closed in 1874 and the building utilized as a machine shop for the adjacent works.

Barrow (FR) SD2068.1/1B

A stone built 8TS dead ended shed with four slated pitched roofs, the facilities and opening and closing dates are not known but by 1901 it was in use as an erecting shop as part of the adjacent works.

Replaced by ...
Barrow (FR) SD2068.2/2A

A stone built 10TS shed with two through roads and a slated multi-pitched roof, it was located at SD20656856 and was opened in 1874. The facilities included a coaling shed, water tank and turntable.

The shed was rebuilt ....
Barrow (LMS) SD2068.2/2B

The building was reduced in length and an asbestos clad LMS single pitched style roof installed in c1939. The depot was closed to steam by BR on December 12th, 1966 and saw further use for servicing diesel locomotives until 1977. The building was later demolished.

Site SD5425.1; On the south side of the line, east of Lostock Hall Station.

Farington (B&PR) SD5425.1/1A

A 1TS shed, located at SD54772551 and opened on June 1st, 1846 by the Blackburn & Preston Railway. No further details are known except that it closed in 1848 and was removed to Blackburn for further use at SD6827.1.

Site SD5525.1; On the north side of the line, east of Lostock Hall Station.

Lostock Hall (L&YR) SD5525.1/1A

A shed which was in use here until October 30th, 1881 is believed to be the 2TS through road building located at SD55012566. No further details are known except that it still stood into BR days, in works use.

Replaced by ...
Site SD5425.2; On the south side of Lostock Hall Station.

Lostock Hall (L&YR) SD5425.2/1A

A brick built 8TS dead ended shed with a northlight pattern roof, located at SD54682547 and opened on October 30th, 1881. The facilities included a coal stage, with water tank over, and a turntable.

The shed was re-roofed ...
Lostock Hall (BR) SD5425.2/1B

A transverse pitched roof, covering a smaller area, was installed by the London Midland Region in 1953. The depot was one of the last to close, on August 4th, 1968, and remained standing for many years afterwards, being utilized for a time by the Civil Engineers' Department.

Site SD6827.1; On the west side of the line, south of Blackburn Station.

Blackburn (ELR) SD6827.1/1A

A 1TS shed, it was located at SD68222754 and was opened on June 1st, 1846 by the East Lancs Railway. Details of the facilities are not known.

The shed was enlarged ...

Blackburn (B&PR) SD6827.1/1B

The depot was enlarged to a 2TS shed in 1849 by the Blackburn & Preston Railway following the installation of the redundant shed building from Farington (SD5425.1/1A).

The shed was enlarged again ...

Blackburn (B&PR) SD6827.1/1C

The building was "extended for 16 engines" in 1863 by the Blackburn & Preston Railway. No further details are known except that the depot closed in 1881.

Site SD6727.1; On the east side of the line, south of Blackburn Station.

Blackburn (BD&BR) SD6727.1/1A

A 2TS shed, located at SD67952723 and opened by the Blackburn, Darwen & Bolton Railway on August 3rd, 1847. No further details are known except that the line was absorbed by the East Lancs & L&YR in 1855 with the depot closing in the same year.

Site SD6727.2; In the fork of King Street Sidings and the Chorley line, south of Blackburn Station.

Blackburn (L&NWR) SD6727.2/1A

A brick built 4TS dead ended shed, located at SD67852722 and opened in 1882. The facilities included a turntable. The depot closed in 1922 but remained standing until the 1960s. No further details are known.

Site SD6827.2; On the west side of Blackburn Station.

Blackburn (L&YR) SD6827.2/F1

A servicing area consisting of a turntable, located at SD68432786, and siding. No further details are known.

Site SD6827.0; In the vicinity of Blackburn Station.

Blackburn (L&YR) SD6827.0/F1

A servicing area consisting of a coal stage opened in 1914. No further details are known.

Site SD6825.1; On the west side of the Bolton line, south of Blackburn Station.

Lower Darwen (L&YR) SD6825.1/1A

A brick built 8TS dead ended shed with a glazed and slated transverse pitched roof, it was located at SD68252561 and opened on September 3rd, 1881. The facilities included a coal stage, with water tank over, and turntable.

The shed was truncated ...

Lower Darwen (LMS) SD6825.1/1B

Just prior to nationalization the roof was cut back by four bays over six of the tracks. BR closed the depot on February 14th, 1966 and immediately demolished it.

EXTRACT FROM LANCASHIRE 62.16 (1910) & 70.4 (1910)

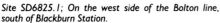

EXTRACT FROM LANCASHIRE 70.8 (1911)

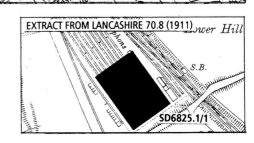

BOLTON Cont ....

Site SD7208.1; In the triangle of the Bury, Manchester and Trinity Street lines, south of Bolton Trinity Street Station.

Bolton Burnden (MB&BCN&R) SD7208.1/1A

A through road shed, located at SD72250808 and opened by the Manchester, Bolton & Bury Canal Navigation & Railway Co. in 1840.

The shed was enlarged ...

Bolton Burnden (MB&BCN&R) SD7208.1/1B

At some stage it was enlarged to a 3TS through road building. Details of the facilities are not known. The line was absorbed by the LYR in 1847 and the depot closed in 1874.

Replaced by ...
Site SD7207.1; On the west side of the Manchester line, south of Bolton Trinity Street Station.

Bolton (L&YR) SD7207.1/1A

A brick built 4TS dead ended shed with a slated hipped roof, located at SD72550750 and opened in 1874.

The shed was enlarged in 1888 ...

Bolton (L&YR) SD7207.1/1B

A brick built 8TS dead ended shed with a northlight pattern roof was built along the western wall of SD7207.1/1A. The facilities included a coal stage, with water tank over, and turntable.

The shed was re-roofed ...

Bolton (LMS) SD7207.1/1C

An LMS style louvre roof with brick screen was installed in 1946. The depot was closed by BR on July 1st, 1968 and subsequently demolished.

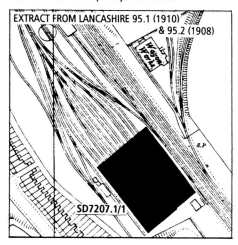
EXTRACT FROM LANCASHIRE 95.1 (1910) & 95.2 (1908)

PADGATE

Site SJ6390.1; On the north side of the line, east of Padgate Station.

Padgate (CLC) SJ6390.1/1A

A timber built 1TS through road shed, it was located at SJ63539016 and was opened on September 1st, 1873. Details of the facilities are not known. The depot was closed by the LNER in 1929 and subsequently demolished

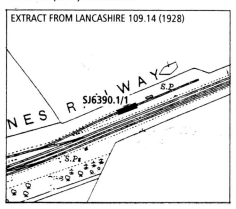
EXTRACT FROM LANCASHIRE 109.14 (1928)

GLAZEBROOK

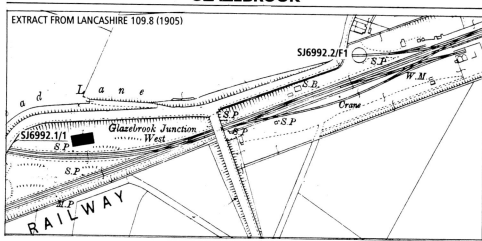
EXTRACT FROM LANCASHIRE 109.8 (1905)

Site SJ6992.1; On the north side of Glazebrook Junction West, west of Glazebrook Station.

Glazebrook (MS&LR) SJ6992.1/1A

A 2TS shed, located at SJ69149238 and opened on October 16th, 1879. No further details are known.

Replaced by ...
Site SJ6992.2; On the north side of the line, at the west end of Glazebrook Station.

Glazebrook (MS&LR) SJ6992.2/F1

A servicing area consisting of a turntable, located at SJ69409247, and siding. No further details are known.

PATRICROFT

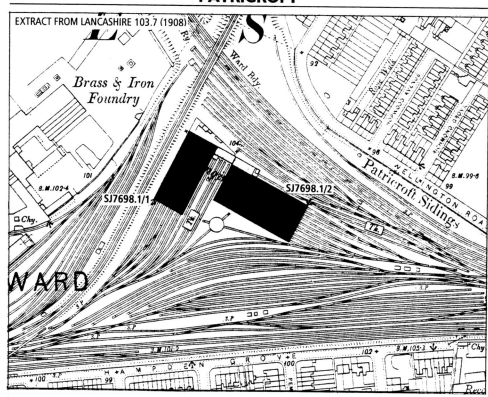
EXTRACT FROM LANCASHIRE 103.7 (1908)

Site SJ7698.1; In the fork of the Eccles to Patricroft and Monton Green lines, west of Eccles Station.

Patricroft (L&NWR) SJ7698.1/1A

A brick built 8TS dead ended shed with a northlight pattern roof, it was located at SJ76769897 and was opened on January 1st, 1885. The facilities included a coal stage, with water tank over, and a turntable.

The shed was reduced in length ...

Patricroft (LMS) SJ7698.1/1B

By 1938 the building had been partially demolished and reduced in length to four bays.

The shed was re-roofed ...

Patricroft (BR) SJ7698.1/1C

A transverse pitched roof with corrugated steel screen was installed in 1957.

Adjoined by ...

Patricroft (L&NWR) SJ7698.1/2A

A brick built 10TS dead ended shed with a northlight pattern roof was constructed at right angles to SJ7698.1/1A, located at SJ76839892. The building opened in 1904 and additional facilities included a coal stage with water tank over.

The shed was re-roofed ...

Patricroft (LMS) SJ7698.1/2B

In 1934 an LMS style multi-pitched roof was installed and a mechanical coaling plant was built in the yard.

The depot was closed by BR on July 1st, 1968 and subsequently demolished.

BURY

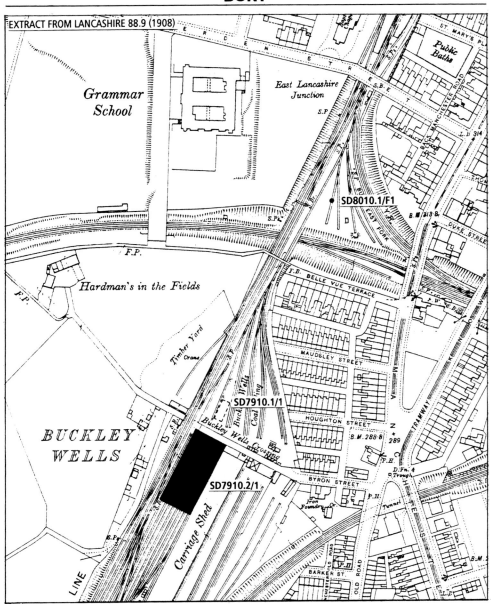

EXTRACT FROM LANCASHIRE 88.9 (1908)

NEWTON HEATH

Site SD8700.1; On the south side of the line, at the west end of Newton Heath Station.

Newton Heath (L&YR) SD8700.1/1A

A brick built 24TS shed with 23 through roads and six hipped roofs, it was located at SD87680090 and opened in 1876. The facilities included two coal stages, with water tanks over, and two 42ft turntables.

The shed was re-roofed ...

Newton Heath (LMS) SD8700.1/1B

In 1935 the five northernmost hipped sections were replaced with a multi-pitched roof. At the same time alterations were made to the coal stages and turntables.

The shed was reduced in size ...

Newton Heath (BR) SD8700.1/1C

The southern half of the building, with the exception of the southernmost bay which was retained for dmu servicing, was demolished by the London Midland Region in c1959 and a purpose-built diesel depot (SD8700.1/1D) erected on the site. The shed closed to steam on February 1st, 1968 and demolition of the northern portion took place in 1969.

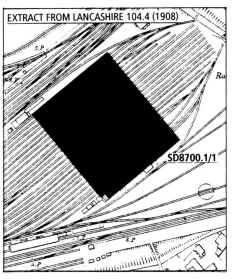

EXTRACT FROM LANCASHIRE 104.4 (1908)

CASTLETON

Site SD8810.1; On the east side of the line, south of Castleton Station.

Castleton Blue Pits (L&YR) SD8810.1/1A

A brick built 2TS dead ended shed with a slated gable style roof, located at SD88301047 and opened in 1844. Details of the facilities are not known. It was closed in 1878 and thereafter utilized as a goods shed, surviving until demolition in 1980.

Site SD8810.2; In the vicinity of Castleton East Junction, south of Castleton Station.

Castleton (L&YR) SD8810.2/F1

A servicing area consisting of a coal stage and siding, approximately located at SD881101 and opened in 1914. No further details are known.

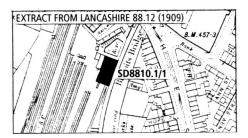

EXTRACT FROM LANCASHIRE 88.12 (1909)

WESTHOUGHTON

Site SD6506.1; On the north side of the line, east of Westhoughton Station.

Westhoughton (L&YR) SD6506.1/F1

A servicing area consisting of a coal stage and siding, located at SD65800695 and opened in 1909. No further details are known.

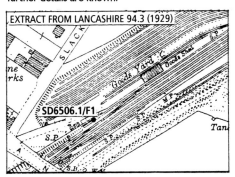

EXTRACT FROM LANCASHIRE 94.3 (1929)

TYLDESLEY

Site SD6802.1; In the vicinity of Tyldesley Station.

Tyldesley (L&NWR) SD6802.1/1A

A 1TS shed, opened on September 1st, 1864 and approximately located at SD689028. No further details are known.

Site SD7910.1; On the east side of the line, south of Bury Bolton Street Station.

Bury Buckley Wells (MB&RR) SD7910.1/1A

A 2TS shed, located at SD79991026 and opened on September 25th, 1846 by the Manchester, Bury & Rossendale Railway. Details of the facilities are not known. The depot was closed by the L&YR on January 1st, 1876.

Replaced by ...

Site SD7910.2; On the east side of the line, south of Bury Bolton Street Station.

Bury (L&YR) SD7910.2/1A

A brick built 8TS dead ended shed with a triple hipped roof, the easternmost roof section half-merging with the adjacent works/carriage shed building. It was located at SD79951020 and opened in 1876. The facilities included a coal stage, with water tank over, and turntable. The depot was closed by BR on November 12th, 1965 with the building immediately utilized for the storage of electric locomotives awaiting modification. The shed was later demolished.

Site SD8010.1; In the fork of the Radcliffe and Castleton lines, at the south end of Bury Bolton St Station.

Bury Bolton Street (L&YR) SD8010.1/F1

A servicing facility consisting of a turntable, located at SD80101044, and siding. No further details are known except that it had been removed by 1908.

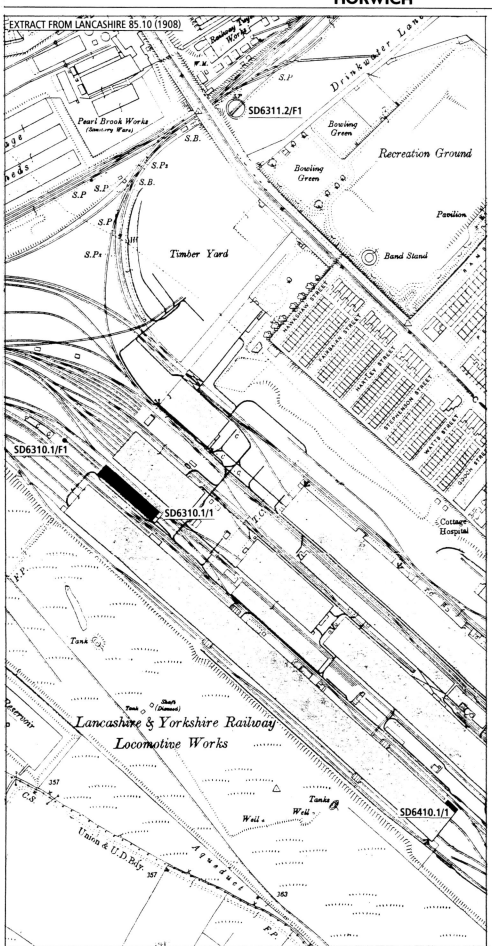

EXTRACT FROM LANCASHIRE 85.10 (1908)

Site SD6311.1; In the vicinity of Horwich Station.
Horwich (L&YR) SD6311.1/1A
A shed was opened here on February 14th, 1870 and closed in 1887. No further details are known.

Replaced by ...
Site SD6310.1; At the western end of Horwich Works.
Horwich (L&YR) SD6310.1/1A
A brick built 2TS through road shed with a northlight pattern roof, it was located at SD63711089 and opened in 1887. The facilities included water columns and a coal stage. The depot was closed by the LMS in July 1928 and the building was still standing in the 1990s, having been utilized as a store for the adjacent works.

A servicing area was then established ...
Horwich (LMS) SD6310.1/F1
The coal stage, water columns, engine pits and siding, located at SD63651095, were then utilized as a stabling point for the standard gauge works locomotives and steam railcar. It was officially closed by BR upon the withdrawal of the ex-L&YR Rail Motor No.50617 on April 17th, 1948 although the works locomotives continued to utilize the area until the end of steam working in the mid-1960s.

Site SD6311.2; On the south side of the line, at the west end of Horwich Station.
Horwich (L&YR) SD6311.2/F1
A servicing area consisting of a turntable, located at SD63811126 and siding, it was opened in 1887. No further details are known.

Site SD6410.1; At the east end of Horwich Works, alongside the north wall of the main erecting shop.
Horwich (L&YR) SD6410.1/1A
A 1ft 6in gauge brick built 3TS dead ended shed with a slated gable style roof, it was located at SD64011060 and opened in 1887. There were no facilities. The depot was closed by BR upon the abandonment of the narrow gauge works system in the late 1950s, with the building finding further use as a store.

ECCLES

Site SJ7898.1; On the north side of the line, at the east end of Eccles Station.
Eccles (L&MR) SJ7898.1/1A
A 1TS shed, opened in 1830 by the Liverpool & Manchester Railway and approximately located at SJ783988. No further details are known.

RAMSBOTTOM

Site SD7916.1; In the vicinity of Ramsbottom Station.
Ramsbottom (ELR) SD7916.1/1A
A 1TS shed, probably sited on the east side of the station and approximately located at SD793168, was opened here on September 28th, 1846. No further details are known except that it was removed to accommodate enlargement of the goods facilities prior to 1870.

Site SD7917.1; In the vicinity of Ramsbottom Sidings, north of Ramsbottom Station.
Ramsbottom (ELR) SD7917.1/F1
A servicing area consisting of a coal stage and siding, it was approximately located at SD793174 and was opened in 1914. No further details are known.

LONGSIGHT

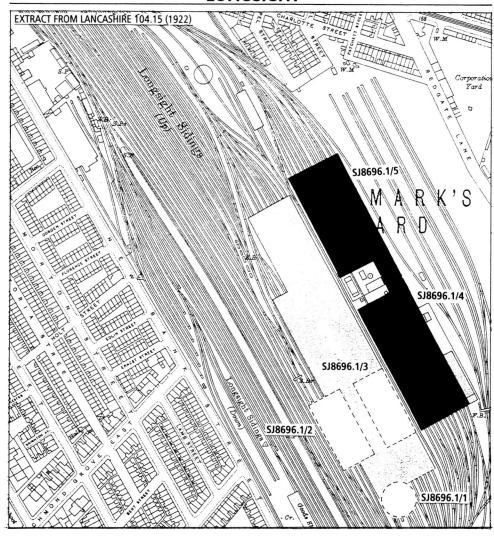

EXTRACT FROM LANCASHIRE 104.15 (1922)

Site SJ8696.1; *On the east side of the line, north of Longsight Station.*
Longsight (M&BR) SJ8696.1/1A
A brick built 12-stall polygonal 1RH building located at SJ86749616 and opened in 1842 by the Manchester & Birmingham Railway. The facilities included a coke/coal stage. The shed was closed in 1870, but did not suffer demolition until 1876.

Longsight (M&BR) SJ8696.1/2A
A brick built 4TS dead ended building, located at SJ86699614 and converted from part of an adjacent carriage shed in 1845. Additional facilities included a 42ft turntable.

The shed was enlarged ...
Longsight (L&NWR) SJ8696.1/2B
In 1866 the remainder of the carriage shed building was converted to form an 8TS dead ended shed. The building was dispensed with upon the opening of SJ8696.1/3A in 1876 and converted back to carriage use. It was demolished in 1907.

Longsight (L&NWR) SJ8696.1/3A
A brick built 8TS dead ended shed converted from a works building and located at SJ86739625. The shed opened in 1876 but was severely damaged by fire in 1901 and was demolished in 1907.

Longsight South (L&NWR) SJ8696.1/4A
A brick built 12TS dead ended shed with a slated triple hipped roof, located at SJ86769630 and opened in 1870. The facilities were improved by the provision of a coal stage, with water tank over and, in 1876, a repair shop. Following the opening of SJ8696.1/5A and the demolition of the repair shop it was also known as the "old" shed.

The shed was re-roofed ...
Longsight South (LMS) SJ8696.1/4B
The roof was renewed in c1933 and access to the building improved by the removal of the 50ft turntable.

The shed was rebuilt ...
Longsight South (BR) SJ8696.1/4C
The building was demolished and a new brick built 6TS dead ended shed with a louvre style roof and brick screen constructed by the London Midland Region in 1957.

Longsight North (L&NWR) SJ8696.1/5A
A brick built 12TS shed with a northlight pattern roof, located at SJ86699642 and opened in 1903. The North or "new" shed was built back-to-back with the "old" and the four easternmost tracks ran through to connect the two buildings via an extension. The facilities were improved by the installation of a new water tank and replacement of the old coal stage with a 50ft turntable.

The shed was rebuilt ...
Longsight North (BR) SJ8696.1/5B
The shed was reduced to an 8TS structure and an LMS style louvre roof with brick screen was installed in 1948.

Longsight South (SJ8696.1/4C) closed to steam in 1961 and Longsight North (SJ8696.1/5B) on February 14th, 1965. The shed was then used for diesel locomotive and dmu servicing and both buildings were still in use in 1998.

TRAFFORD PARK

Site SJ8096.1; *On the north side of the line, east of Trafford Park & Stretford Station.*
Trafford Park (CLC) SJ8096.1/1A
A brick built 20TS dead ended shed with seven slated hipped roofs, located at SJ80359635 and opened in March 1895. The facilities included two turntables, coal stages and water tanks, for the separate use of MR, GNR and GCR locomotives. By nationalization much of the roof cladding had disintegrated and some of the facilities had reached the point of total dereliction.

The shed was altered in 1952/3 ...
Trafford Park (BR) SJ8096.1/1B
The six most northerly tracks were stripped of all roofing by the London Midland Region and the covering over the remaining 14 roads cut back. Some of the bays were then re-clad in corrugated sheeting. The depot closed on March 4th, 1968 and was demolished, the site being utilized for a Freightliner depot.

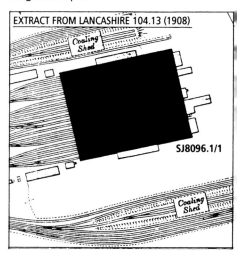

EXTRACT FROM LANCASHIRE 104.13 (1908)

AGECROFT

Site SD8000.1; *In the fork of the Swinton and Clifton Junction lines, north of Pendleton Broad Street.*
Agecroft (L&YR) SD8000.1/1A
A brick built 8TS dead ended shed with a northlight pattern roof, it was located at SD80470075 and was opened in 1889. The facilities included a coal stage, with water tank over, and a turntable.

The shed was partially re-roofed ....
Agecroft (LMS) SD8000.1/1B
In 1933 an LMS style multi-pitched roof was installed over the four westernmost tracks.

The shed was reduced in size ....
Agecroft (LMS) SD8000.1/1C
Either during LMS or early BR days the remaining northlight pattern roof was removed and the depot reduced to a 4TS building with a wooden partition effecting a wall between the roofed and open sections. The shed closed on October 22nd, 1966 and was demolished in 1968.

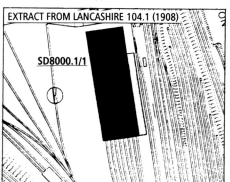

EXTRACT FROM LANCASHIRE 104.1 (1908)

Site SD9104.3; On the north side of the line, at the east end of Oldham Werneth Station.
Werneth (L&YR) SD9104.3/F1
A servicing area consisting of a coal stage and siding, it was located at SD91690469. No further details are known.

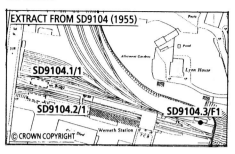

EXTRACT FROM SD9104 (1955)

SD9104.1/1
SD9104.2/1   SD9104.3/F1
© CROWN COPYRIGHT   Werneth Station

Site SD9104.1; On the north side of the line, at the west end of Oldham Werneth Station.
Werneth (M&LR) SD9104.1/1A
A 1TS shed, located at SD91530463 and opened on March 31st, 1842 by the Manchester & Leeds Railway.

Site SD9104.2; On the south side of the line, at the west end of Oldham Werneth Station.
Werneth (M&LR) SD9104.2/1A
A 1TS shed, located at SD91530461 and opened on March 31st, 1842 by the Manchester & Leeds Railway.

The two sheds were considered to be one depot and it may have been that one of the buildings was utilized as a coaling shed. The depot was closed on November 1st, 1847.

Replaced by ...
Site SD9303.1; Within the vicinity of Oldham Mumps Station.
Mumps (M&LR) SD9303.1/1A
A 2TS shed, approximately located at SD934039 and opened on November 1st, 1847 by the Manchester & Leeds Railway. No further details are known.

Site SD9304.1; On the south side of the Huddersfield line, at the south end of Oldham Mumps Station.
Mumps (L&NWR) SD9304.1/1A
A 1TS shed, located at SD93310496 and opened on July 5th, 1856. The depot was closed in 1878. No further details are known.

Replaced by ...
Site SD9504.1; On the north side of Oldham Lees Station.
Lees (L&NWR) SD9504.1/1A
A brick built 6TS dead ended shed with a northlight pattern roof, located at SD95590483 and opened in 1878. The facilities included a water tank, coal stage and 42ft turntable.

The shed was rebuilt ...
Lees (BR) SD9504.1/1B
The building was reduced to a 5TS shed and a louvre style roof with brick screen and steel girder lintel was installed by the London Midland Region in 1955. The depot was closed on April 13th, 1964 and the building subsequently demolished.

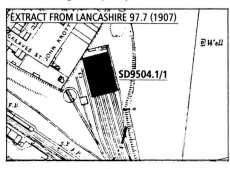

EXTRACT FROM LANCASHIRE 97.7 (1907)

SD9504.1/1

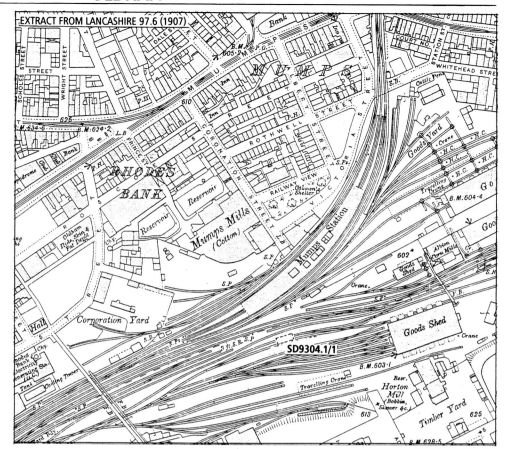

EXTRACT FROM LANCASHIRE 97.6 (1907)

SD9304.1/1

ROYTON JUNCTION

Site SD9306.1; On the west side of the line, at the south end of Royton Junction Station.
Royton Junction (L&YR) SD9306.1/F1
A servicing area consisting of a coal stage and siding, located at SD93380641 and opened in 1909. No further details are known.

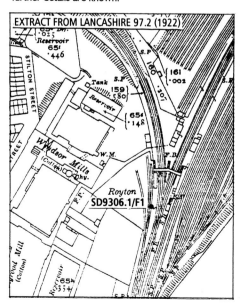

EXTRACT FROM LANCASHIRE 97.2 (1922)

Royton
SD9306.1/F1

SMITHY BRIDGE

Site SD9215.1; In the vicinity of Smithy Bridge Station.
Smithy Bridge (L&YR) SD9215.1/F1
A servicing area consisting of a coal stage and siding, it was approximately located at SD925151 and was opened in 1914. No further details are known.

HALLIWELL

Site SD7210.1; On the south side of the Astley Bridge line, west of Astley Bridge Junction.
Halliwell (L&YR) SD7210.1/F1
A servicing area consisting of a coal stage and siding, it was located at SD7214101 and opened in 1914. No further details are known.

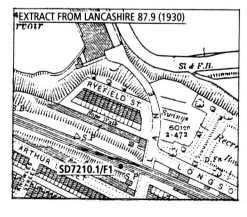

EXTRACT FROM LANCASHIRE 87.9 (1930)

RYEFIELD ST

SD7210.1/F1

FACIT

Site SD8819.1; In the vicinity of Facit Station.
Facit (L&YR) SD8819.1/1A
A timber shed, probably 1TS and approximately located at SD887191, was in use here between 1871 and 1881. No further details are known.

LEIGH

Site SJ6699.1; At Leigh Canal Wharf.
Leigh (L&NWR) SJ6699.1/1A
A 1TS shed, opened in 1867 and approximately located at SJ661998. No further details are known.

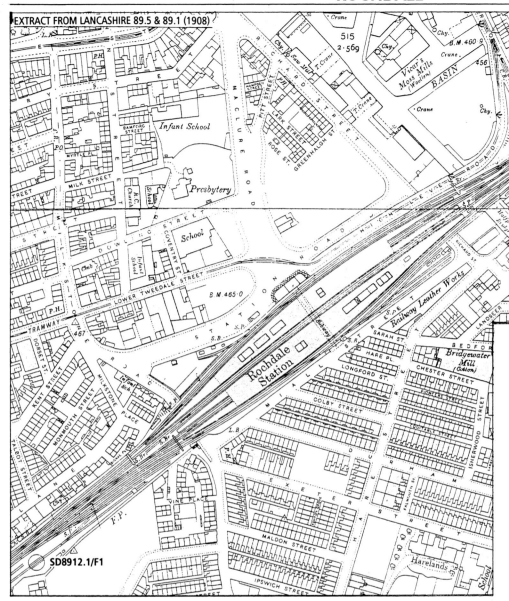

EXTRACT FROM LANCASHIRE 89.5 & 89.1 (1908)

SD9012.1/1

SD8912.1/F1

Site SD9012.1; On the west side of the line, at the north end of Rochdale (1st) Station

Rochdale (M&LR) SD9012.1/1A

A brick built 2TS dead ended shed with a gable style pitched roof incorporating a water tank, located at SD90331290 and opened in 1849 by the Manchester & Leeds Railway. Details of other facilities are not known. The depot was closed by the L&YR in 1863 and demolished to accommodate track improvements.

Site SD8912.1; On the east side of the line, south of Rochdale Station.

Rochdale Station (L&YR) SD8912.1/F1

A servicing area consisting of a turntable, located at SD89681240, and sidings. No further details are known.

Site SD9013.1; In Rochdale Goods Yard, north of Rochdale Station.

Rochdale (L&YR) SD9013.1/F1

A servicing area consisting of a coal stage and siding, approximately located at SD906132 and opened in 1909. No further details are known.

CHEQUERBENT

Site SD6705.1; At Chequerbent, on the west side of the line at the top of the Atherton Incline.

Chequerbent (B&LR) SD6705.1/1A

A 1TS dead ended shed, probably the building located at SD67290596, was opened here on August 1st, 1828 by the Bolton & Leigh Railway. It was destroyed by a fire in 1831. No further details are known.

Replaced, presumably on the same site, by ...

Chequerbent (B&LR) SD6705.1/1B

A 1TS shed, it was opened in 1831 by the Bolton & Leigh Railway. The line was absorbed by the L&NWR on July 16th, 1846 and the depot was closed in 1867. No further details are known.

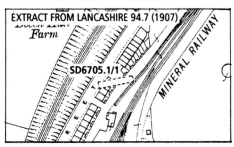

EXTRACT FROM LANCASHIRE 94.7 (1907)

SD6705.1/1

ATHERTON

Site SD6603.1; On the east side of the line, at the south end of Atherton (Bag Lane) Station.

Atherton (L&NWR) SD6603.1/1A

A 1TS dead ended shed, it was located at SD66660376 and was opened in 1849. No further details are known.

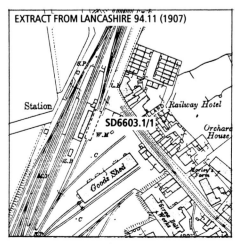

EXTRACT FROM LANCASHIRE 94.11 (1907)

SD6603.1/1

KENYON JUNCTION

Site SJ6496.1; On the north side of Kenyon Junction Station.

Kenyon Junction (B&LR) SJ6496.1/1A

A 2TS shed, opened in 1840 by the Bolton & Leigh Railway and is believed to be the building located at SJ64269645. The line was absorbed by the L&NWR on July 16th, 1846 and the depot closed in c1868. No further details are known.

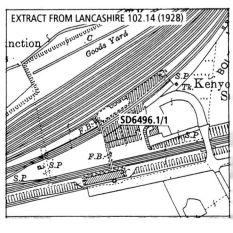

EXTRACT FROM LANCASHIRE 102.14 (1928)

SD6496.1/1

SALFORD & MANCHESTER

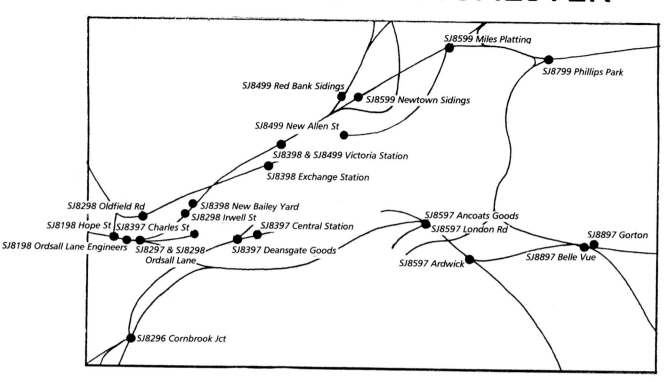

MILES PLATTING

Site SJ8599.1; In the fork of the Oldham Road Goods and Victoria lines, west of Miles Platting Station.
Miles Platting (M&LR) SJ8599.1/1A
A polygonal 1RH shed, probably built in brick, located at SJ85509965 and opened on July 4th, 1839 by the Manchester & Leeds Railway. The building was adjacent to the works and other facilities included a coke store.

Miles Platting (M&LR) SJ8599.1/2A
A 3TS through road shed, located at SJ85559968 and opened in 1845. The facilities included a turntable and water column.

The shed was enlarged ...
Miles Platting (L&YR) SJ8599.1/2B
The building was increased in size to a 5TS through road shed in 1849.

The depot closed in 1872 upon the opening of Newton Heath Shed (SD8700.1/1) and the buildings were demolished in c1880 to accommodate the construction of a flyover from Oldham Road Goods to the eastbound main line.

Replaced, on the same site, by ...
Collyhurst Street Sidings (L&YR) SJ8599.1/F1
A servicing area consisting of a turntable, located at SJ85509952, and siding was established at some time prior to 1902.

The facility was remodelled ...
Collyhurst Street Sidings (LMS) SJ8599.1/F2
At some stage, possibly during LMS days the turntable was removed and a coal stage, water tank and engine pit installed. It was probably not dispensed with until the end of steam in the area.

Site SJ8599.2; On the south side of the Oldham Road Goods line, west of Miles Platting Station.
Miles Platting (L&YR) SJ8599.2/1A
An 11TS dead ended shed, located at SJ85489953 and opened in 1850. The facilities included a water tank and coke store. The depot closed at the same time as SJ8599.1/1&2, in 1872 on the opening of Newton Heath Shed (SD8700.1/1).

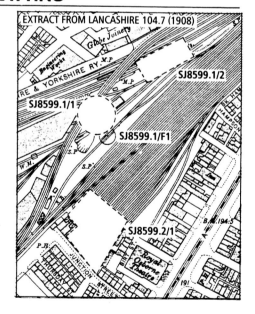

EXTRACT FROM LANCASHIRE 104.7 (1908)

NEW ALLEN STREET

Site SJ8499.1; On the north side of Oldham Road Goods Station.
New Allen Street (L&YR) SJ8499.1/F1
A servicing area consisting of a coal stage and siding, located at SJ84949914 and opened in 1914. The facility was closed by BR.

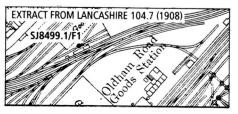

EXTRACT FROM LANCASHIRE 104.7 (1908)

CORNBROOK JUNCTION

Site SJ8296.1; On the west side of Cornbrook Junction, south of Central Station.
Cornbrook Junction (MS&LR) SJ8296.1/1A
A partially curved brick built 3TS through road shed, located at SJ82149684 and opened on January 1st, 1880. The facilities included a turntable and coal stage. The depot was closed in March 1895 and demolished to accommodate track widening.

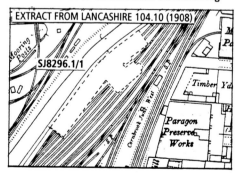

EXTRACT FROM LANCASHIRE 104.10 (1908)

ANCOATS GOODS

Site SJ8597.3; At the east end of Ancoats Goods Yard.
Ancoats Goods (MR) SJ8597.3/F1
A facility consisting of a water column and siding, located at SJ85589788 and opened on May 2nd, 1870. No further details are known except that although officially closed by the LMS in 1923 it remained in use until the end of steam in the area.

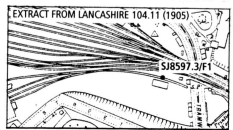

EXTRACT FROM LANCASHIRE 104.11 (1905)

BELLE VUE

Site SJ8897.2; In the fork of the Ashburys to Belle Vue and Gorton lines, east of London Road Station.
Belle Vue (MR) SJ8897.2/1A
A brick built 1RH shed with a slated multi-pitched roof, located at SJ88959701 and opened in 1870. The facilities included a ramped coal stage, fitting shop and an additional 46ft turntable installed in 1877.

The building was re-roofed ...
Belle Vue (LMS) SJ8897.2/1B
A flat concrete roof was installed in 1947 and, at the same time, the turntable enlarged to 57ft. The depot was closed by BR on April 16th, 1956 and let out for private use. Parts of the building were still standing in 1998 with the site being utilized as a scrap yard.

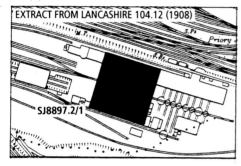
EXTRACT FROM LANCASHIRE 104.12 (1908)

SJ8897.2/1

LONDON ROAD

Site SJ8597.1; On the south side of the line, at the east end of London Road Station.
London Road (L&NWR) SJ8597.1/F1
A servicing area consisting of a turntable, located at SJ85059775, engine pits, water tank and sidings. The opening date is not known but the facility was utilized into BR days.

Site SJ8597.2; On the north side of the line, at the east end of London Road Station.
London Road (MS&LR) SJ8597.2/F1
A servicing area consisting of a turntable, located at SJ85079782, water tank and sidings. The opening date is not known.

At some stage the facility was re-modelled ...
London Road (MS&LR) SJ8597.2/F2
Prior to the grouping the turntable was removed but the water tank and sidings remained in use for servicing into BR days.

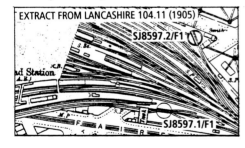
EXTRACT FROM LANCASHIRE 104.11 (1905)

SJ8597.2/F1

SJ8597.1/F1

PHILLIPS PARK

Site SJ8799.1; On the south side of the line, at the west end of Park Station.
Phillips Park (L&YR) SJ8799.1/F1
A servicing area consisting of a coal stage and siding, located at SJ87129960 and opened in 1914. No further details are known.

SJ8799.1/F1

EXTRACT FROM LANCASHIRE 104.8 (1932)

GORTON

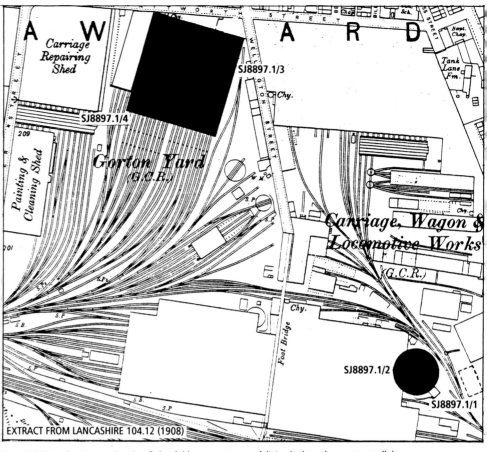
SJ8897.1/3

SJ8897.1/4

SJ8897.1/2

SJ8897.1/1

EXTRACT FROM LANCASHIRE 104.12 (1908)

Site SJ8897.1; On the north side of the Ashburys to Gorton line, west of Gorton Station.
Gorton (MR) SJ8897.1/1A
A 3TS shed, located at SJ88589700 and opened on October 1st, 1866. No further details are known except that although it closed to MR use in 1870, upon the opening of Belle Vue shed (SJ8897.2/1), MS&LR locomotives continued to utilize the building until it was demolished in 1879.

Gorton (MS&LR) SJ8897.1/2A
A brick built circular 1RH shed with a continuous pitched roof, it was located at SJ88549701 and opened in 1848. The building contained a unique double-track turntable to allow the roof to be supported by a large central column. It closed in 1879 and became absorbed as part of the adjacent works, remaining in use until 1963. Demolition followed in November 1965.

Replaced by ...
Gorton (MS&LR) SJ8897.1/3A
A brick built 10TS dead ended shed with a north-light pattern roof, located at SJ88339729 and opened in 1879.

RED BANK SIDINGS

Site SJ8499.5; On the east side of the Bury line, north of Victoria Station.
Red Bank Sidings (L&YR) SJ8499.5/F1
A servicing area consisting of a turntable, located at SJ84549960, and sidings. No further details are known.

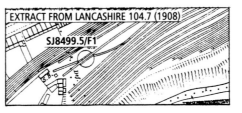
EXTRACT FROM LANCASHIRE 104.7 (1908)
SJ8499.5/F1

Adjoined, along the western wall, by ....
Gorton (MS&LR) SJ8897.1/4A
A brick built 10TS dead ended shed with a north-light pattern roof, located at SJ88299730 and opened in 1879. The facilities, which were up-graded in c1900 and c1930, included a coal stage, turntables and a water tank.

The shed was rebuilt...
Gorton (LNER) SJ8897.1/4B
At some stage the building was reduced to an 8TS dead ended shed and possibly re-roofed.

The depot was closed by BR on June 14th, 1965, the site cleared and replaced with a wholesale market.

ARDWICK

Site SJ8597.4; In the vicinity of Ardwick Station.
Ardwick (MS&LR) SJ8597.4/1A
A 1TS shed approximately located at SJ859972. No further details are known.

NEWTOWN SIDINGS

Site SJ8599.3; On the north side of the line, west of Miles Platting Station.
Newtown Sidings (L&YR) SJ8599.3/F1
A servicing area consisting of a turntable, located at SJ85029952, and sidings. No further details are known.

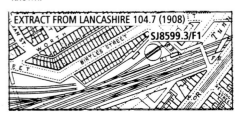
EXTRACT FROM LANCASHIRE 104.7 (1908)
SJ8599.3/F1

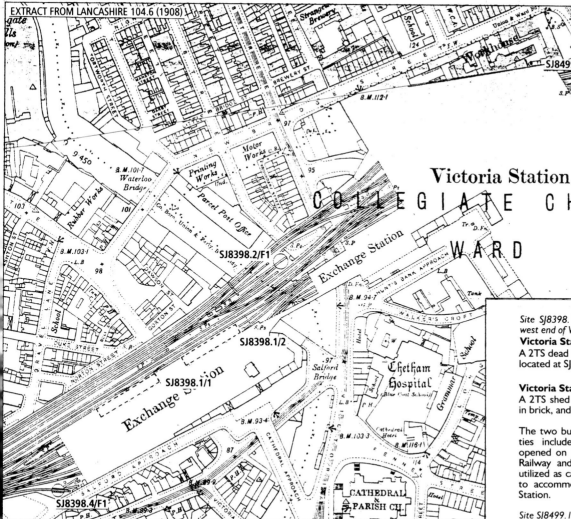

EXTRACT FROM LANCASHIRE 104.6 (1908)

Site SJ8398.1; On the south side of the line, at the west end of Victoria Station.
Victoria Station (GJR) SJ8398.1/1A
A 2TS dead ended shed, probably built in brick, and located at SJ83659885.

Victoria Station (GJR) SJ8398.1/2A
A 2TS shed with one through road, probably built in brick, and located at SJ83729889.

The two buildings faced each other and the facilities included two turntables. The depot was opened on May 4th, 1844 by the Grand Junction Railway and closed in 1860, the buildings being utilized as carriage sheds until the site was cleared to accommodate the enlargement of Exchange Station.

Site SJ8499.1; On the north side of the line, at the east end of Victoria Station
Victoria Station (L&YR) SJ8499.1/1A
A 2TS dead ended shed, located at SJ84109915 and opened on January 1st, 1844. The facilities included a turntable sited outside of the shed entrance. The depot was closed in c1876 and the site cleared to accommodate station enlargements.

Site SJ8499.2; On the north side of the line, at the east end of Victoria Station.
Victoria Station (L&YR) SJ8499.2/F1
A servicing area consisting of a turntable, located at SJ84149919, water column and siding. No further details are known.

Site SJ8499.3; On the south side of the line, at the east end of Victoria Station.
Victoria Station (L&YR) SJ8499.3/F1
A servicing area consisting of a turntable, located at SJ84149912, water tank and siding. No further details are known.

Site SJ8398.2; On the north side of the line, at the west end of Victoria Station.
Victoria Station (L&YR) SJ8398.2/F1
A servicing area consisting of a turntable, located at SJ83799898, water column and sidings. No further details are known.

DEANSGATE GOODS

Site SJ8397.2; On the west side of the line at the south end of Deansgate Goods Station.
Deansgate (GNR) SJ8397.2/1A
A brick built 2TS dead ended shed with a slated northlight pattern roof incorporating a water tank, and located at SJ83289765. Although it officially opened on July 1st, 1898 the local council prohibited its use as an engine shed in view of the siting of the building high above a road. (There was a potential risk of a runaway locomotive passing through the back wall of the shed and out into the street). Locomotives stabled in the shed yard whilst the building was utilized as a wagon shop until at least 1950.

CENTRAL STATION

Site SJ8397.1. On the east side of the line, at the south end of Central Station.
Central Station (CLC) SJ8397.1/F1
A servicing area, consisting of a turntable and sidings, located at SJ83559758 and opened on July 1st, 1880.

The facility was improved ...
Central Station (LNER) SJ8397.1/F2
At some stage, probably during LNER days, the turntable was enlarged. The facility was closed by BR in January 1968.

EXCHANGE STATION

Site SJ8398.4; On the south side of the line, at the west end of Exchange Station.
Exchange Station (L&YR) SJ8398.4/F1
A facility consisting of a turntable, located at SJ83589876, and sidings. No further details are known.

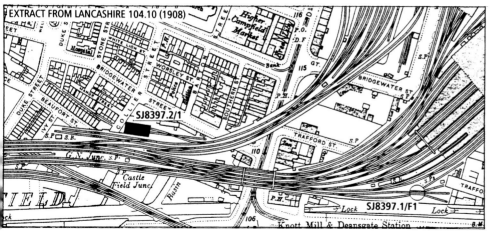

EXTRACT FROM LANCASHIRE 104.10 (1908)

ORDSALL LANE

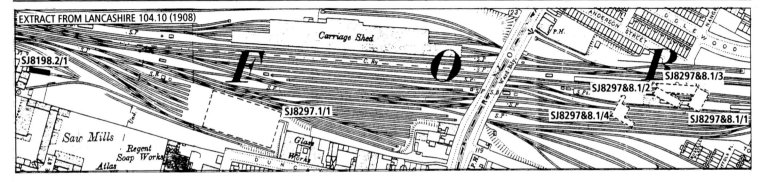

EXTRACT FROM LANCASHIRE 104.10 (1908)

Site SJ8297&8.1; On the south side of the line, at the west end of Ordsall Lane Station.
Ordsall Lane (L&MR)^{SJ8297&8.1/3A}
A 1TS dead ended shed located at SJ82489801.

Adjoined by ...
Ordsall Lane (L&MR)^{SJ8297&8.1/1A}
A 2TS through road shed located at SJ82509799.

Adjoined by ...
Ordsall Lane (L&MR)^{SJ8297&8.1/2A}
A 2TS shed with one through road located at SJ82469799

Ordsall Lane (L&MR)^{SJ8297&8.1/4A}
A 3TS dead ended shed located at SJ82439798

The depot was opened in 1830 by the Liverpool & Manchester Railway and had use of full facilities as all four shed buildings, which were probably constructed in brick with pitched roofs, formed an integral part of Ordsall Lane Works. The depot was closed by the L&NWR in 1874 and the whole site cleared to accommodate station enlargements and track widening.

Replaced by ...
Site SJ8297.1; On the south side of the line, west of Ordsall Lane Station.
Ordsall Lane (L&NWR)^{SJ8297.1/1A}
An 8TS dead ended shed, probably built in brick, located at SJ82079798 and opened in 1874. The facilities included a turntable. The depot closed on June 20th, 1904 upon the enlargement of Patricroft shed (SJ7698.1/2), the building being subsequently demolished.

Site SJ8198.2; On the south side of the line, west of Ordsall Lane Station.
Ordsall Lane Engineers (L&NWR)^{SJ8198.2/1A}
A 1TS dead ended shed, located at SJ81879804 and opened in 1874. Sited at the west end of the yard to Ordsall Lane (SJ8297.1/1) locomotives were able to utilize the depot's facilities. The shed closed in 1904 but was not demolished immediately and may have found further use as a store.

Site SJ8298.1; In the fork of the lines at the east end of Ordsall Lane Station.
Ordsall Lane Station (L&NWR)^{SJ8298.1/F1}
A servicing area consisting of a turntable, located at SJ82789800, water column and siding. No further details are known other than it lasted into BR days.

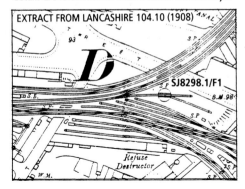

EXTRACT FROM LANCASHIRE 104.10 (1908)

OLDFIELD ROAD

Site SJ8298.2; On the south side of the line, west of Salford Station.
Oldfield Road (MB&BCN&R)^{SJ8298.2/1A}
A 2TS dead ended shed, located at SJ82599825 and opened on May 4th, 1844 by the Manchester, Bolton & Bury Canal Navigation & Railway Company. The shed building housed an unusual track configuration with a line exiting through the side of the building, via a small turntable, and accessing the adjacent works. The line was absorbed by the L&YR in 1847 and the depot closed in 1871.

Replaced by ...
Oldfield Road (L&YR)^{SJ8298.2/F1}
A servicing area consisting of a coal stage and water column located at SJ82609822. No further details are known.

Site SJ8298.3; On the north side of the line, west of Salford Station.
Oldfield Road (ELR)^{SJ8298.3/1A}
A 2TS shed, located at SJ82599830, was opened here by the East Lancs Railway.

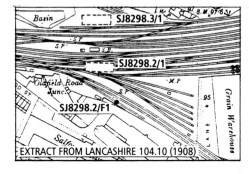

EXTRACT FROM LANCASHIRE 104.10 (1908)

IRWELL STREET

Site SJ8298.4; In Irwell Street Sidings.
Irwell Street (L&YR)^{SJ8298.4/F1}
A servicing area consisting of a coal stage, water column and siding located at SJ82949823. No further details are known except that it was still being utilized in BR days.

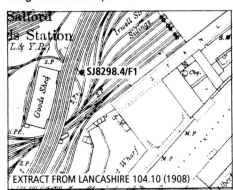

EXTRACT FROM LANCASHIRE 104.10 (1908)

HOPE STREET

Site SJ8198.1; On the east side of Windsor Bridge Cattle Station, west of Ordsall Lane Station.
Hope Street (ELR)^{SJ8198.1/1A}
A 3TS shed, probably located at SJ81889843 and opened by the East Lancs Railway in 1856. The line was absorbed by the L&YR in 1859 and no further details are known except that it closed in 1871.

Replaced, on the same site, by ....
Hope Street* (L&YR)^{SJ8198.1/1B}
A brick built 8TS dead ended shed with a slated triple gable style roof, it opened in 1871. The facilities included a turntable and coal stage. The depot closed in 1899 and found further use as a wagon works, the building not being demolished until January 1983 to make way for a new chord line into Manchester.

Replaced by ....
Hope Street* (L&YR)^{SJ8198.1/F1}
A servicing area consisting of a turntable, located at SJ81859846, coal stage, engine pit and siding was then established. No further details are known.

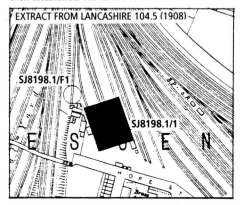

EXTRACT FROM LANCASHIRE 104.5 (1908)

* The depot was also known as Windsor Bridge.

NEW BAILEY YARD

Site SJ8398.3; In New Bailey Yard, on the south side of Salford Station.
New Bailey Yard (L&YR)^{SJ8398.3/F1}
A servicing area, consisting of a coal stage and approximately located at SJ832984, was established here. It was closed by BR in 1968.

CHARLES STREET

Site SJ8397.3; In the Goods Yard on the north side of Liverpool Road Station.
Charles Street (GJR)^{SJ8397.3/1A}
A 2TS shed, approximately located at SJ83109795 was opened here by the Grand Junction Railway on July 4th, 1837 and closed in 1843. No further details are known.

LANCASHIRE (SW)

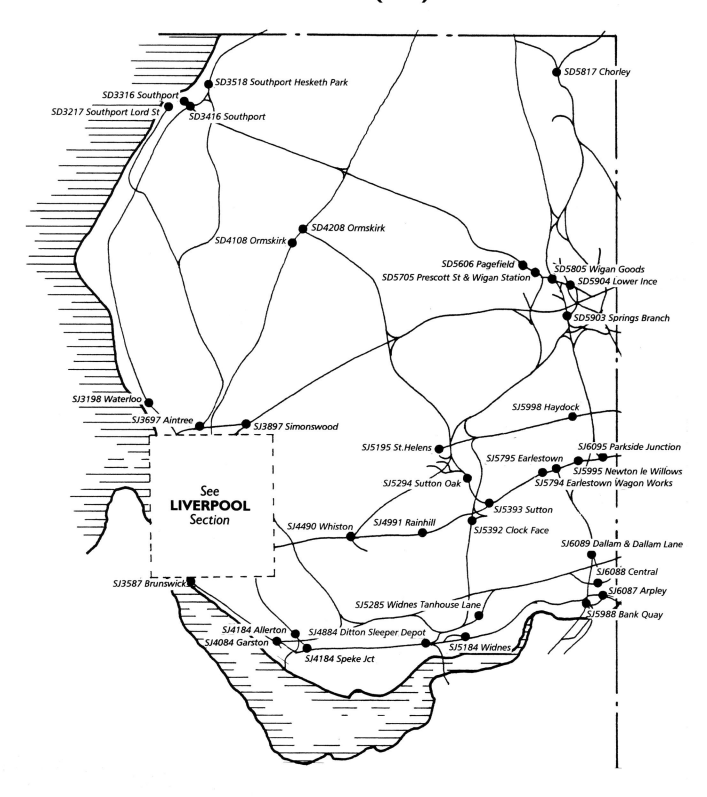

SD5817 Chorley

SD3518 Southport Hesketh Park

SD3316 Southport

SD3217 Southport Lord St

SD3416 Southport

SD4208 Ormskirk

SD4108 Ormskirk

SD5606 Pagefield

SD5805 Wigan Goods

SD5705 Prescott St & Wigan Station

SD5904 Lower Ince

SD5903 Springs Branch

SJ3198 Waterloo

SJ3697 Aintree

SJ3897 Simonswood

SJ5998 Haydock

SJ5195 St.Helens

SJ6095 Parkside Junction

SJ5795 Earlestown

SJ5995 Newton le Willows

SJ5294 Sutton Oak

SJ5794 Earlestown Wagon Works

See **LIVERPOOL** Section

SJ4490 Whiston

SJ4991 Rainhill

SJ5393 Sutton

SJ5392 Clock Face

SJ6089 Dallam & Dallam Lane

SJ6088 Central

SJ3587 Brunswick

SJ6087 Arpley

SJ5285 Widnes Tanhouse Lane

SJ5988 Bank Quay

SJ4184 Allerton

SJ4884 Ditton Sleeper Depot

SJ4084 Garston

SJ4184 Speke Jct

SJ5184 Widnes

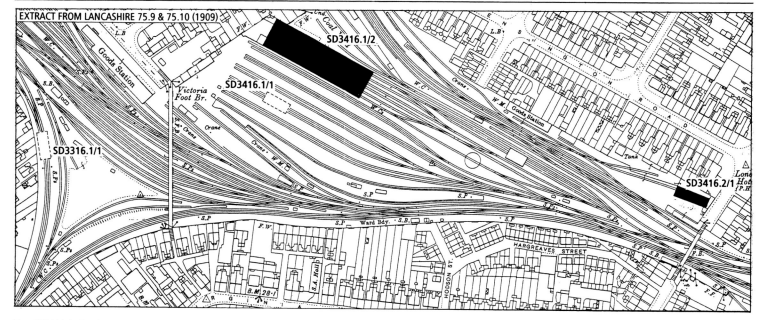

EXTRACT FROM LANCASHIRE 75.9 & 75.10 (1909)

Site SD3416.1; On the north side of the line, east of Chapel Street Station.
Southport (M&SR) SD3416.1/1A

A 2TS dead ended shed, located at SD34181696 and opened by the Manchester & Southport Railway on April 9th, 1855. The line was worked by the East Lancashire Railway and it was absorbed by the L&YR in 1859. Details of the facilities are not known.

The shed was enlarged ...
Southport (L&YR) SD3416.1/1B

The building was extended in 1870 and the depot closed in 1885. The site was later utilized for additional sidings.

Southport Derby Road (L&YR) SD3416.1/2A

A brick built 3TS shed with a northlight pattern roof, located at SD34221699 and opened in March 1890. The facilities included a coal stage with water tank over and turntable.

The shed was enlarged ...
Southport Derby Road (L&YR) SD3416.1/2B

At some stage, prior to 1909, the building was increased in size to a 6TS dead ended shed.

The shed was partially re-roofed ...
Southport Derby Road (LMS) SD3416.1/2C

A multi-pitched roof was installed over the rear half of the shed in 1939.

The re-roofing was completed ...
Southport Derby Road (BR) SD3416.1/2D

The installation was completed over the whole building by the London Midland Region in 1953. The depot closed on June 6th, 1966 and the building was taken over by *Steamport*, a railway preservation group. By 1997 the roof was in such a bad state of repair that the society decided to relocate, with the last public steaming at the depot taking place on November 29th of that year.

Site SD3316.1; On the south side of the line, at the east end of Chapel Road Station.
Southport (LC&SR) SD3316.1/1A

A timber built 1TS shed, located at SD33961693 and opened on July 24th, 1848 by the Liverpool, Crosby & Southport Railway. The line was absorbed by the L&YR in 1855.

The shed was enlarged ...
Southport (L&YR) SD3316.1/1B

Prior to 1856 the building was enlarged to a 2TS through road structure. The facilities included a turntable. The depot closed in 1858 and was demolished to accommodate track widening.

Site SD3416.2; On the north side of the line, at the east end of St. Luke's Station.
Southport Windsor Road (WLR) SD3416.2/1A

A brick built 2TS dead ended shed with a slated gable style roof, located at SD34571688 and opened by the West Lancashire Railway on September 5th, 1882. Details of the facilities are not known. The line was absorbed by the L&YR on July 1st, 1897 and the depot closed in the same year. The building was not demolished but found further use, housing an electricity sub-station, and remained standing in the 1970s.

Site SD3518.1; In the vicinity of Hesketh Park Station.
Southport Hesketh Park (WLR) SD3518.1/1A

A timber built 1TS shed, approximately located at SD354180 and opened on February 19th, 1878 by the West Lancs Railway. No further details are known other than the depot was closed on September 5th, 1882.

Site SD3217.1; On the west side of Lord Street Station.
Southport Lord Street (CLC) SD3217.1/1A

A brick built 2TS dead ended shed with a slated gable style roof, located at SD32911710 and opened on September 1st, 1884. The facilities included a turntable, coal stage and water tank. The depot was closed by BR on July 7th, 1952 and subsequently demolished.

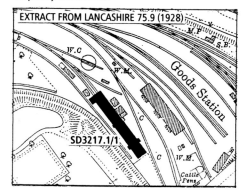

EXTRACT FROM LANCASHIRE 75.9 (1928)

HAYDOCK

Site SJ5998.1; In the vicinity of Haydock (Racecourse) Station.
Haydock (L&MR) SJ5998.1/1A

A 1TS shed, approximately located at SJ596984, it was opened in 1831 by the Liverpool & Manchester Railway. No further details are known.

SIMONSWOOD

Site SJ3897.1; In the fork of the Ford & Fazakerley lines, at Fazakerley Junction.
Simonswood (L&YR) SJ3897.1/1A

A 2TS through road shed located at SJ38349779.

Simonswood (L&YR) SJ3897.1/2A

A 2TS through road shed located at SJ38349776.

The depot opened in 1866 and closed in 1886 upon the opening of Aintree shed (SJ3697.1/1) and the buildings were utilized as a Carriage & Wagon Works. To improve the facility in 1901 they were partially demolished and rebuilt but parts of the original buildings remained until the works were closed by BR.

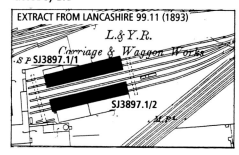

EXTRACT FROM LANCASHIRE 99.11 (1893)

RAINHILL

Site SJ4991.1; On the north side of the line, at the east end of Rainhill Station.
Rainhill (L&MR) SJ4991.1/F1

A facility was established here *"...in Tasker Terrace opposite the Coach and Horses "* in 1829 by the Liverpool & Manchester Railway. It probably consisted of a few sidings and was approximately located at SJ49269155. No further details are known.

EXTRACT FROM LANCASHIRE 107.12 (1907)

Site SJ6087.1; On the south side of Warrington Arpley Station.

Warrington Arpley (W&AJR) SJ6087.1/1A

A brick built 2TS through road shed with a slated gable style roof, located at SJ60558773 and opened by the Warrington & Altrincham Junction Railway on May 1st, 1854. The facilities included a coal stage, with water tank over, and a turntable. By the time the depot was closed to steam by BR on May 27th, 1963 the building was roofless, the site being subsequently utilized as a Diesel Stabling Point.

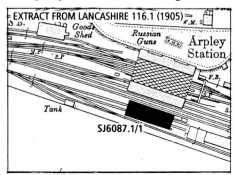

Site SJ6088.1; On the south side of Warrington Central Station.

Warrington Central (CLC) SJ6088.1/1A

A 1TS through road shed, located at SJ60748850 and opened on August 1st, 1873. No further details are known other than it was removed at some point after 1905.

A servicing point was then established ...

Warrington Central (CLC) SJ6088.1/F1

An additional siding was installed and locomotives utilized the engine pit until the facility was closed by BR in c1966.

Site SJ6089.1; On the east side of the line, north of Warrington Bank Quay Station.

Warrington Dallam Lane (W&NR) SJ6089.1/1A

A 2TS shed, believed to be located at SJ60288949, and opened by the Warrington & Newton Railway on July 25th, 1831. The line was absorbed by the Grand Junction Railway on June 12th, 1836. No further details are known.

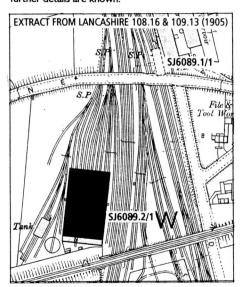

Replaced by ...
Site SJ5988.1; On the west side of the line, at the north end of Warrington Bank Quay Station.

Warrington Bank Quay (L&NWR) SJ5988.1/1A

A 5TS dead ended shed, located at SJ59868818, opened here in c1850 and closed in 1888. No further details are known other than the building remained standing for many years, probably in use as a goods shed.

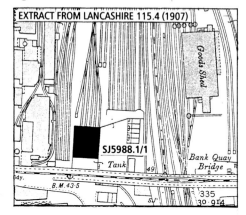

Replaced by ...
Site SJ6089.2; On the west side of the line, north of Warrington Bank Quay Station.

Warrington Dallam (L&NWR) SJ6089.2/1A

A brick built 10TS dead ended shed with a northlight pattern roof, located at SJ60168936 and opened in 1888. The facilities included a coal stage, with water tank over, and a 42ft turntable which was later enlarged to 65ft.

The shed was rebuilt ...
Warrington Dallam (BR) SJ6089.2/1B

The building was reduced to 9TS and a louvre style roof with brick screen was installed by the London Midland Region in 1957. The depot was closed on October 2nd, 1967 and the building let out for private use, surviving into the 1990s.

EARLESTOWN

Site SJ5795.0; In the vicinity of Earlestown Station.
Earlestown (GJR) SJ5795.0/1A

A 1TS shed, approximately located at SJ579951, was opened here on July 4th, 1837 by the Grand Junction Railway. The line was absorbed by the L&NWR on July 16th, 1846.

Earlestown (L&MR) SJ5795.0/2A

A 1TS shed, approximately located at SJ578952, was opened here in 1836 by the Liverpool & Manchester Railway and closed in 1868.

Site SJ5794.1; In Earlestown Wagon Works on the north side of the line, west of Earlestown Station.
Earlestown Wagon Works (L&NWR) SJ5794.1/1A

A brick built 1TS dead ended shed with a slated gable style roof, it was located at SJ57319496. The facilities included a water column. No further details are known except that it closed, along with the works, in 1963 and still stood in 1998, as part of an industrial estate.

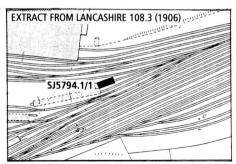

WIDNES

Site SJ5184.1; On the south side of the line, east of Widnes Station.
Widnes (L&NWR) SJ5184.1/1A

A 2TS shed, located at SJ51538492 and opened in 1874. No further details are known.

The shed was enlarged and rebuilt ...
Widnes (L&NWR) SJ5184.1/1B

A brick built 6TS dead ended shed with a northlight pattern roof was constructed on the same site in 1888. The facilities included a coal stage, with water tank over, and a turntable.

The shed was re-roofed ...
Widnes (LMS) SJ5184.1/1C

A louvre style roof with brick screen was installed in 1946 and the depot was closed by BR on April 13th, 1964 with the building being sold for private use. It was subsequently demolished.

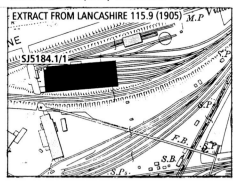

Site SJ5285.1; On the north side of the line, at the west end of Tanhouse Lane Station.
Widnes Tanhouse Lane (GCR/MR) SJ5285.1/1A

A brick built 2TS shed with one through road and a twin slated gable style roof, it was located at SJ52568531 and opened in 1880. The facilities included a water tank, coal stage and turntable. Although the depot was closed by BR on April 16th, 1956 and the shed building immediately demolished, locomotives continued to utilize the facilities in the yard until March 16th, 1961.

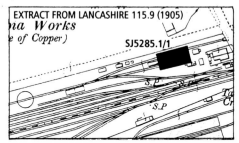

PARKSIDE JUNCTION

Site SJ6095.1; In the fork of the Wigan and Liverpool lines, at Parkside Junction.
Parkside Junction (L&MR) SJ6095.1/1A

A stone built 1TS shed with a gable style roof, located at SJ60719558 and opened in 1831 by the Liverpool & Manchester Railway. The facilities included a water tank. No further details are known except that after closure it was utilized for the adjacent Pumping Station.

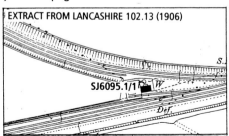

SUTTON

Site SJ5393.1; In the vicinity of St.Helens Junction Station.
Sutton (StH&RGR) SJ5393.1/1A
A 1TS shed, approximately located at SJ535932, was opened here by the St.Helens & Runcorn Gap Railway on February 2nd, 1833 and closed in 1858. No further details are known.

Replaced by ...
Site SJ5393.3; In the vicinity of St.Helens Junction.
Sutton St.Helens Junction (StHC&RC) SJ5393.3/1A
A shed, approximately located at SJ535932 was opened here by the St.Helens Canal & Railway Company in 1858. The line was absorbed by the L&NWR on August 1st, 1864 and the depot closed in 1880 with demolition following in 1889. No further details are known.

Site SJ5393.2; In the James Cross & Co. Locomotive Works, on the south side of St.Helens Junction.
Sutton St.Helens (L&NWR) SJ5393.2/1A
A shed, approximately located at SJ532930 and converted from a works building opened here in 1872 and closed in 1880 reverting to a wagon tarpaulin store. No further details are known.

Replaced by ...
Site SJ5294.1; On the east side of the line, between Sutton Oak and Peasley Cross Stations.
Sutton Oak* (L&NWR) SJ5294.1/1A
A brick built 10TS dead ended shed with a north-light pattern roof, located at SJ52739411 and opened in 1880. The facilities included a ramped coal stage, with water tank over, and a turntable which was enlarged to 60ft in 1937.

The shed was re-roofed ...
Sutton Oak* (LMS) SJ5294.1/1B
A louvre style roof with brick screen was installed in 1946 and although closed by BR on June 19th, 1967 the building remained standing in 1998, in use as a supermarket.

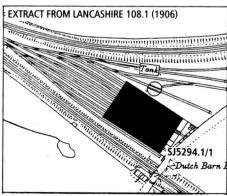
EXTRACT FROM LANCASHIRE 108.1 (1906)
SJ5294.1/1

*The depot was also known as Peasley Cross.

GARSTON

Site SJ4084.1; On the west side of the line, south of Garston Dock Station.
Garston (StHR&CC) SJ4084.1/1A
A 2TS through road shed, located at SJ40158447 and opened in 1861 by the St.Helens Railway and Canal Company. The facilities included a turntable and water tank. The depot closed in 1886 and, until BR days, found further use as a wagon repair shop.

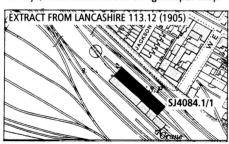
EXTRACT FROM LANCASHIRE 113.12 (1905)
SJ4084.1/1

ST.HELENS CENTRAL

Site SJ5195.1; On the east side of the line, at the north end of St.Helens Central Station.
St.Helens Central (StH&WJR) SJ5195.1/1A
A brick built 2TS dead ended shed with a slated gable style roof, located at SJ51319590 and opened by the St.Helens & Wigan Junction Railway on January 3rd, 1900. The facilities included a water tank and turntable. The line was absorbed by the GCR on January 1st, 1906 and the depot was closed by the LNER in 1928. The building remained standing in 1997, having stood derelict for many years until taken over by a firm manufacturing pine furniture and absorbed into their factory premises.

A servicing point was then established ...
St.Helens Central (LNER) SJ5195.1/F1
The turntable, located at SJ51269581, water tank and sidings were then utilized, probably well into BR days.

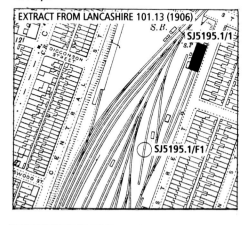
EXTRACT FROM LANCASHIRE 101.13 (1906)
SJ5195.1/1
SJ5195.1/F1

ORMSKIRK

Site SD4108.0; In the vicinity of Ormskirk Station.
Ormskirk (L&YR) SD4108.0/1A
A timber built shed, approximately located at SD417084, was opened here on November 20th, 1848. No further details are known other than it closed in 1855.

Replaced, probably on the same site by ...
Ormskirk (L&YR) SD4108.0/1B
A shed was opened here in 1855 and demolished on August 5th, 1891.

Replaced by ...
Site SD4208.1; In the fork of the St.Helens and Preston lines, north of Ormskirk Station.
Ormskirk (L&YR) SD4208.1/1A
A brick built 4TS dead ended shed with a slated northlight pattern roof, located at SD42020879 and opened on December 5th, 1894. The facilities included a turntable, coal stage and water tank. The depot was closed by the LMS on September 29th, 1935 and subsequently demolished.

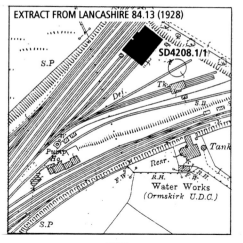
EXTRACT FROM LANCASHIRE 84.13 (1928)
SD4208.1/1

CLOCK FACE

Site SJ5392.1; On the west side of the line, north of Clock Face Station.
Clock Face (St.H&RGR) SJ5392.1/1A
A 2TS dead ended shed located at SJ53079283 and opened by the St.Helens & Runcorn Gap Railway on February 1st, 1833.

Site SJ5392.2; On the east side of the line, north of Clock Face Station.
Clock Face (St.H&RGR) SJ5392.2/1A
A 2TS dead ended shed located at SJ53089283 and opened by the St.Helens & Runcorn Gap Railway on February 1st, 1833.

The line was absorbed by the L&NWR on August 1st, 1864 and the sheds, which were sited opposite to each other, closed in 1880.

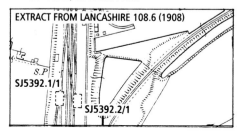
EXTRACT FROM LANCASHIRE 108.6 (1908)
SJ5392.1/1
SJ5392.2/1

BRUNSWICK

Site SJ3587.1; On the west side of the line, south of Liverpool Central Station.
Brunswick No.1 (G&LR) SJ3587.1/1A
A timber built 3TS shed, probably located at SJ35278766 and opened by the Garston & Liverpool Railway on June 1st, 1864. Details of the facilities are not known. The depot was closed in 1880 and demolished by 1893, with additional sidings then occupying the site.

Adjoined by ...
Brunswick No.2 (CLC) SJ3587.1/2A
A timber built 3TS dead ended shed with a gable style pitched roof, located at SJ35258765 and probably built adjacently to the western wall of No.1 shed (SJ3587.1/1A). Details of the facilities are not known. By 1878 it was let exclusively to the MR and the LMS closed the depot in February 1929 with the locomotives transferring across the line to Brunswick (LNER) Shed (SJ3587.2/1). The building was subsequently demolished.

Site SJ3587.2; On the east side of the line, south of Liverpool Central Station.
Brunswick No.3 (MS&LR) SJ3587.2/1A
A curved brick built 5TS dead ended shed with a twin slated gable style roof, located at SJ35358764 and opened in 1879. The facilities included a turntable, coal stage and water tank. By BR days the front part of the roof had been removed.

The shed was rebuilt ...
Brunswick No.3 (BR) SJ3587.2/1B
A transverse pitch louvre style roof with a steel sheeted screen was installed by the London Midland Region in 1956. The depot closed on September 11th, 1961 and was subsequently demolished.

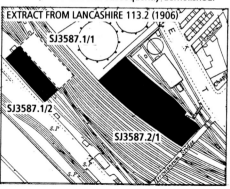
EXTRACT FROM LANCASHIRE 113.2 (1906)
SJ3587.1/1
SJ3587.1/2
SJ3587.2/1

Site SD5805.1; *Adjacent to Wigan North Western Goods Station.*

Wigan (L&MR)SD5805.1/1A

A shed, approximately located at SD584051, was opened here in 1832 by the Liverpool & Manchester Railway. No further details are known.

Site SD5705.0; In the vicinity of Wigan (L&YR) Station.

Wigan (L&YR)SD5705.0/1A

A 1TS shed was opened here in 1862 and destroyed by a fire in 1869. No further details are known.

Replaced, on the same site, by ...

Wigan (L&YR)SD5705.0/1B

A 1TS shed, it was opened in 1870 and closed in 1878. No further details are known.

Replaced by ...

Site SD5606.1; On the east side of the line, north of Wigan L&YR Station.

Wigan Pagefield (L&YR)SD5606.1/1A

A brick built 8TS dead ended shed with a slated transverse multi-pitched roof, located at SD56970622 and opened in 1878. The facilities included a coal stage and water columns. The site suffered badly from mining subsidence and, although there was room for the expansion in capacity required at this time, the depot was closed in 1905.

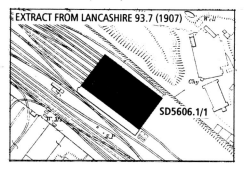

EXTRACT FROM LANCASHIRE 93.7 (1907)
SD5606.1/1

Replaced by ...

Site SD5705.2; On the west side of the line, north of Wigan L&YR Station.

Wigan Prescott Street (L&YR) SD5705.2/1A

A brick & timber built 14TS dead ended shed with a northlight pattern roof, located at SD57450567 and opened in 1905. The facilities included a coal stage, 55ft turntable and water columns.

The shed was reduced in size ...

Wigan Prescott Street (LMS)SD5705.2/1B

At some stage the covering over the six westernmost tracks was removed and the pits filled in, with this area being given over to wagon storage. At the same time all but the roof over the two easternmost tracks was cut back by half its length leaving it as an "L" shaped 8TS dead ended structure. The depot was closed by BR on April 13th, 1964 and subsequently demolished.

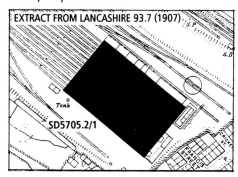

EXTRACT FROM LANCASHIRE 93.7 (1907)
SD5705.2/1

Site SD5805.2; In Wigan Goods Yard.

Wigan Goods (L&YR)SD5805.2/F1

A servicing area consisting of a coal stage and siding and approximately located at SD582054 opened here in 1911. No further details are known.

Site SD5903.1; *On the east side of the Springs Branch line, south of Wigan L&NWR Station.*

Wigan Springs Branch (L&NWR)SD5903.1/1A

A brick built 2TS through road shed located at SD59240398 and opened prior to 1847. The facilities included a turntable.

Wigan Springs Branch (L&NWR)SD5903.1/2A

A temporary timber built shed, probably located at the south end of the shed yard at SD59220392, opened here in 1864.

The two shed buildings were closed and demolished in 1869.

Replaced by ...

Wigan Springs Branch No.1 (L&NWR)SD5903.1/3A

A brick built 8TS dead ended shed with a twin slated hipped roof, located at SD59260382 and opened in 1869.

The shed was rebuilt in 1946 ...

Wigan Springs Branch No.1 (LMS)SD5903.1/3B

A louvre style roof with brick screen was installed and the building reduced to a 6TS dead ended shed.

Adjoined by ...

Wigan Springs Branch No.2 (L&NWR)SD5903.1/4A

A brick built 8TS dead ended shed with a northlight pattern roof, it was constructed in 1882 along the eastern wall of No.1 shed (SD5903.1/3A) and was located at SD59290383.

The shed was re-roofed ...

Wigan Springs Branch No.2 (BR)SD5903.1/4B

A steel framed roof covered in corrugated sheeting was installed by the London Midland Region in 1955.

The facilities originally included a coal stage, with water tank over, and a turntable. A mechanical coaling plant and larger water tank were installed by the LMS in the 1930s. The depot was closed to steam by BR on December 4th, 1967 and No.2 shed was demolished and replaced by a purpose-built Diesel Depot (SD5903.1/4C). No.1 shed (3B) remained in use, initially as additional locomotive stabling room and later as a store until demolition in 1984. The depot finally closed in May 1997 and the sidings were utilized for the storing of withdrawn locomotives.

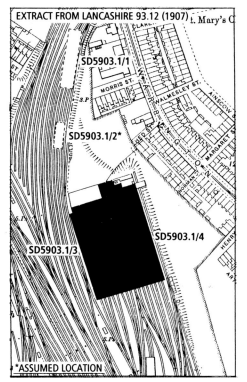

EXTRACT FROM LANCASHIRE 93.12 (1907)
SD5903.1/1
SD5903.1/2*
SD5903.1/3
SD5903.1/4
*ASSUMED LOCATION

Site SD5904.1; *On the west side of the line, north of Lower Ince Station.*

Wigan Lower Ince (WJR)SD5904.1/1A

A brick built 2TS dead ended shed with a slated gable style roof, located at SD59070493 and opened on October 16th, 1879 by the Wigan Junction Railway. The facilities included a water tank. The line was worked by the MS&LR and absorbed by the GCR on January 1st, 1906.

The building was modified ...

Wigan Lower Ince (LNER)SD5904.1/1B

At some stage the shed was rebuilt to two through roads. The depot was closed by BR on March 24th, 1952 and subsequently demolished.

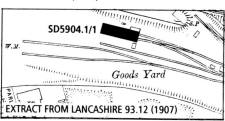

SD5904.1/1
Goods Yard
EXTRACT FROM LANCASHIRE 93.12 (1907)

Site SD5805.3; On the south side of the line, east of the junction of the Liverpool and Southport lines.

Wigan (L&YR)SD5805.3/1A

A 1TS shed, located at SD58060557, was in existence here in 1845. It was removed to make way for the construction of Wigan Wallgate Station.

EXTRACT FROM LANCASHIRE 93 (1845)
SD5805.3/1

Site SD5705.1; On the south side of Wigan Wallgate Station.

Wigan Station (L&YR)SD5705.1/F1

A servicing area consisting of a turntable, located at SD57970556, and siding. No further details are known.

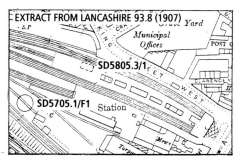

EXTRACT FROM LANCASHIRE 93.8 (1907)
SD5805.3/1
SD5705.1/F1 Station

SPEKE JUNCTION

Site SJ4184.2; In the triangle of the Allerton to Garston Docks to Ditton Junction lines, west of Speke Station.
Speke Junction (L&NWR) SJ4184.2/1A
A brick built 12TS dead ended shed with a north-light pattern roof, located at SJ41378446 and opened on May 10th, 1886. The facilities included a turntable and coal stage with water tank over.

The shed was re-roofed ...
Speke Junction (LMS) SJ4184.2/1B
A louvre style roof with brick screen was installed in 1946/7 and a mechanical coaling plant was later supplied by BR in the 1950s. The depot closed on May 6th, 1968 and was later demolished.

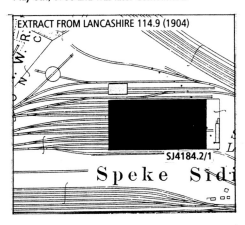

EXTRACT FROM LANCASHIRE 114.9 (1904)
SJ4184.2/1

NEWTON LE WILLOWS

Site SJ5995.1; On the south side of the line, at the east end of Newton le Willows Station.
Newton le Willows (L&MR) SJ5995.1/1A
A 1TS dead ended shed, located at SJ59449533, and opened in 1830 by the Liverpool & Manchester Railway. No further details are known.

EXTRACT FROM LANCASHIRE 101.16 (1906)
SJ5995.1/1

WHISTON

Site SJ4490.1; On the south side of Huyton Quarry Junction, west of Huyton Quarry Station.
Whiston (L&MR) SJ4490.1/1A
A 1TS shed, located at SJ44899068 and opened in 1830 by the Liverpool & Manchester Railway. No further details are known.

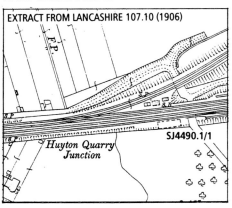

EXTRACT FROM LANCASHIRE 107.10 (1906)
SJ4490.1/1

ALLERTON

Site SJ4184.1; On the east side of the line, at the south end of Allerton Station.
Allerton (CLC) SJ4184.1/1A
A brick built 10TS dead ended shed, located at SJ41028497 and opened in January 1882. The facilities included a coal stage, turntable and water tank. The depot closed in 1897 and saw further use, for wagon repairs and carriage cleaning, until it was demolished by BR.

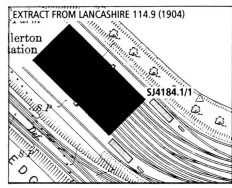

EXTRACT FROM LANCASHIRE 114.9 (1904)
SJ4184.1/1

AINTREE

Site SJ3697.1; In the fork of the Ford to Aintree and Kirkby Goods lines.
Aintree (L&YR) SJ3697.1/1A
A brick built 8TS shed with one through road and a northlight pattern roof. The depot was located at SJ36329748 and opened in 1886. The facilities included a 50ft turntable, ramped coal stage with water tank over and a fitting shop.

The shed was re-roofed ...
Aintree (LMS) SJ3697.1/1B
A louvre style roof was installed in 1937. At the same time the yard was reorganized with improved coal and ash plants and a new turntable was re-sited adjacent to the south side of the building. Although BR closed the depot on June 12th, 1967 it stood, trackless and derelict, until demolished in February 1996.

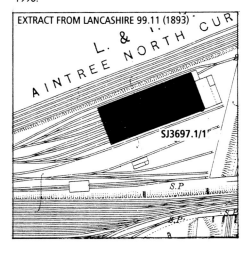

EXTRACT FROM LANCASHIRE 99.11 (1893)
SJ3697.1/1

CHORLEY

Site SD5817.1; In the vicinity of Chorley Station.
Chorley (L&YR) SD5817.1/1A
A 2TS shed opened here in 1868 and closed in 1873. No further details are known.

Replaced by ...
Site SD5817.2; In the fork of the Preston and Blackburn lines, north of Chorley Station.
Chorley (L&YR) SD5817.2/1A
A brick built 2TS dead ended shed with a slated hipped roof, located at SD58641789 and opened in 1873. The facilities included a coal stage and 42ft turntable. The depot was closed in July 1922 and later demolished.

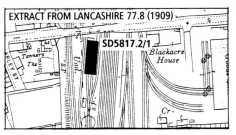

EXTRACT FROM LANCASHIRE 77.8 (1909)
SD5817.2/1

DITTON SLEEPER DEPOT

Site SJ4884.1; In Ditton Sleeper Depot, on the north side of the line at the west end of Ditton Junction Station.
Ditton Sleeper Depot (LMS) SJ4884.1/1A
A 1TS through road shed located at SJ48188492. No further details are known other than the building may have housed the steam works shunter prior to the arrival of ED2 in c1950 and that it was demolished in the 1990s.

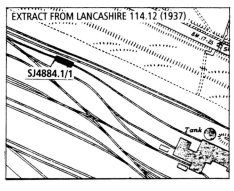

EXTRACT FROM LANCASHIRE 114.12 (1937)
SJ4884.1/1

WATERLOO

Site SJ3198.1; On the west side of the line, at the south end of Waterloo (LC&SR) Station.
Waterloo (LC&SR) SJ3198.1/1A
A 1TS shed, approximately located at SJ31959810 and opened by the Liverpool, Crosby & Southport Railway on July 24th, 1848. The line was worked by the L&YR. Details of the facilities and closure date are not known but it was demolished after the extension of the line to Sandhills and the subsequent rebuilding of the station.

LIVERPOOL

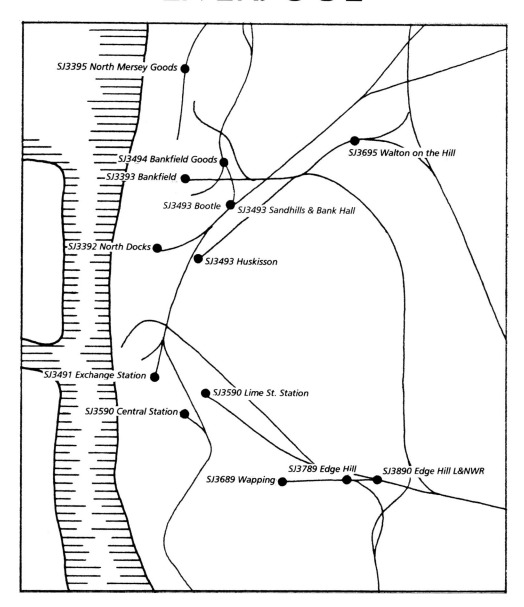

SJ3395 North Mersey Goods

SJ3494 Bankfield Goods
SJ3393 Bankfield
SJ3493 Bootle
SJ3493 Sandhills & Bank Hall
SJ3695 Walton on the Hill
SJ3392 North Docks
SJ3493 Huskisson

SJ3491 Exchange Station
SJ3590 Lime St. Station
SJ3590 Central Station

SJ3789 Edge Hill
SJ3890 Edge Hill L&NWR
SJ3689 Wapping

EXCHANGE STATION

Site SJ3491.1; On the west side of the line, at the north end of Exchange Station*.

Exchange Station (L&YR) SJ3491.1/1A
A 3TS shed with one through road, located at SJ34029100 was opened here on March 13th, 1850 and closed in 1868. No further details are known except that the facilities included a turntable.

A servicing facility was then established ...
Exchange Station (L&YR) SJ3491.1/F1
The turntable, located at SJ34009101, sidings and engine pits were then utilized. No further details are known.

Site SJ3491.2; North of Exchange Station*.
Exchange Station (ELR) SJ3491.2/1A
A brick built dead ended shed, approximately located at SJ340915 and opened in 1849 by the East Lancashire Railway. The facilities included a turntable. The depot closed in 1876.

Also known as Tithebarn Street.

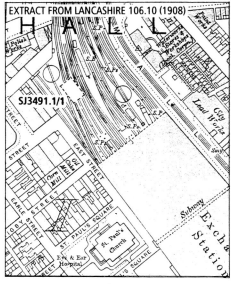

EXTRACT FROM LANCASHIRE 106.10 (1908)

SJ3491.1/1

CENTRAL STATION

Site SJ3590.1; On the east side of the line, at the south end of Liverpool Central Station.

Central Station (CLC) SJ3590.1/1A
A stone built 1TS dead ended tank shed, located at SJ35129006 and opened on March 1st, 1874. The facilities also included a turntable. At some stage the building may have ceased to be utilized as a shed depot with locomotives making use of the remainder of the facility until closed by BR on September 4th, 1966.

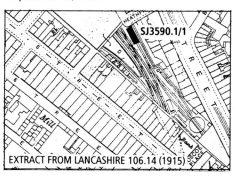

SJ3590.1/1

EXTRACT FROM LANCASHIRE 106.14 (1915)

EDGE HILL

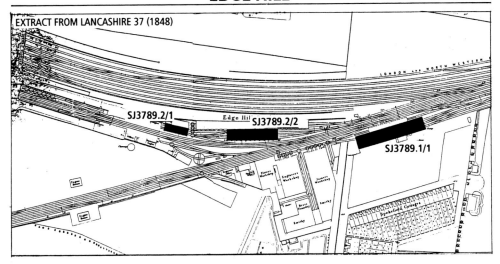

EXTRACT FROM LANCASHIRE 37 (1848)

Site SJ3789.2; On the south side of Edge Hill Station.
Edge Hill (L&MR) SJ3789.2/1A
A 2TS through road shed, located at SJ37198994, and opened by the Liverpool & Manchester Railway in 1831. Details of the facilities are not known but by 1841 heavy running repairs, including locomotive rebuilds, were being undertaken.

Edge Hill (GJR) SJ3789.2/2A
A 3TS through road shed, located at SJ37368992, and opened by the Grand Junction Railway in 1839.

Site SJ3789.1; On the south side of the Wapping line, at the east end of Edge Hill Station.
Edge Hill (GJR) SJ3789.1/1A
A 3TS shed, with one through road, located at SJ37498992, and opened by the Grand Junction Railway on July 4th, 1837. Following the opening of the second GJR shed (SJ3789.2/2A) the building was given over to heavy locomotive repairs.

Further details of the facilities are not known. The Grand Junction Railway buildings were vacated after the heavy repair facility was removed to Crewe Works and all three sheds were then utilized by the Liverpool & Manchester Railway. The depot was closed by the L&NWR in 1865.

Site SJ3890.1; On the south side of Manchester line, east of Edge Hill Station.
Edge Hill (L&NWR) SJ3890.1/1A
A brick built 20TS dead ended shed with five slated hipped roofs, located at SJ38359009 and opened in 1865. The facilities included a coal stage with water tank over and two 42ft turntables.

The shed was rebuilt in 1938 ...
Edge Hill (LMS) SJ3890.1/1B
The building was reduced in length, one road was removed and a multi-pitched roof installed.

The shed was partially demolished ...
Edge Hill (BR) SJ3890.1/1C
A 6TS dead ended section of the building was demolished by the London Midland Region and a 2TS Diesel Depot (SJ3890.1/1D) erected on the site.

Adjoined by ...
Edge Hill (L&NWR) SJ3890.1/2A
A brick built 12TS shed, with a northlight pattern roof and located at SJ38429011 was built along the eastern rear wall of SJ3890.1/1A in 1902. Six of the tracks were adjoined to those in the first shed creating through roads whilst the remaining six terminated within the "new" building.

The shed was re-roofed ...
Edge Hill (LMS) SJ3890.1/2B
A louvre style roof with brick screen was installed in 1944 and the building reduced to an 11TS shed.

The facilities were improved in 1914 by the installation of a concrete built ramped coaling plant, the design of which was unique in Britain. The depot was closed to steam by BR on May 6th, 1968 and the remaining steam shed buildings demolished. The custom-built diesel depot suffered a similar fate on September 26th, 1986.

WAPPING

Site SJ3689.1; On the south side of the line, west of Edge Hill Station.
Wapping, Bankhead (L&MR) SJ3689.1/1A
It is believed* that this was a stone built 2TS dead ended shed, located at SJ36808980 and opened in 1830 by the Liverpool & Manchester Railway. The depot was at right angles to the line, access being gained via a turntable, and was partially hewn out of the rock which formed the sides of the cutting. It could have closed in 1831 upon the opening of Edge Hill shed (SJ3789.1/1A) nearby or in 1836 when the line reached Lime Street Station.

*It is open to some conjecture as to whether this was ever used as an engine shed. The interior design of a pear-shaped chamber could indicate that space was created to allow the locomotive chimney to clear the roof. A flue had been constructed to allow smoke and steam to escape and one theory is that it was originally used as an engine shed and that boilers were then installed later after locomotive use ceased.

Site SJ3689.2; In Crown Street Tunnel, west of Edge Hill Station.
Wapping, Bankhead (L&MR) SJ3689.2/1A
A short section of tunnel to Crown Street Coal Depot was utilized as a 1TS shed. It was located at SJ36758982 and opened in October 1832. It was dispensed with in March 1845. No further details are known.

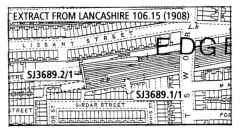

EXTRACT FROM LANCASHIRE 106.15 (1908)

WALTON ON THE HILL

Site SJ3695.1; On the east side of the line, at the north end of Walton on the Hill Station.
Walton on the Hill (CLC) SJ3695.1/1A
A brick built 4TS dead ended shed with a northlight pattern roof, located at SJ36039507 and opened on May 13th, 1881. The facilities included a turntable, coal stage and water tank.

The building was enlarged ...
Walton on the Hill (CLC) SJ3695.1/1B
The shed was increased in size to a 6TS dead ended structure in 1885.

The building was reduced in size ...
Walton on the Hill (BR) SJ3695.1/1C
The shed was modified to a 4TS dead ended structure and re-roofed by the London Midland Region in 1952. The depot closed on December 15th, 1963 and remained standing into the 1970s until demolition.

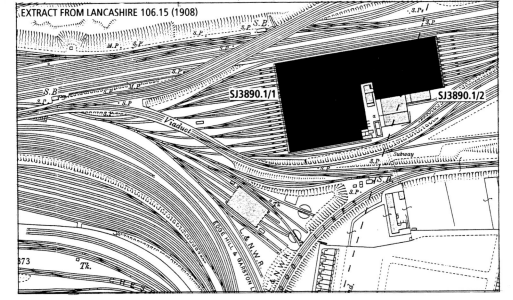

EXTRACT FROM LANCASHIRE 106.15 (1908)

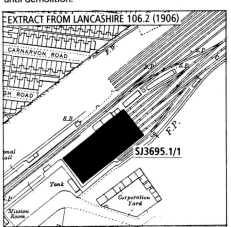

EXTRACT FROM LANCASHIRE 106.2 (1906)

BOOTLE

Site SJ3493.1; On the east side of the line, south of Bootle Station.

Bootle (ELR/L&YR) SJ3493.1/1A

A 2TS through road shed located at SJ34509357 and opened jointly by the East Lancs and Lancashire & Yorkshire Railways in 1848. The depot closed after only two years with the ELR locomotives moving to Liverpool Exchange (SJ3490.1/2) and the L&YR to Sandhills (SJ3493.2/1).

BANK HALL

Site SJ3493.2; On the west side of the line between Sandhills and Kirkdale Stations.

Bank Hall* (L&YR) SJ3493.2/1A

A dead ended shed, located at SJ34619381, was opened here in 1850 and, as the result of fire damage, closed in 1865.

Replaced, on the same site, by ...

Bank Hall* (L&YR) SJ3493.2/1B

A brick built 8TS shed with five through roads and a slated twin gable style roof, it opened in 1865. Following the construction of SJ3493.2/2A in 1875 this building became known as No.1 shed. The facilities included a coal stage, water columns and turntable.

The shed was rebuilt in 1935 ...

Bank Hall No.1 (LMS) SJ3493.2/1C

To accommodate the installation of a mechanical coaling plant and re-modelling of the shed yard the westernmost 4TS portion of the building was demolished, leaving a 4TS shed with a single pitched roof and two through roads.

Bank Hall No.2* (L&YR) SJ3493.2/2A

A brick built 8TS dead ended shed with slated twin hipped roofs, it opened in 1875 and was sited at the north end of the shed yard, being located at SJ34639395.

The depot was closed by BR on October 22nd, 1966 and the site cleared.

* Until 1920 the depot was known as Sandhills.

Site SJ3493.4; On the east side of the line south of Kirkdale Station.

Sandhills (ELR) SJ3493.4/1A

A dead ended shed, located at SJ34739384, was opened here in c1850 by the East Lancs Railway. No further details are known other than it was demolished to accommodate the lines to Sandhills road goods depot.

Site SJ3493.5; On the east side of the line between Sandhills and Kirkdale Stations.

Sandhills (ELR) SJ3493.5/1A

A brick built 3TS dead ended shed located at SJ34569358. The opening date is not known. The facilities included a coal stage with water tank over. The depot may have suffered from fire damage at some stage and was closed in 1865.

LIME STREET STATION

Site SJ3590.2; On the north side of the line, at the east end of Lime Street Station.

Lime Street Station (L&NWR) SJ3590.2/1A

A 4TS dead ended shed with all tracks radiating from a turntable, it was located at SJ35269055. No further details are known.

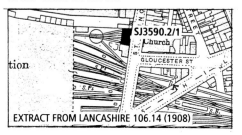

EXTRACT FROM LANCASHIRE 106.14 (1908)

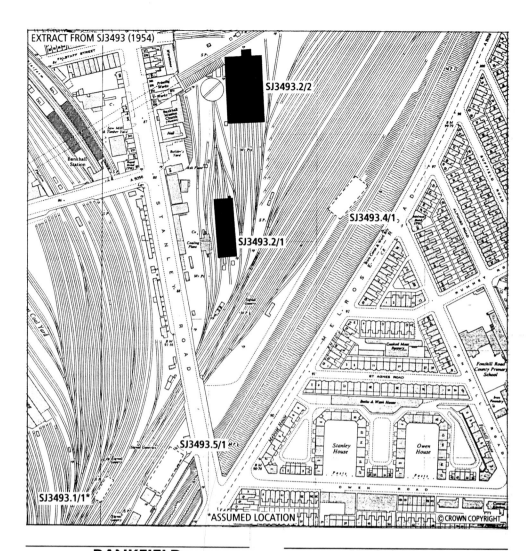

EXTRACT FROM SJ3493 (1954)

SJ3493.2/2

SJ3493.4/1

SJ3493.2/1

SJ3493.5/1

SJ3493.1/1*

*ASSUMED LOCATION

© CROWN COPYRIGHT

BANKFIELD

Site SJ3494.1; In the fork of the Bankfield Goods and Bank Hall lines, south of Bootle Station.

Bankfield Goods, Bootle Jct (L&YR) SJ3494.1/1A

A 1TS through road shed, located at SJ34109437 and opened in 1887. No further details are known other than it had been closed and removed by 1906.

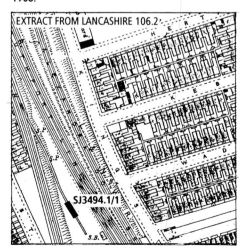

EXTRACT FROM LANCASHIRE 106.2

SJ3494.1/1

Probably replaced by ...
Site SJ3393.1; In Bankfield & Canada Dock Goods Yard.

Bankfield (L&YR) SJ3393.1/F1

A servicing area consisting of a coal stage and approximately located at SJ339939. No further details are known.

HUSKISSON

Site SJ3493.3; On the east side of Huskisson Goods Yard.

Huskisson (CLC) SJ3493.3/F1

A servicing area consisting of a turntable, located at SJ34369300, and siding opened here on July 1st, 1880. No further details are known.

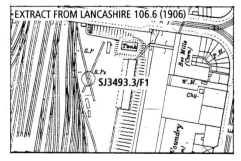

EXTRACT FROM LANCASHIRE 106.6 (1906)

SJ3493.3/F1

NORTH DOCKS

Site SJ3392.1; In North Docks Goods Yard.

North Docks (L&YR) SJ3392.1/F1

A servicing area, approximately located at SJ338926 and consisting of a coal stage and siding. No further details are known.

NORTH MERSEY GOODS

Site SJ3395.1; In North Mersey Goods Yard.

North Mersey Goods (L&YR) SJ3395.1/F1

A servicing area opened here in 1914. It was approximately located at SJ331957 and consisted of a coal stage and siding. No further details are known.

YORKSHIRE

For ease of reference the county has been split into 4 sections:

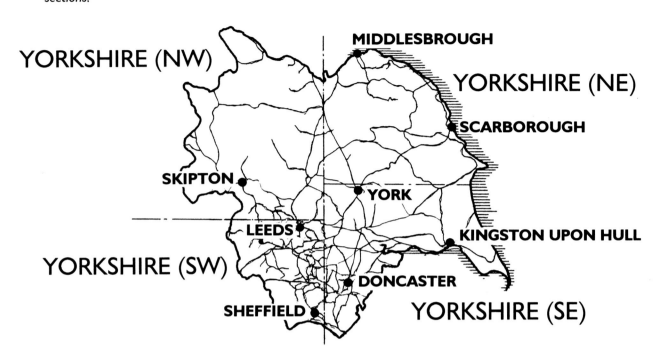

YORKSHIRE (NW)

YORKSHIRE (NE)

MIDDLESBROUGH

SCARBOROUGH

SKIPTON

YORK

LEEDS

KINGSTON UPON HULL

YORKSHIRE (SW)

DONCASTER

SHEFFIELD

YORKSHIRE (SE)

Pateley Bridge saw three engine sheds over the years, with that of the Nidd Valley Railway illustrated on Page 214. The two other buildings served the NER station with the first shed (SE1565.1/1A), of 1862, being distantly seen in this picture dated from around 1905. Built on the edge of the River Nidd, the building's stone construction was its downfall - lierally! Faced with the danger of its engine shed falling into the river, the NER demolished it, at a date yet unknown, and replaced it with a timber building (SE1565.1/1B) on the same site. That shed finally closed in 1951.

Bernard Matthews Collection

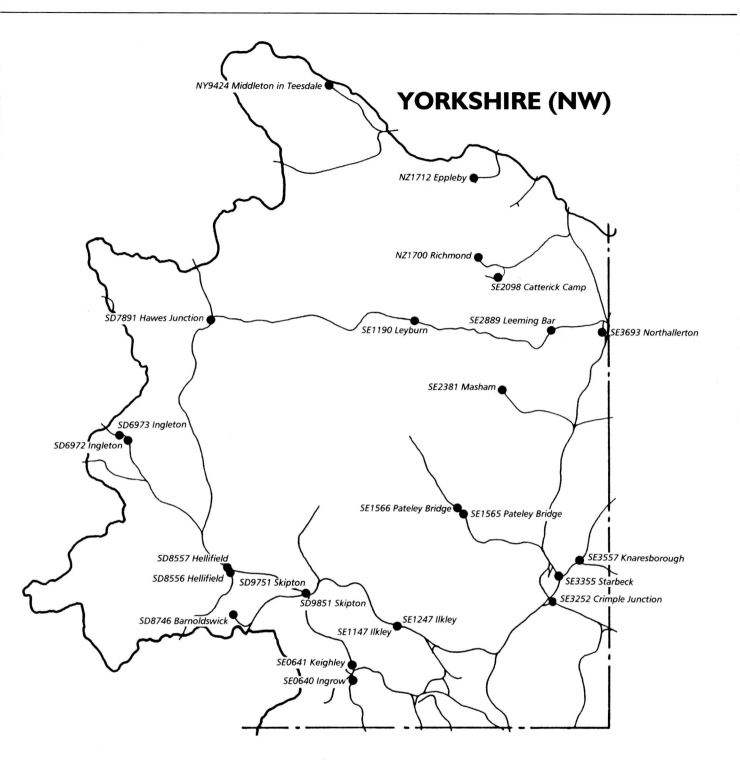

YORKSHIRE (NW)

NY9424 Middleton in Teesdale

NZ1712 Eppleby

NZ1700 Richmond

SE2098 Catterick Camp

SD7891 Hawes Junction

SE1190 Leyburn

SE2889 Leeming Bar

SE3693 Northallerton

SE2381 Masham

SD6973 Ingleton

SD6972 Ingleton

SE1566 Pateley Bridge

SE1565 Pateley Bridge

SE3557 Knaresborough

SD8557 Hellifield

SD8556 Hellifield

SD9751 Skipton

SE3355 Starbeck

SD9851 Skipton

SE3252 Crimple Junction

SD8746 Barnoldswick

SE1247 Ilkley

SE1147 Ilkley

SE0641 Keighley

SE0640 Ingrow

ILKLEY

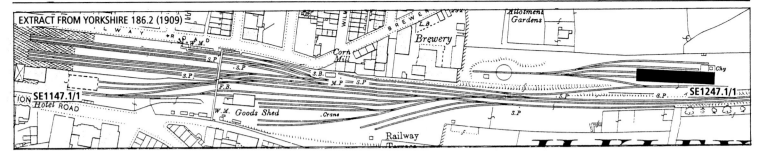

EXTRACT FROM YORKSHIRE 186.2 (1909)

SE1147.1/1

SE1247.1/1

Site SE1147.1; On the south side of Ilkley Station.
Ilkley (MR/NER)^{SE1147.1/1A}
A 2TS dead ended shed, probably built in brick, located at SE11844762 and opened on July 1st, 1866. The facilities included a turntable. The depot was closed and demolished in 1892.

Replaced by ...
Site SE1247.1; On the north side of the line, east of Ilkley Station.
Ilkley (MR/NER)^{SE1247.1/1A}
A brick built 2TS dead ended shed with a slated gable style roof, located at SE12404763 and opened in 1892. The facilities included a turntable, coal stage and water tank. The depot was closed by BR on January 5th, 1959 and subsequently demolished.

INGLETON

Site SD6973.1; On the north side of the line, at the east end of Ingleton (L&NWR) Station.
Ingleton (L&NWR)^{SD6973.1/1A}
A timber built 1TS dead ended shed, probably with a gable style roof, located at SD69037333 and opened on September 16th, 1861. The facilities included a turntable, sited outside of the shed entrance. The building was destroyed by a fire in 1899.

Replaced, on the same site, by ...
Ingleton (L&NWR)^{SD6973.1/1B}
A corrugated iron built 1TS dead ended shed with a corrugated iron dutch barn style roof, it was opened in 1899. The depot was closed by the LMS in 1923 and subsequently demolished.

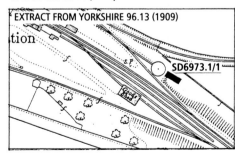

EXTRACT FROM YORKSHIRE 96.13 (1909)

SD6973.1/1

Site SD6972.1; On the east side of the line, south of Ingleton (MR) Station.
Ingleton (MR)^{SD6972.1/1A}
A timber built 1TS dead ended shed with a slated gable style roof, located at SD69687287 and opened in 1878. The facilities included a water tank. The depot was closed by BR on January 30th, 1954 and subsequently demolished.

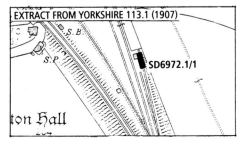

EXTRACT FROM YORKSHIRE 113.1 (1907)

SD6972.1/1

NORTHALLERTON

Site SE3693.1; On the west side of Northallerton Station.
Northallerton (NER)^{SE3693.1/1A}
A brick built 1TS shed* with a slated gable style roof, located at SE36359316 and opened in 1858.

The shed was enlarged ...
Northallerton (NER)^{SE3693.1/1B}
A brick built 1TS shed* with a slated gable style roof was added to the original building in 1882.

The shed was enlarged again...
Northallerton (NER)^{SE3693.1/1C}
One of the buildings was extended in 1886.

The facilities included a water tank. The depot was closed by BR on March 3rd, 1963 and demolished in November 1964.

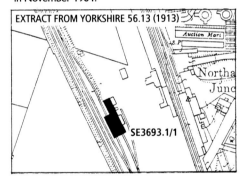

EXTRACT FROM YORKSHIRE 56.13 (1913)

SE3693.1/1

*One of the shed buildings was of the through road type and the other, with the later extension, a dead ender. It is not known in which sequence they were built.

INGROW

Site SE0640.1; On the west side of the line, north of Ingrow (GNR) Station.
Ingrow (GNR)^{SE0640.1/1A}
A brick built 2TS dead ended shed with a northlight pattern roof, located at SE06034005 and opened in April 1884. The facilities included a turntable. Although the depot was closed by the LNER in 1936 the building remained standing, in private use, until demolished in 1989.

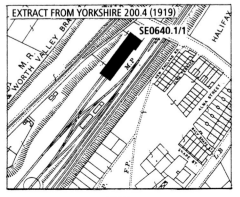

EXTRACT FROM YORKSHIRE 200.4 (1919)

SE0640.1/1

HELLIFIELD

Site SD8556.1; In the fork of the Blackburn and Skipton lines, east of Hellifield Station.
Hellifield (L&YR)^{SD8556.1/1A}
A brick built 3TS dead ended shed with a slated hipped roof, located at SD85515685 and opened in 1881. The facilities included a water tank, coal stage and turntable. The depot was closed by the LMS on November 2nd, 1927 and later demolished.

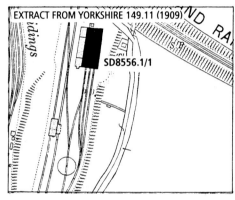

EXTRACT FROM YORKSHIRE 149.11 (1909)

SD8556.1/1

Site SD8557.1; On the north side of the line at the west end of Hellifield Station.
Hellifield (MR)^{SD8557.1/1A}
A brick built 4TS through road shed with a slated twin gable style roof, located at SD85045737 and opened in 1880. The facilities included a ramped coal stage, water tank, turntable (enlarged to 60ft in 1940) and, after 1948, a repair shop. The depot was closed by BR on June 17th, 1963 and it was then renovated and utilized as a store for some of the preserved locomotives from the National Collection pending the opening of York Museum. It was demolished in the 1970s.

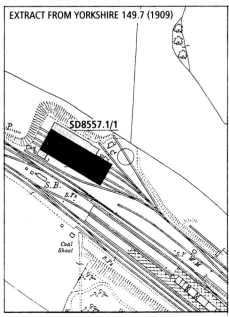

EXTRACT FROM YORKSHIRE 149.7 (1909)

SD8557.1/1

SCARBOROUGH

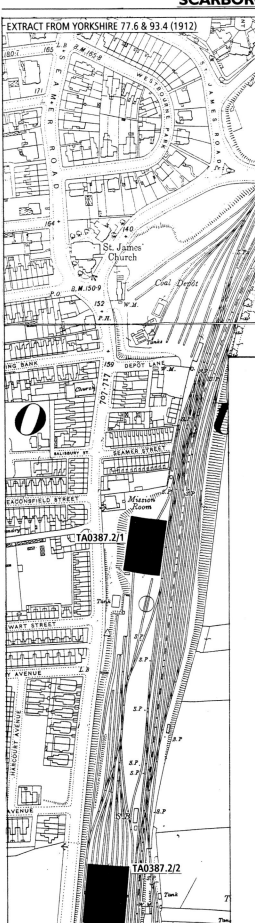

EXTRACT FROM YORKSHIRE 77.6 & 93.4 (1912)

TA0387.1/1

TA0387.2/1

TA0387.2/2

Site TA0387.1; On the west side of the line, south of Scarborough Station.
Scarborough (Y&NMR) TA0387.1/1A
A 2TS through road shed, located at TA03528781 and opened on July 7th, 1845 by the York & North Midland Railway. The facilities included a turntable. The depot was closed by the NER in 1882 and utilized as a store until demolition in 1906 to make way for Londesborough Road Excursion Station.

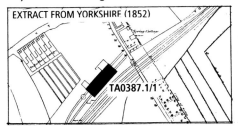

EXTRACT FROM YORKSHIRE (1852)

TA0387.1/1

Replaced by ...
Site TA0387.2; On the west side of the line, south of Scarborough Station.
Scarborough (NER) TA0387.2/1A
A brick built rectangular 1RH shed with a slated multi-pitched roof, located at TA03428733 and opened in 1882. After the opening of TA0387.2/2 it was mainly utilized for engine repairs and storage.

Scarborough (NER) TA0387.2/2A
A brick built 8TS dead ended shed with a slated twin pitched roof, sited at the south end of the yard and located at TA03298702. It was opened in 1890 and the facilities included a turntable and water tank.

The building was partially demolished ...
Scarborough (BR) TA0387.2/2B
Due to subsidence the section covering the four easternmost tracks was removed in 1955 by the North Eastern Region.

Although the depot officially closed on July 20th, 1963 visiting locomotives continued to utilize the facilities until the end of steam in the area.

Site TA0388.1; In the vicinity of Gallows Close Goods Depot.
Scarborough, Gallows Close (NER) TA0388.1/F1
A servicing area consisting of a turntable, water tank and coal stage opened on June 8th, 1908 and closed by BR in 1958.

THIRSK

Site SE4281.1; On the south side of the line at the west end of Thirsk Town Station.
Thirsk Town (L&TR) SE4281.1/1A
A 2TS through road shed, located at SE42528178 and opened on January 5th, 1848 by the Leeds & Thirsk Railway. No further details are known other than the depot closed in 1855.

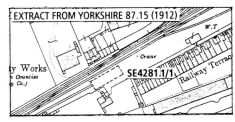

EXTRACT FROM YORKSHIRE 87.15 (1912)

SE4281.1/1

Site SE4181.1; In the vicinity of Thirsk Station.
Thirsk (NER) SE4181.1/F1
A servicing area consisting of an engine pit and siding, approximately located at SE410816 and opened in 1857. The facility closed in 1887.

Replaced by ...
Site SE4181.2; In the fork of the Leeds and York lines, south of Thirsk Station.
Thirsk (NER) SE4181.2/1A
A brick built 2TS dead ended shed with a slated gable style roof, located at SE41178123 and opened in 1887. The facilities included a turntable, coaling crane and water tank. The depot was closed by the LNER on November 10th, 1930 and demolished in 1965.

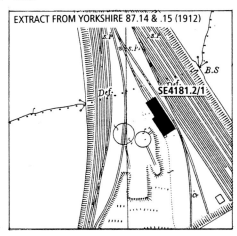

EXTRACT FROM YORKSHIRE 87.14 & .15 (1912)

SE4181.2/1

BATTERSBY JUNCTION

Site NZ5807.1; On the east side of Battersby Junction Station.
Battersby Junction (NER) NZ5807.1/1A
A brick built 3TS dead ended shed with a slated gable style roof, located at NZ58890722 and opened in 1877. The facilities included a water tank and turntable. The depot was closed a few years later, re-opened again on January 1st, 1889 and finally closed on November 30th, 1895. The building was not actually demolished until 1965, having being utilized for a variety of purposes including the the storage of redundant rolling stock.

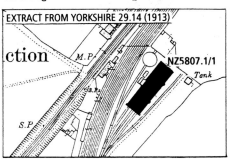

EXTRACT FROM YORKSHIRE 29.14 (1913)

NZ5807.1/1

NEWPORT

Site NZ4719.1; West of Newport Station.
Newport (NER)^{NZ4719.1/1A}
A brick built 1RH building was opened here in 1881. The facilities included a coal stage. No further details are known except that, as a result of subsidence, the building became unsafe and was closed in November 1890.

Replaced by ...
Site NZ4719.2; On the north side of the line, west of Newport Station.
Newport (NER)^{NZ4719.2/1A}
A brick built 2RH building with a slated triple gable style roof, located at NZ47051921 and opened in November 1890. The facilities included a water tank.

Adjoined by ...
Newport (LNER)^{NZ4719.2/2A}
A 3TS dead ended shed, built in corrugated sheeting with a gable style roof, located at NZ47111926 and constructed along the eastern wall of the main building (NZ4719.2/1A) in c1940. It was originally used as a repair shop.

The depot was closed by BR on June 1st, 1958 and demolished in 1959, the site being utilized for sidings as part of the Tees Marshalling Yard.

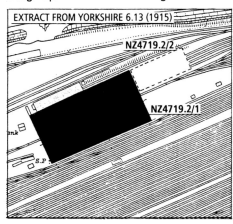
EXTRACT FROM YORKSHIRE 6.13 (1915)

EASINGWOLD

Site SE5269.1; On the west side of the line, at the south end of Easingwold Station.
Easingwold (Easingwold)^{SE5269.1/1A}
A corrugated iron built 1TS dead ended shed, located at SE52236971 and opened on July 25th, 1891 by the Easingwold Railway. No further details are known other than at some stage it was destroyed by a runaway coal wagon.

Replaced on the same site by ...
Easingwold (Easingwold)^{SE5269.1/1B}
A brick built 1TS dead ended shed with a slated gable style roof. Details of the facilities are not known. The shed fell out of use in the early 1940s when an LNER Class J71 0-6-0T, which was too tall to enter the shed, was utilized on the branch. The building was demolished in 1989.

EXTRACT FROM YORKSHIRE 121.11 (1911)

THORNABY

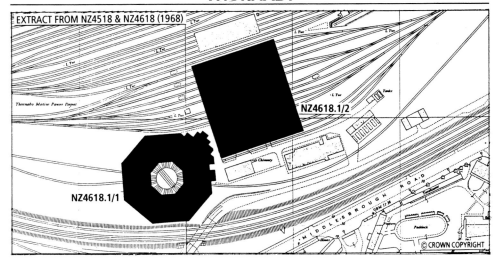
EXTRACT FROM NZ4518 & NZ4618 (1968)
© CROWN COPYRIGHT

Site NZ4618.1; On the north side of the line, east of Thornaby Station.
Thornaby (BR)^{NZ4618.1/1A}
A brick built polygonal 1RH shed with a glazed and corrugated sheeted continuous pitched roof, located at NZ46001845.

Thornaby (BR)^{NZ4618.1/2A}
A brick built 13TS shed with nine through roads and a glazed louvre style roof with a brick screen, located at NZ46051853.

The depot was opened by the North Eastern Region on June 5th, 1958 and possessed all major facilities. It closed to steam in December 1964, and the roundhouse (NZ4618.1/1A) found further use for wagon repairs until demolished in 1988.

SALTBURN

Site NZ6521.1; In the fork of the Saltburn and Whitby lines, west of Saltburn Station.
Saltburn (S&DR)^{NZ6521.1/1A}
A brick built 2TS shed, located at NZ65932135 and opened in 1864.

The shed was enlarged ...
Saltburn (NER)^{NZ6521.1/1B}
The building was extended in 1877 and the roof was destroyed by a fire on April 17th, 1907.

The shed was rebuilt in 1907 ...
Saltburn (NER)^{NZ6521.1/1C}
A brick built 2TS through road shed, with a dutch barn style roof was constructed on the same site, utilizing the original shed walls. The facilities included a water tank, coaling crane and turntable. The depot was closed by BR on January 27th, 1958 and demolished in 1960.

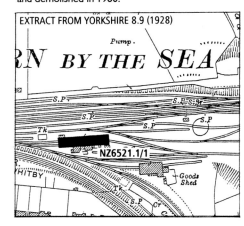
EXTRACT FROM YORKSHIRE 8.9 (1928)

SLAPEWATH

Site NZ6415.1; In the vicinity of Slapewath Station.
Slapewath (NER)^{NZ6415.1/1A}
A timber built shed, probably 1TS and approximately located at NZ641159 was removed from here to Brusselton Bank Foot (as NZ2125.1/1A) in 1870. No further details are known.

GUISBOROUGH

Site NZ6115.1; On the east side of the line, at the south end of Guisborough Station.
Guisborough (M&GR)^{NZ6115.1/1A}
A 1TS dead ended shed, located at NZ61461578 and opened on November 11th, 1853 by the Middlesbrough & Guisborough Railway. The line was worked by the Stockton & Darlington Railway, absorbed by the S&D in July 1858 and taken over by the NER in 1863. No further details are known other than the building was destroyed by a fire on February 27th, 1903.

Replaced, probably on the same site, by ...
Guisborough (NER)^{NZ6115.1/1B}
A corrugated iron 1TS dead ended shed with a corrugated iron gable style roof, opened in 1908. The facilities included a turntable and water tank. The depot was closed by BR on September 20th, 1954.

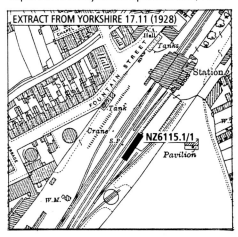
EXTRACT FROM YORKSHIRE 17.11 (1928)

SAND HUTTON

Site SE6958.1; In the vicinity of Sand Hutton.
Sand Hutton (SHLR)^{SE6958.1/1A}
A 1ft 6in gauge 2TS shed, approximately located at SE696583 and opened in 1920 by the Sand Hutton Light Railway. No further details are known other than it closed in 1932.

BOROUGHBRIDGE

Site SE3967.1; *On the south side of Boroughbridge Station.*

Boroughbridge (Y&NR)^{SE3967.1/1A}

A brick built 1TS dead ended shed with a slated hipped roof, located at SE39796730 and opened on June 17th, 1847 by the York & Newcastle Railway. Details of the facilities are not known. The depot was closed by the NER on July 1st, 1886 and converted into a goods shed. The building still stood in 1997, in commercial use.

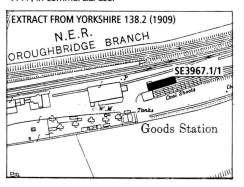

EXTRACT FROM YORKSHIRE 138.2 (1909)

PICKERING

Site SE7983.1; *On the east side of the line, south of Pickering Station.*

Pickering (Y&NMR)^{SE7983.1/1A}

A brick built 1TS dead ended shed with a slated hipped roof, located at SE79658387 and opened on July 7th, 1845 by the York & North Midland Railway.

The shed was enlarged ...
Pickering (Y&NMR)^{SE7983.1/1B}

The building was doubled in length in 1876. The facilities included a coaling crane. Although the depot was closed by BR on April 6th, 1959 it still stood in 1998, utilized by a builders' merchant.

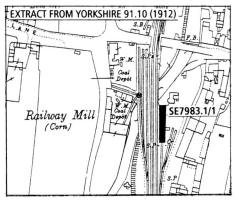

EXTRACT FROM YORKSHIRE 91.10 (1912)

BECKHOLE

Site NZ8202.1; *At the foot of Goathland Incline.*

Beckhole (Y&NMR)^{NZ8202.1/1A}

A 2TS shed, approximately located at NZ821021 and opened in July 1847 by the York & North Midland Railway. The line was absorbed by the NER in 1854 and the depot closed on July 1st, 1865.

MALTON

Site SE7871.1; *On the south side of the line, at the west end of Malton Station.*

Malton (NER)^{SE7871.1/1A}

A brick built 2TS shed with a slated gable style roof, located at SE78557130 and opened in 1853. The facilities included a coaling crane, turntable and water column.

The shed was enlarged ...
Malton (NER)^{SE7871.1/1B}

The building was lengthened to a 2TS through road shed in 1867. The depot was closed by BR on April 15th, 1963 and subsequently demolished.

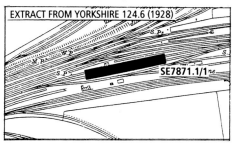

EXTRACT FROM YORKSHIRE 124.6 (1928)

BROTTON

Site NZ6819.1; *On the east side of the line, at the north end of Brotton Station.*

Brotton (NER)^{NZ6819.1/F1}

A servicing area consisting of a turntable, located at NZ68581975, and siding. No further details are known.

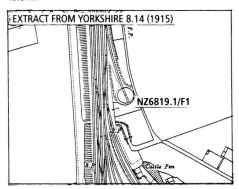

EXTRACT FROM YORKSHIRE 8.14 (1915)

NB. A shed (NZ6819.1/1A) may have existed here in c1906. No further details are known.

CASTLETON

Site NZ6808.1; *On the south side of the line, west of Castleton Station.*

Castleton (NER)^{NZ6808.1/1A}

A 1TS dead ended shed, located at NZ68170851 and in existence in 1856. The facilities included a turntable. No further details are known.

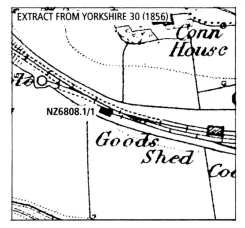

EXTRACT FROM YORKSHIRE 30 (1856)

ROSEDALE

Site SE7195.1; *On the west side of the line, near the end of the Rosedale branch at West Rosedale.*

Rosedale (NER)^{SE7195.1/1A}

A stone built 2TS through road shed with a slated gable style roof, located at SE71989511 and opened on March 27th, 1861.

The building was enlarged ...
Rosedale (NER)^{SE7195.1/1B}

The shed was lengthened in 1862. Details of the facilities are not known. The depot was closed by the LNER on September 29th, 1928 and demolished in 1937 with the stones being utilized in the building of Hutton le Hole Village Hall.

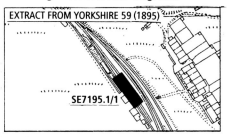

EXTRACT FROM YORKSHIRE 59 (1895)

REDCAR

Site NZ6024.1; *On the north side of the line, at the west end of Redcar Station.*

Redcar (S&DR)^{NZ6024.1/1A}

A 2TS dead ended shed opened by the Stockton & Darlington Railway in 1848 and closed by the NER in 1863. It is believed to be the building at NZ60092495 which was subsequently utilized as a loading shed. No further details are known.

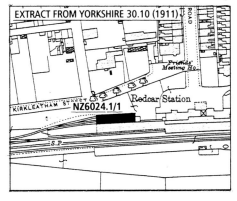

EXTRACT FROM YORKSHIRE 30.10 (1911)

NORMANBY JETTY

Site NZ5221.1; *At the west end of Normanby Jetty.*

Normanby Jetty (Cleveland)^{NZ5221.1/1A}

A 1TS dead ended shed, located at NZ52032111 and opened in 1861 by the Cleveland Railway. Details of the facilities are not known. The line was taken over by the NER in 1865 and the depot was closed in 1885. The site was utilized as an extension to the warrant store until the Jetty was demolished prior to 1915.

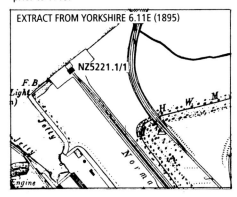

EXTRACT FROM YORKSHIRE 6.11E (1895)

YORKSHIRE (SE)

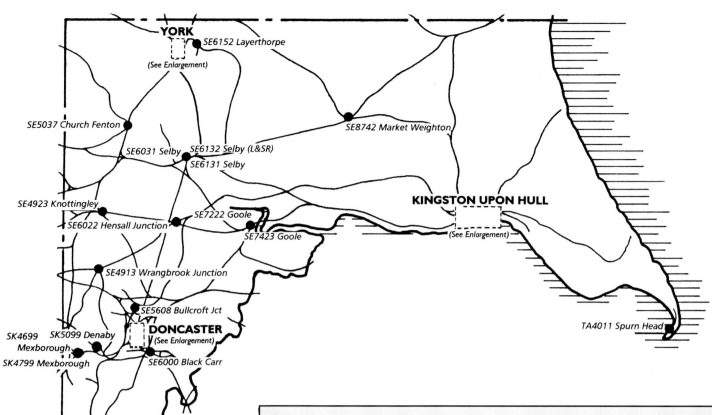

SE6152 Layerthorpe
YORK (See Enlargement)

SE5037 Church Fenton

SE6031 Selby
SE6132 Selby (L&SR)
SE6131 Selby

SE8742 Market Weighton

SE4923 Knottingley

SE6022 Hensall Junction

SE7222 Goole

SE7423 Goole

KINGSTON UPON HULL (See Enlargement)

SE4913 Wrangbrook Junction

SE5608 Bullcroft Jct

DONCASTER (See Enlargement)

SK4699 SK5099 Denaby
Mexborough
SK4799 Mexborough
SE6000 Black Carr

TA4011 Spurn Head

DENABY

Site SK5099.1; On the north side of the line, at Lowfield Junction, east of Mexborough Station.

Denaby (SYR) SK5099.1/1A
A timber built 1TS dead ended shed with a gable style roof, located at SK50219981 and opened by the South Yorkshire Railway. The facilities included a turntable. The roof was damaged by a fire in 1921.

The shed was rebuilt ...
Denaby (H&BR) SK5099.1/1B
The building was re-roofed and shortened in 1921 by the Hull & Barnsley Railway. The depot was closed by the LNER on May 31st, 1927 and subsequently demolished.

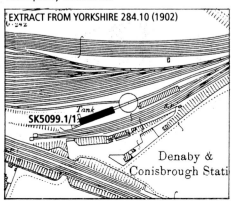

EXTRACT FROM YORKSHIRE 284.10 (1902)

Tank

SK5099.1/1

Denaby & Conisbrough Stati

Once a railway crossroads of considerable importance, **Market Weighton** is today miles from the nearest railway! The Y&NMR opened the first line into the town, providing a 2TS shed (SE8742.1/1A) adjacent to the station. This served until 1917, following which it was turned over to goods use, surviving into the 1960s as this picture of April 24th, 1962 demonstrates.   *K Hoole*

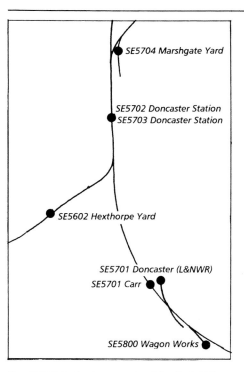

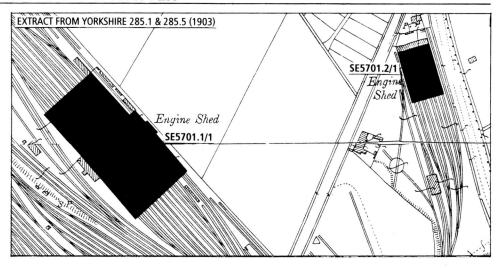

EXTRACT FROM YORKSHIRE 285.1 & 285.5 (1903)

SE5704 Marshgate Yard

SE5702 Doncaster Station
SE5703 Doncaster Station

SE5602 Hexthorpe Yard

SE5701 Doncaster (L&NWR)
SE5701 Carr

SE5800 Wagon Works

SE5701.1/1 — Engine Shed

SE5701.2/1 — Engine Shed

Site SE5602.1; On the east side of the Sheffield line, south of Doncaster Station.

Hexthorpe Yard (MS&LR) SE5602.1/F1
A servicing area consisting of a coal stage, engine pit and siding, located at SE56330215 and opened in 1878. No further details are known.

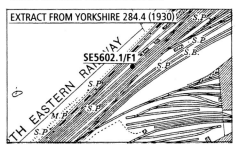

EXTRACT FROM YORKSHIRE 284.4 (1930)

SE5602.1/F1

Site SE5703.1; In Doncaster Station.

Doncaster Station (GNR) SE5703.1/1A
A temporary 1TS shed, located at SE57120320 and opened in 1848. No further details are known other than it was closed in 1849.

Replaced by ...
Site SE5702.1; On the west side of Doncaster Station.

Doncaster Station (GNR) SE5702.1/1A
A 2TS shed, located at SE57080217, and opened in 1849.

The shed was modified ...
Doncaster Station (GNR) SE5702.1/1B
The building was enlarged in 1866. No further details are known except that it was closed on March 25th, 1876.

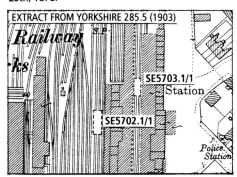

EXTRACT FROM YORKSHIRE 285.5 (1903)

SE5703.1/1

SE5702.1/1

Replaced by ...
Site SE5701.1; On the east side of the line, south of Doncaster Station.

Doncaster Carr (GNR) SE5701.1/1A
A brick built 12TS through road shed with four slated hipped roofs, located at SE57610167 and opened on March 25th, 1876. The facilities included a repair shop, water tank, coal stages and a turntable.

The shed was rebuilt ...
Doncaster Carr (BR) SE5701.1/1B
A corrugated sheeting clad roof with four pitches and corrugated sheeting gables was installed by the Eastern Region in 1957. At the same time it was reduced to a 9TS through road building and shortened in length. The shed closed to steam in May 1966 and was utilized as a diesel depot.

Site SE5701.2; On the east side of the line, south of Doncaster Station.

Doncaster Red Bank (L&NWR) SE5701.2/1A
A timber built 8TS dead ended shed with a northlight pattern roof, located at SE57880183 and opened in 1881. The facilities included a ramped coal stage with water tank over, repair shop and a turntable. By 1893 the L&NWR found the depot to be surplus to requirements and leased it to the GER. The shed closed in 1925 but remained standing until c1972.

Site SE5704.1; On the west side of the Hull line, north of Doncaster Station.

Marshgate West Yard (MS&LR) SE5704.1/F1
A stabling point consisting of a siding located at SE57220409.

Site SE5704.2; On the east side of the Hull line, north of Doncaster Station.

Marshgate East Yard (MS&LR) SE5704.2/F1
A stabling point consisting of a siding located at SE57370418.

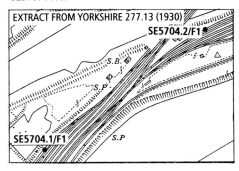

EXTRACT FROM YORKSHIRE 277.13 (1930)

SE5704.2/F1

SE5704.1/F1

The stabling points opened in c1880 and were closed by BR in 1968. There were no facilities, locomotives taking water and coal at Hexthorpe Yard (SE5602.1/F1).

Site SE5800.1; Within Doncaster Wagon Works.

Doncaster Wagon Works (LNER) SE5800.1/1A
A timber built 1TS through road shed with a pitched roof, located at SE58550085. The facilities included a coal stage. No further details are known.

EXTRACT FROM YORKSHIRE 285.5 (1930)

Travelling Crane

SE5800.1/1

Balby Carr Farm

BULLCROFT JUNCTION

Site SE5608.1; On the west side of the Bentley Colliery line at Bullcroft Junction.

Bullcroft Junction (H&BR) SE5608.1/1A
A timber built 2TS dead ended shed with a transverse slated multi-pitched roof, located at SE56960822 and opened on July 20th, 1885 by the Hull & Barnsley Railway. Details of the facilities are not known. The depot was closed by the LNER on December 5th, 1931 and subsequently demolished.

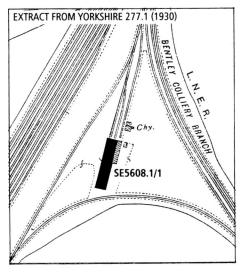

EXTRACT FROM YORKSHIRE 277.1 (1930)

BENTLEY COLLIERY BRANCH

L.N.E.R.

Chy.

SE5608.1/1

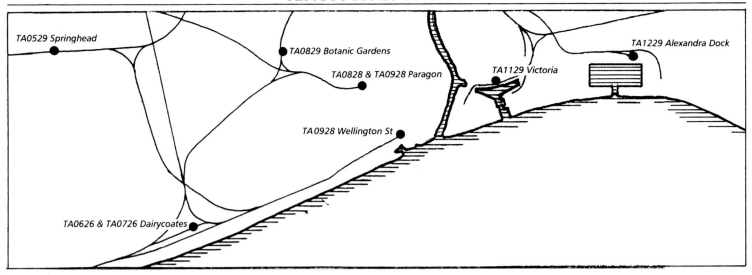

Site TA0928.1; On the south side of the line, at the east end of the Manor House Street branch.
Wellington Street (H&SR) TA0928.1/1A
A 3TS dead ended shed, located at TA09522809 and opened by the Hull & Selby Railway on July 1st, 1840. The facilities included a turntable, coal stage and water tank. The depot closed in 1863 with the building being utilized as part of the goods depot.

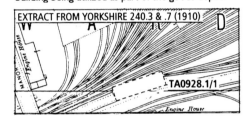

Replaced by ...
Site TA0626&0726.1; On the south side of the Hessle line, west of Hull Paragon Station.
Dairycoates No.1 (NER) TA0626&0726.1/1A
A brick built 1RH shed located at TA07092697 and opened in 1863.

The shed was re-roofed ...
Dairycoates No.1 (BR) TA0626&0726.1/1B
The building was re-roofed by the North Eastern Region in 1953.

Adjoined by ....
Dairycoates No.2 (NER) TA0626&0726.1/2A
A brick built 1RH shed located at TA07052699 and opened in 1876.

The shed was re-roofed ...
Dairycoates No.2 (BR) TA0626&0726.1/2B
The building was re-roofed by the North Eastern Region in 1956.

Adjoined by ....
Dairycoates No.3 (NER) TA0626&0726.1/3A
A brick built 1RH shed located at TA07012698 and opened in 1876.

The shed was re-roofed ...
Dairycoates No.3 (BR) TA0626&0726.1/3B
The building was re-roofed by the North Eastern Region in 1956.

Adjoined by ....
Dairycoates No.4 (NER) TA0626&0726.1/4A
A brick built 1RH shed located at TA06952696 and opened in 1915.

The shed was re-roofed ...
Dairycoates No.4 (BR) TA0626&0726.1/4B
The building was re-roofed by the North Eastern Region in 1956.

Adjoined by ....
Dairycoates No.5 (NER) TA0626&0726.1/5A
A brick built 1RH shed located at TA06882693 and opened in 1915.

The shed was re-roofed ...
Dairycoates No.5 (BR) TA0626&0726.1/5B
The building was re-roofed by the North Eastern Region in 1956.

Adjoined by ....
Dairycoates No.6 (NER) TA0626&0726.1/6A
A brick built 1RH shed located at TA06832692 and opened in 1915. The building was demolished by BR in 1956 with the locomotives then stabling around the turntable in the open until 1962.

Adjoined by ....
Dairycoates (NER) TA0626&0726.1/7A
A brick built 2TS shed located at TA07042696 and probably opened in 1876.

Adjoined by ....
Dairycoates (NER) TA0626&0726.1/8A
A brick built 3TS shed located at TA07052694 and probably opened in 1876.

Nos 1 (1A), 2 (2A) and 3 (3A) roundhouses and the 3TS (8A) and 2TS (7A) sheds were originally covered with a slated multi-hipped roof, with the later additions, Nos 4 (4A), 5 (5A) and 6 (6A) having a slated triple gable style design. The re-roofing of Nos 2-5 (2B, 3B, 4B and 5B) roundhouses in 1956 involved the installation of a flat concrete and glass roof, with a central higher single pitched unit along the whole length and brick screens at each end. With the demolition of No.6 (6A) shed an additional wall was also constructed at the end of No.5 (5B).

The shed had use of all facilities, most of which were steadily improved during its existence. The depot closed to steam on June 24th, 1967 and then completely on September 21st, 1970. Most of the buildings were demolished but Nos 4 & 5 round-houses (4B & 5B) were still in use as warehouses in 1994.

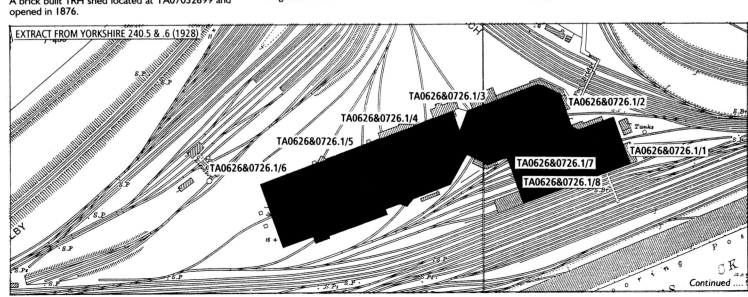

Continued ....

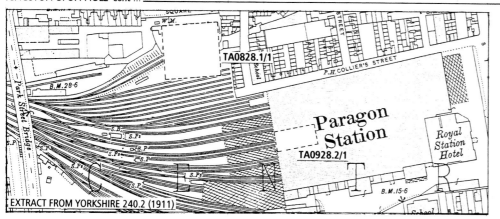

EXTRACT FROM YORKSHIRE 240.2 (1911)

Site TA0928.2; On the north side of Paragon Station.
Paragon (Y&NMR) TA0928.2/1A
A brick built 3TS dead ended shed, located at TA09082879 and opened on May 8th, 1848 by the York & North Midland Railway. The facilities included a turntable, water column and coal stage.

Site TA0828.1; On the north side of the line at the west end of Paragon Station.
Paragon* (NER) TA0828.1/1A
A brick built 1RH shed with a slated triple pitched roof, located at TA08982887 and opened in 1876. The facilities included a water column and use of the coal stage at TA0928.2/1.

*An "additional shed" was authorized in 1865 and extended in 1867. This could either have occupied a site as yet unidentified (as TA0828.2/1) or the site of the roundhouse (as TA0828.1/2).

The depots were closed in 1901 to accommodate enlargements to Paragon Station.

Replaced by ...
Site TA0829.1; On the east side of the line, south of Botanic Gardens Station.
Botanic Gardens (NER) TA0829.1/1A
A brick built 2RH shed with a slated triple gable style roof, located at TA08142924 and opened in 1901. The facilities included a water tank and ramped coal stage.

The shed was rebuilt ....
Botanic Gardens (BR) TA0829.1/1B
Between 1956 and 1959 the turntables and stalls were removed by the North Eastern Region, and a 5TS through road shed created. At the same time a concrete and glass roof with a central arched portion was installed. After completion of the work the depot closed to steam on June 13th, 1959.

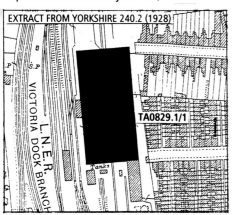

EXTRACT FROM YORKSHIRE 240.2 (1928)

Site TA1129.1; In the vicinity of Victoria Station.
Victoria (H&HR) TA1129.1/1A
A 1TS shed, approximately located at TA110290 was opened here by the Hull & Holderness Railway in May 1858. No further details are known other than it closed in 1866 and was removed to Lockington for use as a goods shed.

Site TA1229.1; In Hull Alexandra Docks.
Alexandra Dock (H&BR) TA1229.1/1A
A timber built 2TS dead ended shed with a slated gable style roof, located at TA12692919 and opened on July 20th, 1885 by the Hull & Barnsley Railway. There were no facilities. The building was demolished by the LNER in 1928.

A stabling point was then established ...
Alexandra Dock (LNER) TA1229.1/F1
Locomotives stabled on the shed site and adjacent sidings until closure to steam by BR on November 14th, 1960. Although the stabling point was then officially closed on October 27th, 1963 diesel shunters still stood there when not in service until the docks closed in 1982.

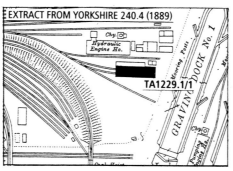

EXTRACT FROM YORKSHIRE 240.4 (1889)

Site TA0529.1; On the north side of the line, east of Springhead Halt.
Springhead (H&BR) TA0529.1/1A
A brick built 8TS through road shed with a slated transverse multi-pitched roof, located at TA05132924 and opened on July 20th, 1885.

The building was lengthened ...
Springhead (H&BR) TA0529.1/1B
The shed was extended in 1890.

The building was lengthened again ...
Springhead (H&BR) TA0529.1/1C
The shed was extended in 1897.

The building was lengthened again ...
Springhead (H&BR) TA0529.1/1D
The shed was extended to its final length in 1906. Being sited adjacently to the locomotive works it had use of all major facilities including a ramped coaling stage, turntable and water tank. By 1955 the building was totally roofless.

The shed was partially re-roofed ...
Springhead (BR) TA0529.1/1E
A lightweight roof was installed over four tracks by the North Eastern Region in 1955. This was to temporarily accommodate dmu stabling and maintenance whilst awaiting the completion of the alterations to Botanic Gardens shed (TA0829.1/1B). The steam locomotives continued to utilize the open roads until the depot closed to steam on December 15th, 1958. It was totally closed in July 1961 and subsequently demolished.

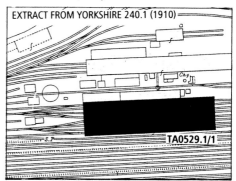

EXTRACT FROM YORKSHIRE 240.1 (1910)

The Y&NMR built a 3TS depot (TA0928.2/1A) beside its 1848 terminus at **Hull Paragon**. The shed was "enlarged" in 1865, probably by erection of another building that must have been of a temporary nature as, in 1876, it was replaced by a roundhouse (TA0828.1/1A) on a site just north of the station.

That building is seen here in 1901, just before it and the original 3TS shed were demolished to make way for enlargement of the station.
Authors' Collection

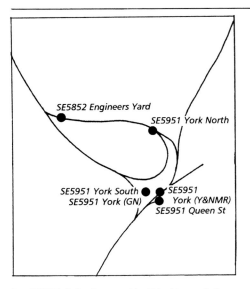

Site SE5951.4; On the west side of the Newcastle line, north of York Station.
York North No.1 (NER) SE5951.4/1A
A brick built square IRH shed with a slated multi-pitched roof, located at SE59485194 and opened in 1878.

The shed was rebuilt in 1957 ...
York North No.1 (BR) SE5951.4/1B
The building was demolished by the North Eastern Region and replaced with a brick built 7TS dead ended shed with a shallow pitched concrete and glass roof. This abutted the east end of the former No.2 shed (SE5951.4/2B).

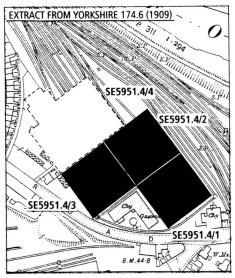
EXTRACT FROM YORKSHIRE 174.6 (1909)

Adjoined by ...
York North No.2 (NER) SE5951.4/2A
A brick built square IRH shed with a slated multi-pitched roof, located at SE59435198 and opened in 1878.

The shed was rebuilt in 1957 ...
York North No.2 (BR) SE5951.4/2B
The building was demolished by the North Eastern Region and replaced with a brick built 7TS through road shed with a shallow pitched concrete and glass roof and a brick screen. This abutted the west end of the former No.1 shed (SE5951.4/1B) creating a single depot building which was utilized as a diesel depot until 1984.

Adjoined by ...
York North No.3 (NER) SE5951.4/3A
A brick built square IRH shed with a slated multi-pitched roof, located at SE59405195 and opened in 1878.

The shed was re-roofed ...
York North No.3 (BR) SE5951.4/3B
A multi-arched concrete and glass roof was installed in 1959 by the North Eastern Region.

Adjoined by ...
York North No.4 (NER) SE5951.4/4A
A brick built square IRH shed, located at SE59375199 and opened in 1915.

The shed was re-roofed ...
York North No.4 (BR) SE5951.4/4B
A multi-arched concrete and glass roof was installed in 1959 by the North Eastern Region.

The facilities included a ramped coal stage, later replaced by a coaling plant, water tank and turntable. The depot closed to steam in June 1967 with the former Nos 3 & 4 sheds (SE5951.4/3B&4B) being refurbished in 1975 and used as the main premises of the National Railway Museum. The remainder of the depot closed in March 1984 and still stood in a derelict condition until it too, as the result of a National Lottery grant of £2m in 1998, became part of the Museum.

Site SE5951.1; On the north side of the line, west of York Old Station.
York (Y&NMR) SE5951.1/1A
A 2TS shed, probably located at SE59455148 and opened on May 29th, 1839 by the York & North Midland Railway.

The shed was enlarged ...
York (Y&NMR) SE5951.1/1B
At some stage the building was enlarged to a 3TS through road shed. The facilities included a turntable. No further details are known other than it was demolished in 1875/6 to make way for the new station.

Site SE5951.2; In the triangle of lines on the west side of the Doncaster line, at the south end of York Station.
York South (GNofER) SE5951.2/1A
A brick built 3TS through road shed with a slated gable style roof, located at SE59315153 and opened on January 4th, 1841 by the Great North of England Railway. Details of the facilities are not known. It was taken over by the GNR in c1850 and in 1923 LMS locomotives were housed there (*The building thereafter being known as the "LMS Shed"*).

The shed was re-roofed ...
York LMS (LMS) SE5951.2/1B
At some stage a dutch barn style roof in corrugated sheeting was installed. Following nationalization the LMS locomotives moved to York North and the building became part of York South depot, closing in May 1961.

Site SE5852.1; On the south side of the Newcastle line, west of York Station.
York Engineers Yard (LNER) SE5852.1/1A
A corrugated iron ITS through road shed, located at SE58555215 and opened in 1930. Details of the facilities are not known. The shed housed Sentinel locomotive No.45 and closed to steam when it was withdrawn by BR in 1959. The replacement diesel shunter Departmental No.84 probably utilized the building thereafter.

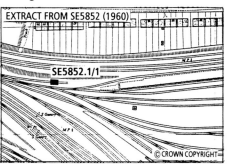
EXTRACT FROM SE5852 (1960)
© CROWN COPYRIGHT

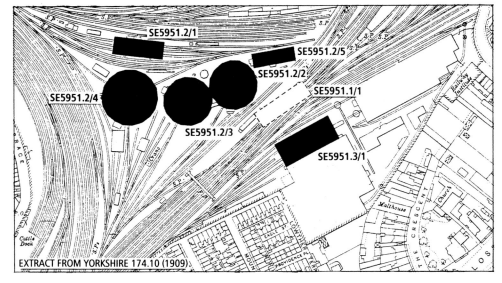
EXTRACT FROM YORKSHIRE 174.10 (1909)

York South No.1 (Y&NMR) SE5951.2/2A
A brick built IRH shed with a conical roof, located at SE59415149 and opened in 1850 by the York & North Midland Railway. Details of the facilities and closure date are not known but by 1921 it was utilized for repairing wagon sheets as well as some stabling of rolling stock. The building was destroyed by a fire on October 21st, 1921, with the site later being utilized for track widening.

York South No.2 (Y&NMR) SE5951.2/3A
A brick built IRH shed with a conical roof, located at SE59365148 and opened in 1852 by the York & North Midland Railway. Details of the facilities are not known.

The building was modified ...
York South No.2 (LNER) SE5951.2/3B
Part of the eastern side of the building was removed in 1936 to accommodate track widening into York Station. The depot was closed by BR in May 1961 and demolished in 1963.

York South No.3 (NER) SE5951.2/4A
A brick built IRH shed with a slated radiating multi-pitched roof surmounted by a central conical section and weather vane. It was located at SE59315148 and opened in November 1864. Details of the facilities are not known. The building was leased to the Midland Railway which utilized it until the grouping when the LMS moved across the line to Queen Street (SE5931.3/1). By the time closure came, by BR in May 1961, the building was roofless and demolition followed in 1963.

Continued ...

York (GNR) SE5951.2/5A ·
brick built 3TS dead ended shed, located at
E59445152 and opened in 1853. No further de-
ails are known other than it closed in 1875 before be-
ng demolished to make way for station enlarge-
ents in 1936.

te SE5951.3; On the east side of the line, at the
uth end of York Station.
York Queen Street (GCR/GER/L&YR) SE5951.3/1A
A brick built 4TS dead ended shed with a twin
lated gable style roof, located at SE59475144 and
pened in 1909. The building originally formed part
f the York & North Midland Railway Works as a
oiler shop and was converted to an engine shed.
he facilities included a water column.

Upon the grouping in 1923 the GCR and GER lo-
omotives moved across the tracks to York South
SE5951.2/3&4) with the MR locomotives crossing
the opposite direction. Although the shed was
losed by the LMS in 1932 it saw further use as a
arriage shed and, in BR days, as a diesel shunter
naintenance depot before being demolished.

LAYERTHORPE

te SE6152.1; On the east side of Layerthorpe (DVLR)
tation.
ayerthorpe (DVLR) SE6152.1/1A
1TS through road shed, located at SE61295205
nd opened in 1919 by the Derwent Valley Light
Railway. Details of the facilities are not known. Al-
hough the line ceased to use its own locomotives
rom 1935 the hired engines, from the LNER and
ater BR, continued to utilize the shed until the end
f steam in c1965. The diesel shunters which took
over the duties were then housed in the building.

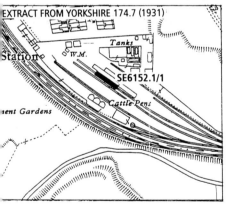

EXTRACT FROM YORKSHIRE 174.7 (1931)

CHURCH FENTON

Site SE5037.1; On the west side of the line, at the
north end of Church Fenton Station.
Church Fenton (Y&NMR) SE5037.1/1A
A brick built 2TS dead ended shed with a slated
gable style roof, located at SE50973729 and opened
in 1847 by the York & North Midland Railway. The
facilities included a pump house and water tank.
The closure date is not known, but it lasted into the
late 1960s having found further use as an
engineering workshop.

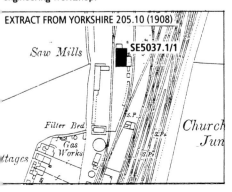

EXTRACT FROM YORKSHIRE 205.10 (1908)

GOOLE

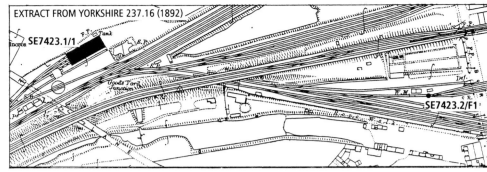

EXTRACT FROM YORKSHIRE 237.16 (1892)

Site SE7423.1; On the north side of the line, at Goods
Yard Junction.
Goole (L&YR) SE7423.1/1A
A 2TS dead ended shed, located at SE74012322
and opened on April 1st, 1848. The facilities included a turntable. No further details are known
except that it was closed in 1871.

Replaced, on the same site, by ...
Goole (L&YR) SE7423.1/1B
A 3TS dead ended shed, probably built in brick,
opened here in 1871. The facilities included a water
tank, coal stage and turntable. The depot closed in
1889.

Replaced by ...
Site SE7222.1; On the north side of the line, west of
Goole West Junction.
Goole (L&YR) SE7222.1/1A
A brick built 6TS dead ended shed with a northlight
pattern roof, located at SE72602236 and opened in
1889. The facilities included a coal stage, with wa-
ter tank over and 50ft turntable.

The shed was re-roofed ...
Goole (BR) SE7222.1/1B
A louvre style roof with brick screen was installed
by the North Eastern Region in 1950 and the depot
closed on May 8th, 1967.

MARKET WEIGHTON

Site SE8742.1; On the north side of Market Weighton
Station.
Market Weighton (NER) SE8742.1/1A
A brick built 2TS through road shed, located at
SE87804204 and opened on October 4th, 1847.
The facilities included a 50ft turntable. The depot
closed on March 1st, 1917 and was utilized as a
goods shed. The building was demolished after
1980, with the site being utilized for housing.

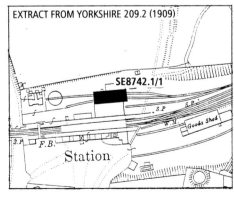

EXTRACT FROM YORKSHIRE 209.2 (1909)

BLACK CARR

Site SE6000.1; At Black Carr Junction, east of Don-
caster Station.
Black Carr (DVR) SE6000.1/1A
A shed, approximately located at SE600001, was
opened here by the Dearne Valley Railway in 1908.
No further details are known.

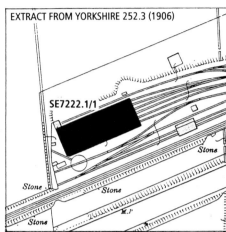

EXTRACT FROM YORKSHIRE 252.3 (1906)

Site SE7423.2; In Goole Goods Yard.
Goole (L&YR) SE7423.2/F1
A servicing area consisting of a coal stage and siding,
located at SE74332319 and opened in 1914.

NB. A servicing area consisting of a coal stage and
siding may have existed at Goole High Level.

KNOTTINGLEY

Site SE4923.0; In the vicinity of Knottingley Station.
Knottingley (Leeds&MR) SE4923.0/F1
Some sort of facility was opened here by the Leeds
& Manchester Railway. No further details are
known.

Replaced by ...
Site SE4923.1; On the south side of Knottingley
Station.
Knottingley (L&YR) SE4923.1/1A
A brick built 1TS through road shed with a slated
gable style roof, located at SE49102354 and opened
in March 1854*. The facilities included a 44ft
turntable. The depot closed on July 1st, 1922 and
the building was let to the adjacent glass works
which utilized it as a bottle warehouse for a number
of years prior to demolition.

EXTRACT FROM YORKSHIRE 235.13 & 235.14 (1907)

*The building was initially utilized, either solely or
partly, by GNR locomotives. This practice continued
until at least 1858 but had ceased by mid-1868.

MEXBOROUGH

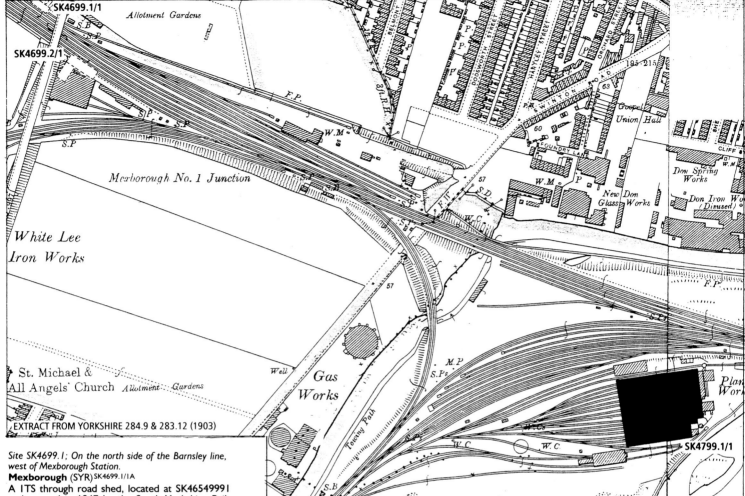

EXTRACT FROM YORKSHIRE 284.9 & 283.12 (1903)

SK4699.1/1

SK4699.2/1

SK4799.1/1

Site SK4699.1; On the north side of the Barnsley line, west of Mexborough Station.
Mexborough (SYR) SK4699.1/1A
A 1TS through road shed, located at SK46549991 and opened in 1847 by the South Yorkshire Railway. Details of the facilities are not known. The depot closed in 1854.

Replaced by ...
Site SK4699.2; On the south side of the Barnsley line, west of Mexborough Station.
Mexborough (SYR) SK4699.2/1A
A 2TS shed with one through road, located at SK46579987 and opened by the South Yorkshire Railway in 1854. The facilities included a repair shop. The depot was closed in 1875 and demolished to make way for additional running lines.

Replaced by ...
Site SK4799.1; On the south side of the Sheffield line, at Mexborough No.2 Junction, west of Mexborough Station.
Mexborough (MS&LR) SK4799.1/1A
A brick built 12TS dead ended shed, located at SK47029955 and opened in 1875. The facilities included a coal stage, water tank and 60ft turntable.

The shed was re-roofed ...
Mexborough (BR) SK4799.1/1B
At some stage a multi-pitched roof and brick screen was installed, probably by the Eastern Region. The depot closed in February 1964 and was later demolished.

HENSALL JUNCTION

Site SE6022.1; On the north side of Hensall Junction, east of Hensall Station.
Hensall Junction (H&BR) SE6022.1/1A
A brick built 2TS dead ended shed with a northlight pattern roof, located at SE60702261 and opened on July 20th, 1885 by the Hull & Barnsley Railway. The facilities included a turntable and water tank. The depot closed in 1914 and remained standing in a derelict condition until 1997.

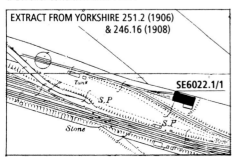

EXTRACT FROM YORKSHIRE 251.2 (1906) & 246.16 (1908)

SE6022.1/1

WRANGBROOK JUNCTION

Site SE4913.1; On the west side of the Wath line, south of Wrangbrook Junction.
Wrangbrook Junction (H&BR) SE4913.1/F1
A servicing area consisting of a turntable, located at SE49091301, and siding was opened here by the Hull & Barnsley Railway. No further details are known.

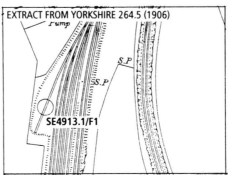

EXTRACT FROM YORKSHIRE 264.5 (1906)

SE4913.1/F1

SPURN HEAD

Site TA4011.1; On the east side of the line at Spurn Point.
Spurn Head (Spurn Head) TA4011.1/1A
A 2TS dead ended shed, located at TA40381131 and opened by the Spurn Head Railway. No further details are known other than it closed in 1951.

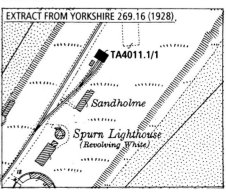

EXTRACT FROM YORKSHIRE 269.16 (1928)

TA4011.1/1

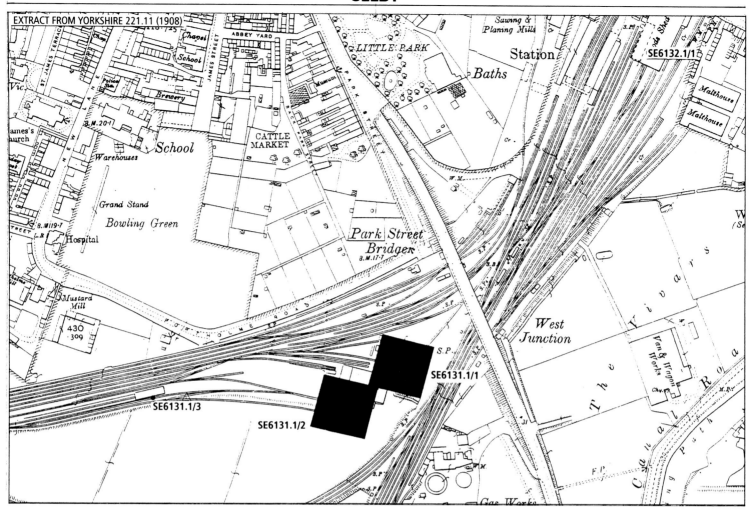

EXTRACT FROM YORKSHIRE 221.11 (1908)

Site SE6132.1; On the east side of Selby Station.
Selby (L&SR) SE6132.1/1A
A 2TS dead ended shed, located at SE61873227 and opened by the Leeds & Selby Railway on September 22nd, 1834. The facilities included a repair shop and water column. No further details are known other than it probably closed in 1871 and saw further use as part of a goods shed.

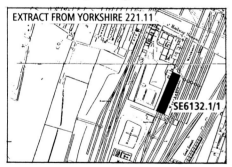

EXTRACT FROM YORKSHIRE 221.11

SE6132.1/1

Replaced by ...
Site SE6131.1; In the fork of the Leeds and Doncaster lines, south of Selby Station.
Selby* (NER) SE6131.1/1A
A brick built square 1RH shed with a slated triple hipped roof, located at SE61643196 and opened in 1871.

Adjoined by ...
Selby New (NER) SE6131.1/2A
A brick built square 1RH shed with a slated triple gable style roof, located at SE61583192 and opened in 1898.

The facilities included a ramped coal stage and water tank. The depot was closed by BR on September 13th, 1959 and demolished a few years later.

*Upon the opening of SE6131.1/2A the original building became known as the "old" shed.

NB. An unusual "shed" (SE6131.1/3A) was constructed in 1912 along the southern side of the coaling stage at SE61403193. This lean-to construction solely housed the Petrol-Electric bogie cars, and their railcar successors, for use on the Cawood Branch and remained in existence until at least 1964.

Site SE6031.1; On the north side of the Leeds line, at Wistow Junction, west of Selby Station.
Selby (CW&SLR) SE6031.1/1A
A 1TS dead ended shed, located at SE60893186 and opened by the Cawood, Wistow & Selby Light Railway on February 16th, 1898. Details of the facilities are not known. The line was taken over by the NER and the depot closed when they withdrew the only locomotive belonging to the CW&SR, *Cawood*, in June 1901, locomotives thereafter being supplied from Selby shed (SE6131.1/1&2). The shed building saw a variety of uses before demolition in 1963.

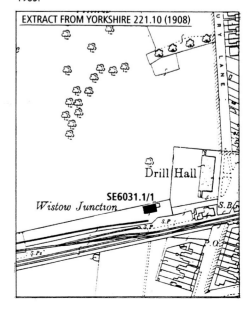

EXTRACT FROM YORKSHIRE 221.10 (1908)

Drill Hall

SE6031.1/1

Wistow Junction

YORKSHIRE (SW)

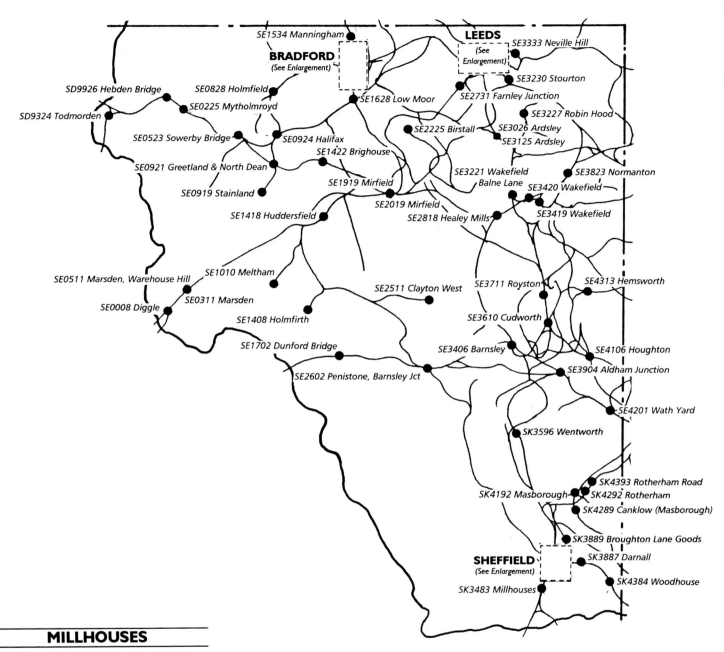

SE1534 Manningham
BRADFORD (See Enlargement)
LEEDS (See Enlargement)
SE3333 Neville Hill
SD9926 Hebden Bridge
SE0828 Holmfield
SE3230 Stourton
SE0225 Mytholmroyd
SE1628 Low Moor
SE2731 Farnley Junction
SD9324 Todmorden
SE3227 Robin Hood
SE0523 Sowerby Bridge
SE0924 Halifax
SE2225 Birstall
SE3026 Ardsley
SE0921 Greetland & North Dean
SE1422 Brighouse
SE3125 Ardsley
SE0919 Stainland
SE3221 Wakefield
SE3823 Normanton
SE1919 Mirfield
Balne Lane
SE3420 Wakefield
SE2019 Mirfield
SE3419 Wakefield
SE1418 Huddersfield
SE2818 Healey Mills
SE0511 Marsden, Warehouse Hill
SE1010 Meltham
SE2511 Clayton West
SE3711 Royston
SE4313 Hemsworth
SE0008 Diggle
SE0311 Marsden
SE3610 Cudworth
SE1408 Holmfirth
SE3406 Barnsley
SE4106 Houghton
SE1702 Dunford Bridge
SE3904 Aldham Junction
SE2602 Penistone, Barnsley Jct
SE4201 Wath Yard
SK3596 Wentworth
SK4393 Rotherham Road
SK4192 Masborough
SK4292 Rotherham
SK4289 Canklow (Masborough)
SK3889 Broughton Lane Goods
SHEFFIELD (See Enlargement)
SK3887 Darnall
SK3483 Millhouses
SK4384 Woodhouse

MILLHOUSES

Site SK3483.1; On the west side of the line, at the north end of Millhouses & Ecclesall Station.

Millhouses (MR) SK3483.1/1A

A brick built 8TS dead ended shed with a slated four pitched roof, located at SK34068369 and opened in 1901. The facilities included a ramped coal stage, water tank and a turntable. The depot was closed by BR on January 1st, 1962 and sold for industrial use. The building still stood in 1998.

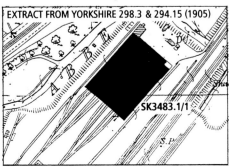

EXTRACT FROM YORKSHIRE 298.3 & 294.15 (1905)

SK3483.1/1

BIRSTALL

Site SE2225.1; On the south side of Birstall Station.

Birstall (L&NWR) SE2225.1/1A

A brick built 1TS dead ended shed, believed to be the building located at SE22522594 and opened on September 30th, 1852. Details of the facilities are not known. The depot closed in 1917 and remained standing until at least 1952 when it was sold for use as part of the adjacent gas works.

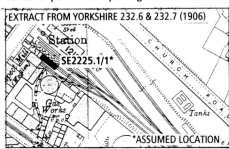

EXTRACT FROM YORKSHIRE 232.6 & 232.7 (1906)

Station
SE2225.1/1*

Gas Works
*ASSUMED LOCATION

ALDHAM JUNCTION

Site SE3904.1; On the west side of the line, north of Wombwell Station.

Aldham Junction (MS&LR) SE3904.1/F1

A servicing area consisting of an engine pit and siding, located at SE39250420 and opened in 1878. The facility was closed by BR in 1965.

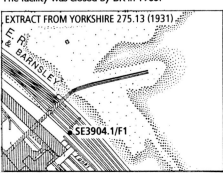

EXTRACT FROM YORKSHIRE 275.13 (1931)

E. R. & BARNSLEY

SE3904.1/F1

BARNSLEY

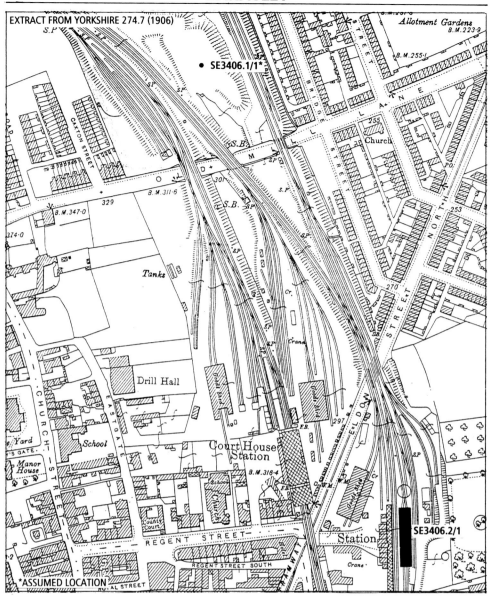

EXTRACT FROM YORKSHIRE 274.7 (1906)

● SE3406.1/1*

Tanks

Drill Hall

Court House
Station

REGENT STREET

REGENT STREET SOUTH

*ASSUMED LOCATION

Station

SE3406.2/1

ARDSLEY

Site SE3026.1; On the north side of the line, west of Ardsley Station.
Ardsley (BW&LR)^{SE3026.1/1A}
A 2TS shed, located at SE30062657 and opened in 1860 by the Bradford, Wakefield & Leeds Railway.

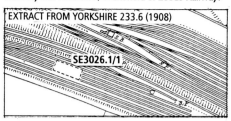

EXTRACT FROM YORKSHIRE 233.6 (1908)

SE3026.1/1

Replaced by ...
Site SE3125.1; On the north side of the line, east of Ardsley Station.
Ardsley (GNR)^{SE3125.1/1A}
A brick built 8TS through road shed with a north-light pattern roof, located at SE31232594 and opened in 1892. The facilities included a ramped coal stage, with water tank over, and turntable.

The shed was partially re-roofed ...
Ardsley (LNER)^{SE3125.1/1B}
A steel framed multi-pitched roof was installed at the eastern end of the depot in 1946.

The shed re-roofing was completed ...
Ardsley (BR)^{SE3125.1/1C}
A louvre style roof with brick screen was installed over the remainder of the depot by the Eastern Region in 1955. The shed was closed in October 1965 and subsequently demolished.

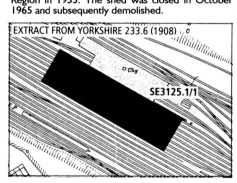

EXTRACT FROM YORKSHIRE 233.6 (1908)

SE3125.1/1

Site SE3406.1; In the fork of the lines, north of Barnsley Station.
Barnsley (SRBWH&GR)^{SE3406.1/1A}
A ITS shed approximately located at SE34520699 and opened on January 1st, 1850 by the Sheffield, Rotherham, Barnsley, Wakefield, Huddersfield and Goole Railway. The facilities included a turntable. The line was absorbed by the L&YR on August 2nd, 1858 and the depot probably closed on the opening of SE3406.2/1B.

Site SE3406.2; On the east side of Barnsley Station.
Barnsley (MS&LR)^{SE3406.2/1A}
A servicing facility, located at SE34730655, was established under the station roof in c1845. No further details are known other than it was probably removed when the overall roof was demolished.

Replaced, on the same site by ...
Barnsley (L&YR/MS&LR)^{SE3406.2/1B}
A brick built 2TS through road shed with a gable style slated roof. The facilities included a turntable, sited outside of the northern entrance to the shed. No further details are known.

The shed was re-roofed ...
Barnsley (BR)^{SE3406.2/1C}
A new gable style roof was installed in c1956 by the Eastern Region. By this time the turntable had been removed. The depot closed on January 4th, 1960 and was demolished the same year, the site later being partially utilized as a bus station.

DIGGLE

Site SE0008.1; At the north end of Diggle Station.
Diggle (L&NWR)^{SE0008.1/1A}
A short section of the southern end of Diggle Tunnel, located at SE00790813, was utilized as a temporary ITS shed during 1856 and 1857. There were no facilities.

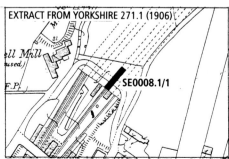

EXTRACT FROM YORKSHIRE 271.1 (1906)

SE0008.1/1

WENTWORTH

Site SK3596.1; In the vicinity of Chapeltown Station.
Wentworth (MS&LR)^{SK3596.1/F1}
A servicing area consisting of a coal stage was opened here in 1878 and closed by BR in 1954. No further details are known.

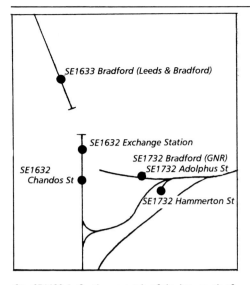

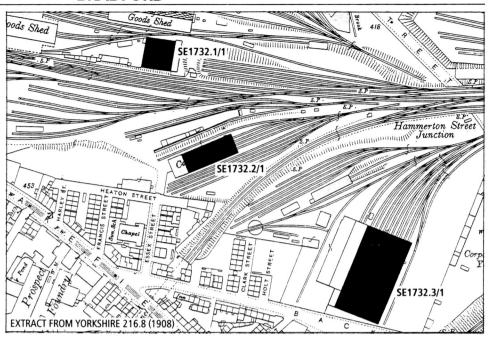

EXTRACT FROM YORKSHIRE 216.8 (1908)

Site SE1632.1; On the west side of the line, south of Bradford Exchange Station.

Chandos Street (L&YR)^{SE1632.1/1A}

A 4TS dead ended shed, located at SE16603257 and opened on September 26th, 1850. The facilities included a turntable. No further details are known except that it closed in 1866, upon the opening of Low Moor shed (SE1628.1/1A), and was demolished in 1882.

Site SE1632.2; On the east side of the line, at the south end of Bradford Exchange Station.

Exchange Station (GNR)^{SE1632.2/1A}

A servicing area consisting of a turntable, located at SE16653285, and siding. No further details are known other than it probably opened in 1888 and had been removed by 1958.

Site SE1632.3; On the west side of the line, at the south end of Bradford Exchange Station.

Exchange Station (L&YR)^{SE1632.3/F1}

A servicing area consisting of a turntable, located at SE16583286, and siding. It probably opened in 1888 and did not close until the end of steam in the area in c1965.

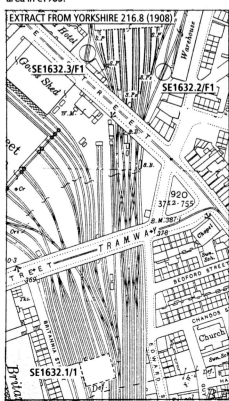

EXTRACT FROM YORKSHIRE 216.8 (1908)

Site SE1732.1; On the north side of the line, east of Bradford (GNR) Station.

Bradford (GNR/LB&HJR)^{SE1732.1/1A}

A 6TS dead ended shed, located at SE17213261 and opened in August 1854 by the Great Northern and Leeds, Bradford & Halifax Joint Railways. No further details are known other than it closed on February 11th, 1867 and saw further use, firstly as stables and later as a goods shed until demolished in 1977.

Replaced by ...
Site SE1732.2; On the south side of the line, east of Bradford (GNR) Station.

Adolphus Street (GNR)^{SE1732.2/1A}

A 4TS dead ended shed, located at SE17263251 and opened on February 11th, 1867. No further details are known other than it closed in March 1883 and saw further use, firstly as a carriage shed and later as a goods shed until demolished in 1977.

Replaced by ...
Site SE1732.3; On the south side of the line at Hammerton Street Junction, east of Bradford (GNR) Station.

Bowling Junction* (GNR)^{SE1732.3/1A}

A brick built 10TS dead ended shed with a north-light pattern roof, located at SE17423241 and opened in March 1883. The facilities included a ramped coal stage, later replaced by a coaling plant, turntable, water tower and repair shop.

The shed was re-roofed ...
Hammerton Street (BR)^{SE1732.3/1B}

A louvre style roof with brick screen was installed by the Eastern Region in 1955. The shed was gradually converted for use as a dmu maintenance depot and by the time that it was closed to steam in January 1958 it had been reduced to a 9TS building. The depot was totally closed in 1984 and remained standing in a derelict condition until demolished in May 1991.

*It was also known as Bowling Back and Hammerton Street.

TODMORDEN

Site SD9324.1; In the triangle of lines, east of Todmorden Station.

Todmorden (L&YR)^{SD9324.1/F1}

A servicing area consisting of a coal stage, approximately located at SD939244, was opened here in 1914. No further details are known.

Site SE1633.1; On the east side of Bradford (Leeds & Bradford) Railway Station.

Bradford (L&BR)^{SE1633.1/1A}

A 2TS dead ended shed, located at SE16493342 and opened on June 30th, 1846 by the Leeds & Bradford Railway. The facilities included a coaling shed, water column and repair shop. The line was absorbed by the MR and they closed the depot in 1854.

Replaced by ...
Site SE1633.2; On the west side of the line, at the north end of Bradford (MR) Station.

Bradford (MR)^{SE1633.2/1A}

A 4TS dead ended shed, located at SE16403350 and opened in 1854. The facilities included a coal stage and turntable. No further details are known other than it probably closed in 1872 upon the opening of Manningham shed (SE1534.1/1).

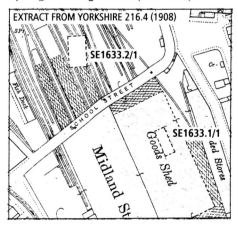

EXTRACT FROM YORKSHIRE 216.4 (1908)

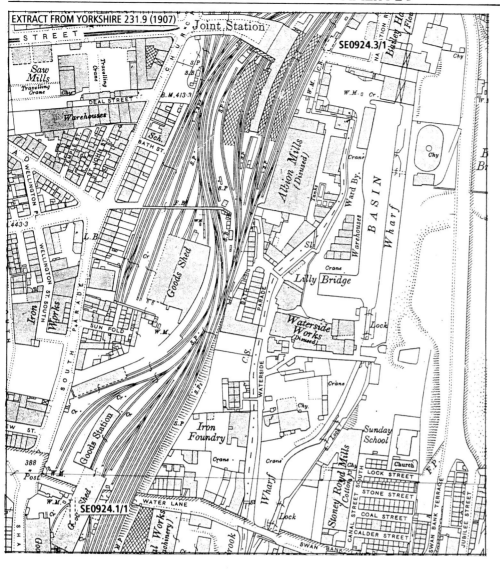

EXTRACT FROM YORKSHIRE 231.9 (1907)

Site SE0924.1; On the east side of Shaw Syke Station.
Shaw Syke (L&MR) SE0924.1/1A
A 1TS dead ended shed, probably constructed in timber, located at SE09572452 and opened by the Leeds & Manchester Railway in 1844. The facilities included a turntable. No further details are known except that it was removed in 1850 to Horbury for further use as a goods shed.

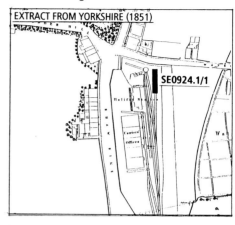

EXTRACT FROM YORKSHIRE (1851)

Site SE0924.2; In the vicinity of Shaw Syke Station.
Shaw Syke (L&YR) SE0924.2/1A
A 1TS shed was opened here at some time after 1850. It was taken over by the GNR August 1st, 1854 and closed by them on June 24th, 1855. No further details are known.

Replaced by ...
Site SE0924.3; On the east side of Halifax Joint Station.
Halifax (GNR/L&YR) SE0924.3/1A
A 2TS dead ended shed, located at SE09792497 and opened on June 24th, 1855. No further details are known other than it closed in 1867 and was not demolished until 1887.

Replaced by ...
Site SE0924.4; In the vicinity of Halifax Joint Station.
Halifax (L&YR) SE0924.4/1A
A shed opened here in 1867. No more details are known.

LOW MOOR

Site SE1628.1; On the west side of Low Moor Station.
Low Moor (L&YR) SE1628.1/1A
A shed opened here in 1866, closed in 1888 and was probably located at SE16562840.

Replaced, on the same site, by ...
Low Moor (L&YR) SE1628.1/1B
A brick built 12TS dead ended shed, probably with a northlight pattern roof. The facilities included a coal stage, with water tank over, and a turntable.

The shed was rebuilt ...
Low Moor (BR) SE1628.1/1C
A louvre style roof with brick screen was installed over the six easternmost tracks by the London Midland Region in 1948. The remaining portion of the shed was left roofless until the depot closed on October 2nd, 1967.

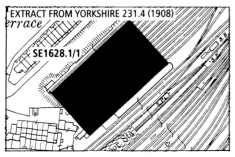

EXTRACT FROM YORKSHIRE 231.4 (1908)

HOLMFIELD

Site SE0828.1; On the east side of the line, south of Holmfield Station.
Holmfield (GNR) SE0828.1/1A
A stone built 2TS dead ended shed with a slated northlight pattern roof, located at SE08412827 and opened in 1890. The facilities included a water tank and coal stage. The depot was closed by the LNER in 1933.

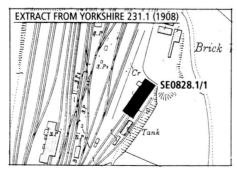

EXTRACT FROM YORKSHIRE 231.1 (1908)

HEALEY MILLS

Site SE2818.1; In the vicinity of Horbury & Ossett Station.
Healey Mills (L&YR) SE2818.1/F1
A servicing area, consisting of a coal stage, was opened here. No further details are known.

HOLMFIRTH

Site SE1408.1; On the west side of Holmfirth Station.
Holmfirth (L&YR) SE1408.1/F1
A servicing area consisting of a turntable, located at SE14450850, coal stage and engine pit. It was opened on July 1st, 1850 and closed by the LMS in 1923.

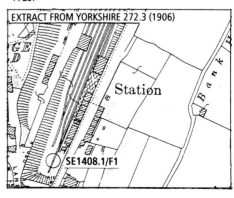

EXTRACT FROM YORKSHIRE 272.3 (1906)

HEMSWORTH

Site SE4313.1; In the vicinity of Hemsworth Station.
Hemsworth (H&BR) SE4313.1/F1
Some sort of facility was opened here by the Hull & Barnsley Railway. No further details are known.

MIRFIELD

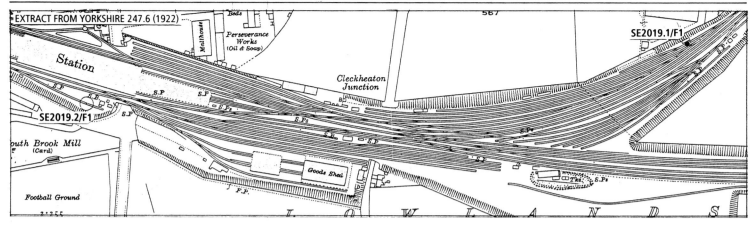

EXTRACT FROM YORKSHIRE 247.6 (1922)

SE2019.1/F1

SE2019.2/F1

Site SE2019.0; In the vicinity of Mirfield Station.
Mirfield (L&YR) SE2019.0/F1
A servicing area consisting of a water tank and sidings, opened in 1849 and closed in 1857. No further details are known.

Replaced by ...
Mirfield (L&YR) SE2019.0/1A
A 3TS shed opened here in 1857 and closed in 1885. No further details are known.

Replaced by ...
Site SE1919.1; On the north side of the line, west of Mirfield Station.
Mirfield (L&YR) SE1919.1/1A
A brick built 8TS dead ended shed with a northlight pattern roof, located at SE19651987 and opened in 1885. The facilities included a ramped coal stage, with water tank over, and a turntable.

The shed was re-roofed ...
Mirfield (LMS) SE1919.1/1B
A multi-pitched roof was installed in 1934. The depot was closed by BR in April 1967 and remained standing, in private use, until the 1990s.

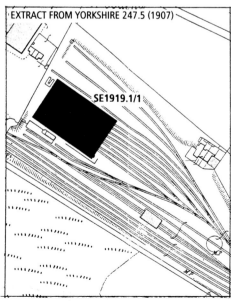

EXTRACT FROM YORKSHIRE 247.5 (1907)

SE1919.1/1

Site SE2019.1; In Mirfield Goods Yard.
Mirfield Goods (L&YR) SE2019.1/F1
A servicing area consisting of a coal stage and siding, located at SE20941952 and opened in 1914. No further details are known.

Site SE2019.2; On the south side of Mirfield Station.
Mirfield Station (L&YR) SE2019.2/F1
A servicing area consisting of a turntable, located at SE20381945, and siding. No further details are known.

WAKEFIELD

Site SE3221.1; On the east side of the line, at the north end of Wakefield Westgate Joint Station.
Wakefield Balne Lane (MR/MS&LR) SE3221.1/1A
A 3TS dead ended shed, located at SE32712107 and opened on July 1st, 1868. The facilities included a turntable. The depot was closed by the LNER in 1923.

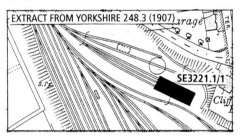

EXTRACT FROM YORKSHIRE 248.3 (1907)

SE3221.1/1

Site SE3420.1; In the fork of the lines, at the east end of Wakefield Kirkgate Joint Station.
Wakefield (L&YR) SE3420.1/1A
A brick built 5TS through road shed, located at SE34302045 and opened in 1847. The facilities included a turntable, coke/coal shed and water column. The depot closed in 1879 and was immediately demolished.

Replaced, on the same site, by ...
Wakefield (L&YR) SE3420.1/1B
A 10TS dead ended shed opened in 1879 and closed in 1898. No further details are known.

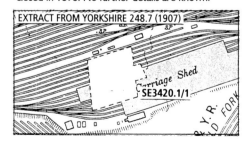

EXTRACT FROM YORKSHIRE 248.7 (1907)

Carriage Shed

SE3420.1/1

Site SE3419.1; On the east side of the Pontefract line, south of Wakefield Kirkgate Joint Station.
Wakefield (L&YR) SE3419.1/1A
A brick built 10TS dead ended shed with a northlight pattern roof, located at SE34831956 and opened in 1893. The facilities included a coal stage, with water tank over and a turntable.

The depot was re-modelled ...
Wakefield (LMS) SE3419.1/1B
The building was converted to a 10TS through road shed and a new coaling plant and turntable were installed in 1932.

The shed was re-roofed ...
Wakefield (LMS) SE3419.1/1C
A new louvre style roof with brick screen was installed by the London Midland Region in 1956 and the depot closed on June 3rd, 1967. The building saw further use as a wagon shop until 1986 and was demolished in 1993.

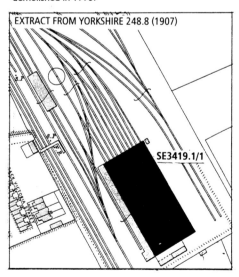

EXTRACT FROM YORKSHIRE 248.8 (1907)

SE3419.1/1

MARSDEN

Site SE0311.1; Adjacent to the entrance to Diggle Tunnel, west of Marsden Station.
Marsden (L&NWR) SE0311.1/1A
A 1TS shed located at SE03961184. No further details are known other than it closed upon the enlarging of the tunnel in August 1894.

Site SE0511.1; In the vicinity of Marsden Station.
Warehouse Hill (L&NWR) SE0511.1/1A
A 1ft 6in gauge 1TS shed was opened here to service locomotives being utilized on civil engineering works. No further details are known.

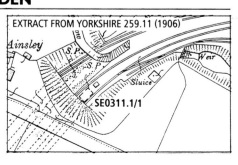

EXTRACT FROM YORKSHIRE 259.11 (1906)

Ainsley

Weir

Sluice

SE0311.1/1

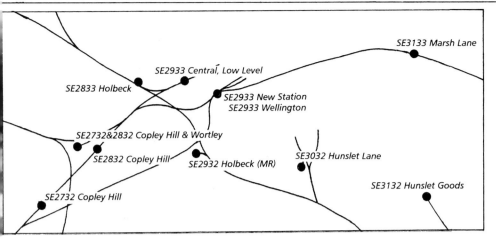

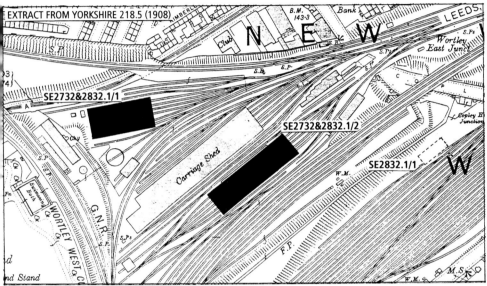

EXTRACT FROM YORKSHIRE 218.5 (1908)

SE2732&2832.1/1

SE2732&2832.1/2

SE2832.1/1

Site SE2732&2832.1; In the triangle of the Leeds Central, Armley Moor and Ardsley lines, west of Leeds Central Station.

Copley Hill (GNR) SE2732&2832.1/2A

A brick built 5TS through road shed with a transverse multi-pitched roof, located at SE28103261 and opened in 1900. The facilities included a ramped coaling stage, water tank and turntable.

The shed was re-roofed ...

Copley Hill (BR) SE2732&2832.1/2B

A louvre style roof with brick screen was installed by the Eastern Region in c1949. The depot closed on September 7th, 1964 and was demolished.

Wortley (GNR/L&YR) SE2732&2832.1/1A

A 6TS shed, composed of 4TS and 2TS adjoining buildings, located at SE27983267 and opened in 1857.

The shed was rebuilt...

Wortley Junction (L&YR) SE2732&2832.1/1B

A brick built 6TS dead ended shed with a northlight pattern roof was constructed on the same site and opened in 1900. The facilities included a turntable and coal stage. The depot was closed by the LMS on July 1st, 1928 but remained standing in a derelict condition for some time before demolition.

Site SE2832.1; On the north side of the Dewsbury line, west of Leeds Wellington Station.

Copley Hill (L&NWR/L&YR) SE2832.1/1A

A 3TS shed located at SE28273264 and opened on September 18th, 1848. The facilities included two turntables, one sited outside of the shed entrance. No further details are known other than it closed in 1868.

Replaced by ...

Site SE2732.1; On the east side of the line, north of Farnley & Wortley Station.

Copley Hill (L&NWR) SE2732.1/1A

A 5TS dead ended shed located at SE27803216 and opened in 1868. Details of the facilities are not known. The building and yard became unstable as the area suffered from mining subsidence and the depot closed in 1882 with the locomotives transferring to Farnley Junction shed (SE2731.1/1).

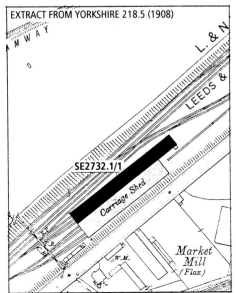

EXTRACT FROM YORKSHIRE 218.5 (1908)

SE2732.1/1

Site SE3132.1; In the vicinity of Hunslet Goods Station.

Hunslet Goods (GNR) SE3132.1/F1

A servicing area consisting of a turntable, water column and engine pits, approximately located at SE316321, and opened on July 3rd, 1899. No further details are known.

Site SE3032.1; On the west side of the line, at the south end of Hunslet Lane Station.

Hunslet Lane (L&YR/NMR) SE3032.1/1A

A brick built 8TS through road shed with a slated multiple gable roof, located at SE30323239 and opened on July 1st, 1840 by the Lancashire & Yorkshire and North Midland Railways. At the rear of the building each of the roads had a small turntable accessing a single track running parallel to the back of the shed and other facilities included a full sized turntable, coking shed and repair shop. The depot was closed by the Midland Railway in 1868 and converted into a goods shed, not being demolished until c1980.

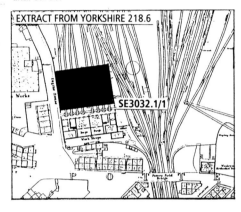

EXTRACT FROM YORKSHIRE 218.6

SE3032.1/1

Site SE3133.1; On the north side of the line, at the east end of Marsh Lane (Leeds & Selby) Station.

Marsh Lane (L&SR) SE3133.1/1A

A brick built 2TS dead ended shed, located at SE31213353 and opened on September 22nd, 1834 by the Leeds & Selby Railway. The building was at right angles to the line and access was via two small turntables. The facilities also included a repair shop. The depot probably closed in 1852 upon the enlargement of Marsh Lane Station by the York & North Midland Railway.

Replaced by ...

Site SE3133.2; On the south side of the line, east of Marsh Lane Station.

Marsh Lane (Y&NMR) SE3133.2/1A

A 2TS dead ended shed, located at SE31383342 and probably opened in 1852 by the York & North Midland Railway. Details of the facilities are not known. The depot probably closed in 1871 upon the opening of New Station shed (SE2933.2/1).

SE3133.1/1

SE3133.2/1

EXTRACT FROM YORKSHIRE 218.6 & 218.2 (1906)

Continued ...

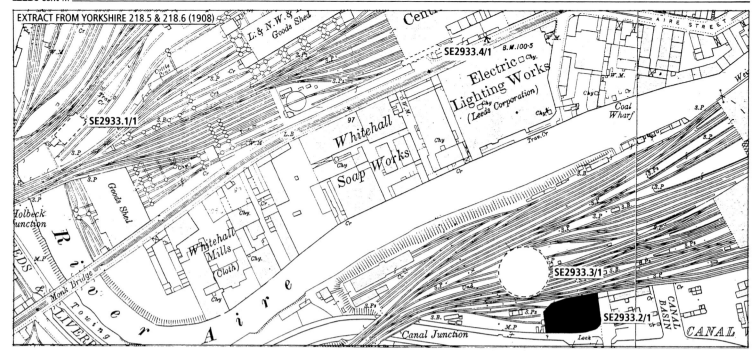

EXTRACT FROM YORKSHIRE 218.5 & 218.6 (1908)

Site SE2933.1; On the south side of the line, at the west end of Leeds Central, Low Level, Station.

Central, Low Level (GNR)SE2933.1/1A

A 3TS shed, located at SE29163325 and opened on May 14th, 1850. The facilities included a turntable sited outside of the shed entrance. The depot closed in 1857.

Site SE2933.4; On the south side of Leeds Central Station.

Central Station (LNER)SE2933.4/1A

A 1TS dead ended lean-to style shed located at SE29483336. It was probably opened by the LNER and the facilities included a water tank and turntable. The closure date is not known but it had been demolished by 1954.

Site SE2933.2; On the south side of the line, at the west end of Leeds New Station.

New Station (NER)SE2933.2/1A

A brick built 1RH shed, located at SE29643309 and opened in 1871. The shape of the building was unusual, conforming to the site upon which it was built, with the internal turntable having radiating stalls on one side only, and the facilities included a second external turntable. The depot closed in 1904 and was subsequently demolished.

A servicing area was then established ...

New Station (NER)SE2933.2/F1

A facility consisting of a 60ft turntable (located at SE29593309), water column and sidings was opened in 1908 and remained in use until the 1950s.

Site SE2933.3; On the south side of the line, at the west end of Leeds Wellington Station.

Wellington (L&BR)SE2933.3/1A

A brick built circular 1RH shed, located at SE29593313 and opened in 1848 by the Leeds & Bradford Railway. The facilities included a water tank, coke shed and repair shop. The depot closed upon the opening of Holbeck shed (SE2932.1/1) on May 9th, 1868 and was immediately demolished to make way for the construction of Leeds New Station.

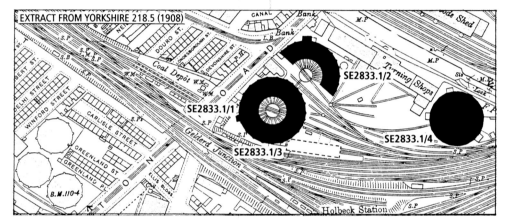

EXTRACT FROM YORKSHIRE 218.5 (1908)

Site SE2833.1; On the north side of the line, at Holbeck Junction, west of Leeds Central Station.

Holbeck No.1 (L&TR)SE2833.1/1A

A brick built circular 1RH shed with a continuous pitched roof, located at SE28783321 and opened on July 9th, 1849 by the Leeds & Thirsk Railway.

Adjoined by ...

Holbeck (L&TR)SE2833.1/3A

A 2TS dead ended shed, located at SE28833324 and opened on July 9th, 1849 by the Leeds & Thirsk Railway.

Holbeck (L&TR)SE2833.1/2A

A brick built semi-roundhouse shed with a continuous pitched roof, located at SE28823324 and opened on July 9th, 1849 by the Leeds & Thirsk Railway. This building may have formed part of the L&TR works.

Holbeck No.2 (NER)SE2833.1/4A

A brick built 1RH shed with a slated radiating multipitched roof surmounted by a central conical section, located at SE28963320 and opened in 1873.

The shed had the use of the facilities of the main works of the railway which was sited adjacently. By the time that the NER closed the depot and transferred the locomotives to the shed at Neville Hill (SE3333.1/1) in 1904 the 2TS shed (SE2833.1/3A) had been demolished. The three remaining buildings were sold off for private use and the former NER shed (SE2833.1/4A) was demolished in the 1970s. The other two sheds were still standing in 1998 as Grade 1 listed buildings.

Site SE2932.1; On the west side of the Woodlesford line, south of Leeds City Station.

Holbeck (MR)SE2932.1/1A

A brick built 2RH shed with two slated triple pitched roofs, located at SE29213253 and opened on May 9th, 1868. The facilities included a ramped coal stage, water tank and repair shop. The depot was closed by BR on October 2nd, 1967 and demolished. The repair shop was converted to a diesel depot and a diesel servicing shed (SE2932.1/2A) was later erected at the site.

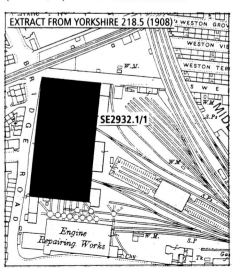

EXTRACT FROM YORKSHIRE 218.5 (1908)

NEVILLE HILL

EXTRACT FROM YORKSHIRE 218.7 (1908)

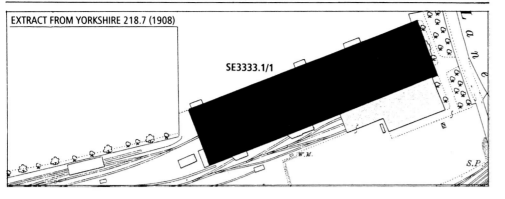

SE3333.1/1

Site SE3333.1; On the north side of the Cross Gates line, east of Leeds City Station.
Neville Hill (NER)SE3333.1/1A
A brick built 4RH shed with a transverse multi-pitched roof, located at SE33083315 and opened in October 1894. The depot had use of all facilities.

The shed was modified ...
Neville Hill (BR)SE3333.1/1B
The building was reduced to a 2RH shed and a flat concrete roof with a central raised pitch was installed by the North Eastern Region in 1960. The depot closed to steam on June 12th, 1966 with the shed subsequently being rebuilt to a straight shed (SE3333.1/1C) for diesel servicing.

MANNINGHAM

Site SE1534.1; On the east side of Manningham Station.
Manningham (MR)SE1534.1/1A
A brick built square 1RH shed with a slated triple gable style roof, located at SE15873496 and opened in 1872.

Manningham (MR)SE1534.1/2A
A timber built 4TS dead ended shed with a slated northlight pattern roof, located at SE15943484 and opened in 1887.

The facilities included a coal shed and water tank. The second shed (SE1534.1/2A) was demolished by the LMS in c1945 and the depot was closed by BR on April 30th, 1967.

EXTRACT FROM YORKSHIRE 201.16 & 216.4 (1908)

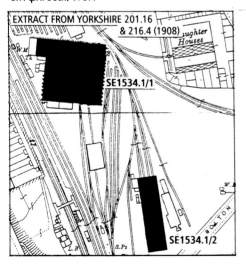

SE1534.1/1

SE1534.1/2

BROUGHTON LANE

Site SK3889.1; On the north side of the line, at the east end of Broughton Lane Station.
Broughton Lane Goods (GCR)SK3889.1/F1
A servicing area consisting of a coal stage located at SK38998938. No further details are known.

EXTRACT FROM YORKSHIRE 295.1 (1923)

SK3889.1/F1

NORMANTON

Site SE3822.1; In the vicinity of Normanton Station.
Normanton (NMR/Y&NMR)SE3822.1/1A
A shed was opened here by the North Midland and York & North Midland Railways in 1850. No further details are known other than it closed in 1867.

Replaced by ...
Site SE3823.1; On the east side of the line, north of Normanton Station.
Normanton (MR/NER)SE3823.1/1A
A polygonal 1RH shed, located at SE38362313 and opened in 1867. Details of its construction are not known.

Normanton (L&YR)SE3823.1/2A
A brick built 5TS dead ended shed with a slated twin gable style roof and located at SE38402318. It was built by the Midland Railway in 1882 for the use of L&YR locomotives.

The facilities included a turntable and coal stage with water tank over. The original roundhouse (SE3823.1/1A) was demolished in c1935 by the LMS and coal and ash plants erected on the site. The depot was closed by BR on January 1st, 1968 and demolished later that year.

EXTRACT FROM YORKSHIRE 234.13 (1908)

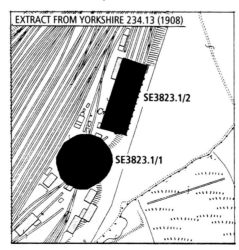

SE3823.1/2

SE3823.1/1

NORTH DEAN

Site SE0921.2; In the vicinity of Greetland Station
North Dean (L&YR)SE0921.2/F1
Some sort of facility was opened here. No further details are known other than it closed in 1858.

SOWERBY BRIDGE

Site SE0523.1; In the vicinity of Sowerby Bridge Station.
Sowerby Bridge (L&YR)SE0523.1/1A
A timber built carriage shed was converted to locomotive use in 1852. No further details are known.

The shed was extended ...
Sowerby Bridge (L&YR)SE0523.1/1B
Additional accommodation for one engine was provided in 1857. No further details are known other than it closed in 1887.

Replaced by ...
Site SE0523.2; On the north side of the line, west of Sowerby Bridge Station.
Sowerby Bridge (L&YR)SE0523.2/1A
A brick built 6TS dead ended shed with a northlight pattern roof, located at SE05532359 and opened in 1887. The facilities included a coal stage, with water tank over, and turntable.

The shed was re-roofed ...
Sowerby Bridge (BR)SE0523.2/1B
A louvre style roof with brick screen was installed by the London Midland Region in 1953 and the depot closed on January 4th, 1964.

EXTRACT FROM YORKSHIRE 230.11 (1907)

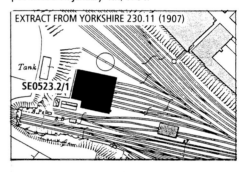

Tank

SE0523.2/1

WATH

Site SE4201.1; On the south side of the Barnsley line, west of Wath Station.
Wath Yard (GCR)SE4201.1/F1
A servicing area consisting of a turntable, located at SE42830169, water columns and two sidings and coal stages opened on August 19th, 1907. The facility was closed by BR in 1961.

EXTRACT FROM YORKSHIRE 283.3 (1930)

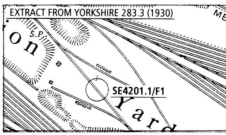

SE4201.1/F1

MYTHOLMROYD

Site SE0225.1; On the south side of the line, at the east end of Mytholmroyd Yard, east of Mytholmroyd Station.
Mytholmroyd (L&YR)SE0225.1/F1
A servicing area consisting of a coal stage and siding, located at SE02242580, was opened here in 1919 and closed by BR on January 4th, 1964. No further details are known.

EXTRACT FROM YORKSHIRE 230.6 (1931)

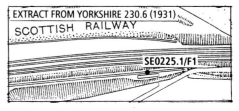

SCOTTISH RAILWAY

SE0225.1/F1

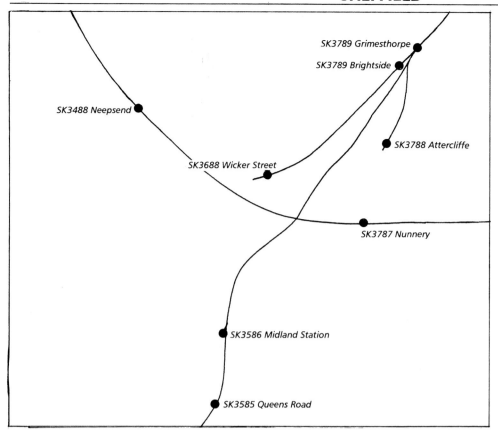

Site SK3688.1; On the north side of the line, at the east end of Wicker Street Station.
Wicker Street (S&RR)^{SK3688.1/1A}
A 2TS shed with one through road located at SK36248831 and opened by the Sheffield & Rotherham Railway on November 1st, 1838. The facilities included a coal stage and water columns. The line was absorbed by the Midland Railway in 1845 and the depot closed in 1861. The building was demolished in March 1862 to allow expansion of the goods depot.

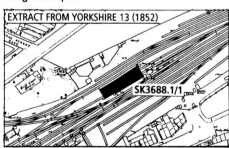

EXTRACT FROM YORKSHIRE 13 (1852)
SK3688.1/1

Replaced by ...
Site SK3789.1; On the west side of the line, south of Brightside Station.
Brightside (MR)^{SK3789.1/1A}
A circular 1RH shed, located at SK37318939 and opened in 1861. No further details are known other than it was closed in 1877 and subsequently demolished, the site being utilized for sidings.

Replaced by ...
Site SK3789.2; On the east side of the line, south of Brightside Station.
Grimesthorpe (MR)^{SK3789.2/1A}
A brick built square 1RH shed with a triple slated gable style roof, located at SK37608950 and opened in 1877. The facilities included a repair shop, ramped coal stage (later replaced with a mechanical coaling plant), water tank and, installed in 1901, an exterior 60ft turntable. The depot was closed by BR on September 11th, 1961 and was utilized as a diesel stabling point prior to demolition in 1963.

Site SK3488.1; On the north side of the line, east of Neepsend Station.
Neepsend (MS&LR)^{SK3488.1/1A}
A brick built 6TS dead ended shed located at SK34858882. No further details are known other than the facilities included a turntable and the depot was closed by the LNER in April 1943. The building saw further use as a wagon works before being demolished in the 1970s.

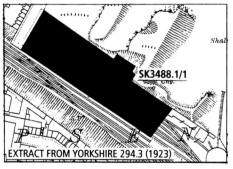

SK3488.1/1
EXTRACT FROM YORKSHIRE 294.3 (1923)

Site SK3788.1; On the east side of Attercliffe Goods Station.
Attercliffe (LD&ECR/GCR/MR)^{SK3788.1/F1}
A servicing area consisting of a coal stage, siding and engine pit, located at SK37468883 and opened by the Lancashire, Derbyshire & East Coast, Great Central and Midland Joint Railway. The opening date of the facility is not known but it was probably closed by BR on November 1st, 1961.

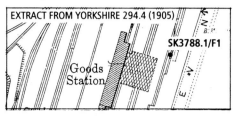

EXTRACT FROM YORKSHIRE 294.4 (1905)
SK3788.1/F1
Goods Station

Site SK3585.1; In Queens Road Goods Yard, on the west side of the line, south of Sheffield Midland Station.
Queens Road (MR)^{SK3585.1/F1}
A servicing area consisting of a siding, coal stage and water column, located at SK35808592 and opened in 1892. The facility was closed by BR in 1965.

EXTRACT FROM YORKSHIRE 294.12 (1923)
SK3585.1/F1

Site SK3787.1; On the south side of the line, east of Sheffield Nunnery Station.
Nunnery (L&NWR)^{SK3787.1/1A}
A brick built 4TS dead ended shed with a northlight pattern roof, located at SK37178776 and opened in 1898. The facilities included a turntable, coal stage and water tank. The depot was closed by the LMS on July 6th, 1925, finding further use as a wagon shop prior to demolition.

SK3787.1/1
EXTRACT FROM YORKSHIRE 294.8 (1923)

Site SK3586.1; On the west side of the line, at the south end of Sheffield Midland Station.
Midland Station (MR)^{SK3586.1/1A}
A servicing area consisting of a turntable, located at SK35848664, sidings, water columns and engine pits. No further details are known.

EXTRACT FROM YORKSHIRE 294.12 (1923)
SK3586.1/F1

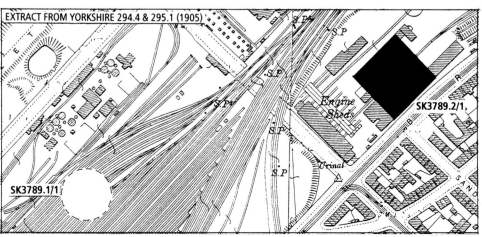

EXTRACT FROM YORKSHIRE 294.4 & 295.1 (1905)
SK3789.1/1
SK3789.2/1
Engine Sheds

ROTHERHAM

Site SK4192.0; In the vicinity of Rotherham Masbrough Station.
Masbrough* (NMR) SK4192.0/F1
Some sort of facility was established here by the North Midland Railway in May 1840 and closed in 1855. No further details are known.

Replaced by ...
Masbrough* (MR) SK4192.0/1A
Some sort of facility, probably a 1TS shed, was established here in 1855 and closed in 1881. No further details are known other than a single 0-6-0 locomotive was allocated here in 1880.

Replaced by ...
Site SK4192.1; On the west side of the line, at the south end of Rotherham Masbrough Station.
Masbrough* (MR) SK4192.1/1A
A 2TS dead ended shed, located at SK41799271 and opened in 1881. The facilities included a turntable. No further details are known other than the depot closed in 1900.

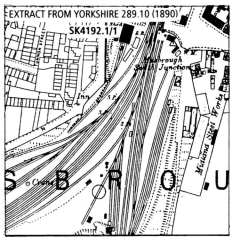

EXTRACT FROM YORKSHIRE 289.10 (1890)
SK4192.1/1

* *An alternative spelling of Masborough was also used.*

Replaced by ...
Site SK4289.1; On the west side of the Staveley line, south of Rotherham Masbrough Station.
Canklow (MR) SK4289.1/1A
A brick built square 1RH shed with a triple slated gable style roof, located at SK42618985 and opened in 1900. The facilities included a ramped coal stage and water tank. The depot was closed by BR on October 11th, 1965 and found further use as a factory prior to demolition in the 1980s.

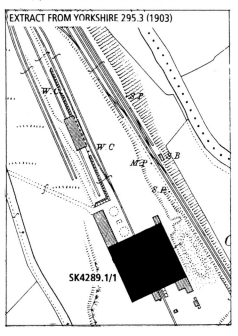

EXTRACT FROM YORKSHIRE 295.3 (1903)
SK4289.1/1

Site SK4292.1; On the west side of the line, south of Rotherham Central Station.
Rotherham Central (MS&LR) SK4292.1/F1
A servicing area consisting of a coal stage, siding and engine pit, located at SK42389256 and opened in 1871. No further details are known.

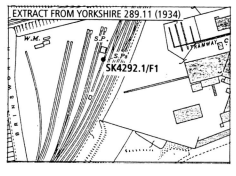

EXTRACT FROM YORKSHIRE 289.11 (1934)
SK4292.1/F1

Site SK4393.1; On the west side of the line, north of Rotherham Central Station.
Rotherham Road (LNER) SK4393.1/F1
A stabling point consisting of a siding, located at SK43059397 and opened in 1925. There were no facilities. Steam locomotives ceased to stable there in 1964 and it closed totally in 1980.

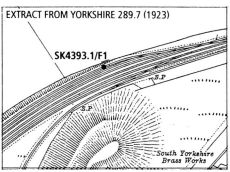

EXTRACT FROM YORKSHIRE 289.7 (1923)
SK4393.1/F1
South Yorkshire Brass Works

FARNLEY JUNCTION

Site SE2731.1; On the west side of the line, south of Farnley & Wortley Station.
Farnley Junction* (L&NWR) SE2731.1/1A
A brick built 12TS dead ended shed with a northlight pattern roof, located at SE27103123 and opened in 1882. The facilities included a coal stage, with water tank over, and turntable.

The shed was re-roofed ...
Farnley Junction (LMS) SE2731.1/1B
A multi-pitched roof was installed in 1932. The depot was closed by BR in November 1966 and demolished.

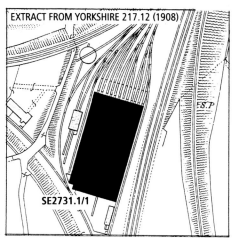

EXTRACT FROM YORKSHIRE 217.12 (1908)
SE2731.1/1

**It was also known as Farnley & Wortley.*

HUDDERSFIELD

Site SE1418.1; On the west side of the line, north of Huddersfield Station.
Hillhouse (L&NWR) SE1418.1/1A
A 4TS dead ended shed, located at SE14901812 and opened in 1849. No further details are known other than the building was shared with the wagon department.

The building was enlarged ...
Hillhouse (L&NWR) SE1418.1/1B
The shed was rebuilt in stone as a 6TS dead ended shed with a northlight pattern roof in 1882. The facilities included a 42ft turntable and coal stage. At the same time the wagon shop was moved into a new building adjacent to the west side.

The building was enlarged again...
Hillhouse (L&NWR) SE1418.1/1C
The building was altered in 1905 with four tracks passing through the depot and the adjacent 3TS wagon shop was taken over for locomotive use. At the same time a new 65ft turntable and coal stage with water tank over were installed.

The building was re-roofed ...
Hillhouse (LMS) SE1418.1/1D
A multi-pitched roof was installed in 1937. Other improvements including the supply of a coaling plant were also undertaken. The depot was closed by BR on January 2nd, 1967 and subsequently demolished.

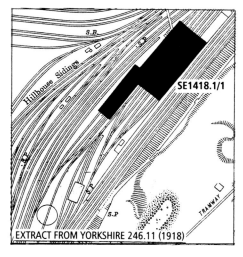

EXTRACT FROM YORKSHIRE 246.11 (1918)
SE1418.1/1

PENISTONE

Site SE2602.1; On the north side of the Sheffield line, at Barnsley Junction.
Penistone, Barnsley Junction (MS&LR) SE2602.1/1A
A 1TS dead ended shed, located at SE26220257 and opened at some point after 1905. The facilities included a coal stage. The depot was closed by the LNER in 1932.

A servicing point was then established ...
Penistone, Barnsley Junction (LNER) SE2602.1/F1
Locomotives utilized the coal stage, engine pit and siding. No further details are known.

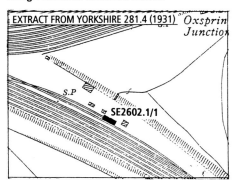

EXTRACT FROM YORKSHIRE 281.4 (1931) Oxsprin Junction
SE2602.1/1

STOURTON

Site SE3230.1; On the west side of the line, north of Woodlesford Station.
Stourton (MR)$^{SE3230.1/1A}$
A brick built square 1RH shed with a triple slated gable style roof, located at SE32293028 and opened in 1893. The facilities included a coal stage and water tank.

The shed was re-roofed ...
Stourton (MR)$^{SE3230.1/1B}$
A flat concrete and steel roof was installed by the London Midland Region in 1950. The depot was closed in January 1967 and subsequently demolished.

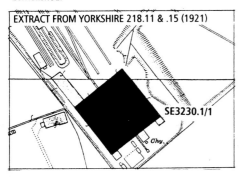
EXTRACT FROM YORKSHIRE 218.11 & .15 (1921)
SE3230.1/1

STAINLAND

Site SE0919.1; On the east side of Stainland Station.
Stainland (L&YR)$^{SE0819.1/F1}$
A servicing area consisting of a coal stage, approximately located at SE091197, was in existence here. No further details are known.

ROBIN HOOD

Site SE3227.1; On the west side of the line, north of Robin Hood Station.
Robin Hood (E&WYUR)$^{SE3227.1/1A}$
A 2TS through road shed, located at SE32962793 and opened on March 27th, 1861 by the East & West Yorkshire Union Railway. No further details are known other than it was absorbed by the LNER in 1923 and closed in July 1926.

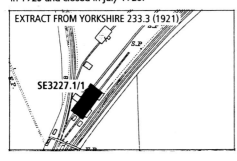
EXTRACT FROM YORKSHIRE 233.3 (1921)
SE3227.1/1

HEBDEN BRIDGE

Site SD9926.1; On the south side of the line, at the west end of Hebden Bridge Station.
Hebden Bridge (M&LR)$^{SD9926.1/1A}$
A timber built 1TS through road shed with a gable style roof, located at SD99382687 and opened on October 5th, 1840 by the Manchester & Leeds Railway. No further details are known other than it closed in 1862.

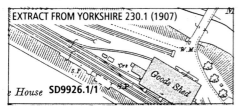
EXTRACT FROM YORKSHIRE 230.1 (1907)
SD9926.1/1

CUDWORTH

Site SE3610.1; On the west side of the Normanton line, north of Cudworth Goods Junction.
Cudworth (H&BR)$^{SE3610.1/1A}$
A brick built 8TS dead ended shed with a northlight pattern roof, located at SE36661071 and opened on July 20th, 1885 by the Hull & Barnsley Railway. The facilities included a water tank, 60ft turntable and a coaling crane, later replaced by a coal plant. By the time that the depot was closed by BR on July 30th, 1951 at least half of the building was roofless.

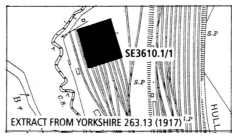
SE3610.1/1
EXTRACT FROM YORKSHIRE 263.13 (1917)

ROYSTON

Site SE3711.1; On the east side of the line, south of Royston & Notton Station.
Royston* (LMS)$^{SE3711.1/1A}$
A brick built 10TS dead ended shed with a slated multi-pitched roof, located at SE37501134 and opened in March 1932. The facilities included a coal plant, water tank and turning triangle. The depot was closed by BR on November 6th, 1967 and subsequently demolished.

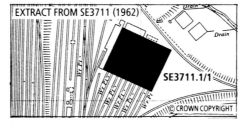
EXTRACT FROM SE3711 (1962)
SE3711.1/1
© CROWN COPYRIGHT

It was also known as Carlton.

MELTHAM

Site SE1010.1; On the north side of the line, at the east end of Meltham Station.
Meltham (L&YR)$^{SE1010.1/1A}$
A 1TS through road shed, probably the building attached to the south side of the goods shed and located at SE10131082. The depot opened in 1868 and closed in 1889, finding further use as a store.

EXTRACT FROM YORKSHIRE 260.9 (1906)
Goods Shed
SE1010.1/1

DUNFORD BRIDGE

Site SE1702.1; On the north side of the line, east of Dunford Bridge Station.
Dunford Bridge (MS&LR)$^{SE1702.1/F1}$
A servicing area consisting of a turntable, located at SE17550259, and siding. No further details are known.

EXTRACT FROM YORKSHIRE 270.4 (1905)
SE1702.1/F1

DARNALL

Site SK3887.1; On the south side of the line, west of Darnall Station.
Darnall (LNER)$^{SK3887.1/1A}$
A brick built 10TS through road shed with a corrugated iron northlight pattern roof, located at SK38598777 and opened on April 11th, 1943. The facilities included a coaling plant, water tank and 70ft turntable. The depot was closed to steam by BR on June 17th, 1963 and totally on October 4th, 1965. The building remained standing, roofless, until demolition in 1995.

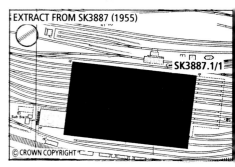
EXTRACT FROM SK3887 (1955)
SK3887.1/1
© CROWN COPYRIGHT

HOUGHTON

Site SE4106.1; On the east side of the Houghton Main Colliery branch, at Houghton Junction.
Houghton (DVR)$^{SE4106.1/1A}$
A 1TS dead ended shed opened in 1902 by the Dearne Valley Railway. It was probably the building located at SE41610666. No further details are known.

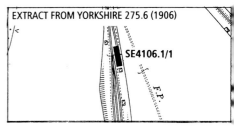
EXTRACT FROM YORKSHIRE 275.6 (1906)
SE4106.1/1

CLAYTON WEST

Site SE2511.1; In the vicinity of Clayton West Station.
Clayton West (L&YR)$^{SE2511.1/F1}$
A servicing area consisting of a coal stage and siding, approximately located at SE256112, was opened here. No further details are known.

BRIGHOUSE

Site SE1422.1; In the vicinity of Brighouse Station.
Brighouse (L&YR)$^{SE1422.1/F1}$
A servicing area consisting of a coal stage, approximately located at SE148224, opened here in 1914. No further details are known.

WOODHOUSE

Site SK4384.1; In the vicinity of Woodhouse Sidings, south of Woodhouse Station.
Woodhouse (MS&LR)$^{SK4384.1/F1}$
A servicing area consisting of a coal stage, approximately located at SE435849. No further details are known.

GREETLAND

Site SE0921.1; In the vicinity of Greetland Station
Greetland (L&YR)$^{SE0921.1/F1}$
A servicing area consisting of a coal stage, approximately located at SE09621, opened here in 1914. No further details are known.

COUNTY DURHAM

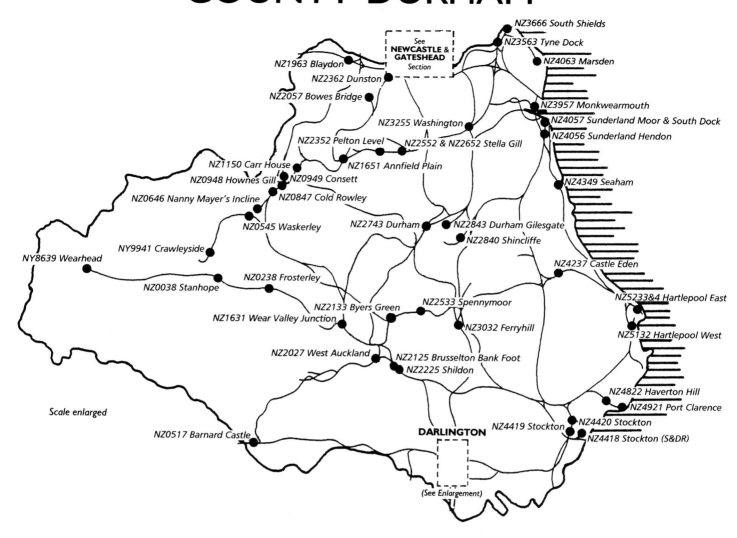

NZ3666 South Shields
NZ3563 Tyne Dock
NZ4063 Marsden
NZ1963 Blaydon
See NEWCASTLE & GATESHEAD Section
NZ2362 Dunston
NZ2057 Bowes Bridge
NZ3957 Monkwearmouth
NZ3255 Washington
NZ4057 Sunderland Moor & South Dock
NZ2352 Pelton Level
NZ2552 & NZ2652 Stella Gill
NZ4056 Sunderland Hendon
NZ1150 Carr House
NZ1651 Annfield Plain
NZ0948 Hownes Gill
NZ0949 Consett
NZ0646 Nanny Mayer's Incline
NZ0847 Cold Rowley
NZ4349 Seaham
NZ0545 Waskerley
NZ2743 Durham
NZ2843 Durham Gilesgate
NY9941 Crawleyside
NZ2840 Shincliffe
NY8639 Wearhead
NZ4237 Castle Eden
NZ0238 Frosterley
NZ5233&4 Hartlepool East
NZ0038 Stanhope
NZ2133 Byers Green
NZ2533 Spennymoor
NZ1631 Wear Valley Junction
NZ5132 Hartlepool West
NZ3032 Ferryhill
NZ2027 West Auckland
NZ2125 Brusselton Bank Foot
NZ2225 Shildon
NZ4822 Haverton Hill
NZ4921 Port Clarence
Scale enlarged
NZ4419 Stockton
NZ4420 Stockton
NZ0517 Barnard Castle
DARLINGTON
NZ4418 Stockton (S&DR)
(See Enlargement)

PELTON LEVEL

Site NZ2352.1; In the fork of the Pontop and South Shields and Craghead lines at Pelton Level.
Pelton Level (S&TR)^{NZ2352.1/1A}
A 1TS dead ended shed, located at NZ23745225 and opened by the Stanhope & Tyne Railway. No further details are known.

Replaced, on the same site, by ...
Pelton Level (NER)^{NZ2352.1/1B}
A brick built 1TS dead ended shed with a slated gable style roof, it was opened in 1894 and closed by BR on January 7th, 1950. The building was later demolished and the site incorporated in a golf course.

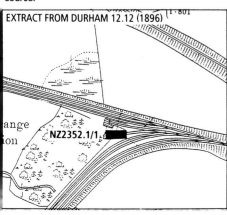

EXTRACT FROM DURHAM 12.12 (1896)
NZ2352.1/1

PORT CLARENCE

Site NZ4921.1; On the south side of the line, west of Port Clarence Station.
Port Clarence (NER)^{NZ4921.1/1A}
A 3TS through road shed, located at NZ49702174 and opened in 1882. It may have incorporated a building that was in use at Stockton (Clarence Junction) Engine Works. No further details are known other than it was demolished.

A servicing area was then established ...
Port Clarence (NER)^{NZ4921.1/F1}
At some stage prior to 1918 a turntable and siding were installed on the same site. No further deatils are known.

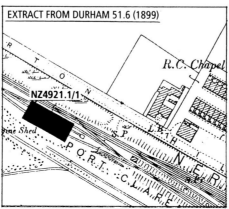

EXTRACT FROM DURHAM 51.6 (1899)
R.C. Chapel
NZ4921.1/1

WEST AUCKLAND

Site NZ2027.1; On the north side of the line, at Fieldon's Bridge Junction, east of West Auckland Station.
West Auckland* (NER)^{NZ2027.1/1A}
A brick built square 1RH shed with a slated triple gable style roof, located at NZ20152719 and opened in 1887. The facilities included a coal stage and water columns. The depot was closed by the LNER on April 13th, 1931 and re-opened on July 8th, 1935 to accommodate locomotives displaced from Wear Valley Junction (NZ1631.1/1A) and Shildon (NZ2225.1/2B) sheds. It was finally closed by BR on February 2nd, 1964 and demolished.

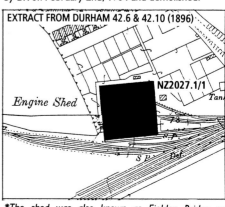

EXTRACT FROM DURHAM 42.6 & 42.10 (1896)
Engine Shed
NZ2027.1/1

*The shed was also known as Fieldon Bridge or Fylands Bridge.

TYNE DOCK

Site NZ3563.1; On the west side of the Pontop and South Shields branch, north of East Boldon Station.
Tyne Dock (NER)^{NZ3563.1/1A}
A brick built 1RH shed with a slated multi-hipped roof, located at NZ35396395 and opened in 1862.

The shed was modified ...
Tyne Dock (NER)^{NZ3563.1/1B}
At some stage prior to 1880 the building was converted to a 5TS shed with one through road.

Adjoined by ...
Tyne Dock (NER)^{NZ3563.1/2A}
A brick built 1RH shed with a slated multi-hipped roof, located at NZ35376391 and probably opened in 1871.

Adjoined by ...
Tyne Dock (NER)^{NZ3563.1/3A}
A brick built 1RH shed with a slated multi-hipped roof, located at NZ35356387 and probably opened in 1877.

Adjoined by ...
Tyne Dock (NER)^{NZ3563.1/4A}
A brick built 1RH shed with a slated gable style multi-pitched roof, located at NZ35326393 and opened prior to 1897.

The facilities included a coal stage, water tank and, in later days, an exterior turntable. By the time that the depot was closed by BR on September 9th, 1967 the buildings were in a derelict condition. The site was cleared during the 1970s and given over to housing.

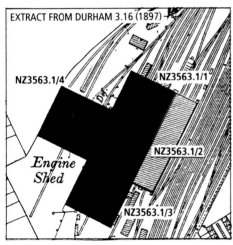
EXTRACT FROM DURHAM 3.16 (1897)
NZ3563.1/4
NZ3563.1/1
NZ3563.1/2
NZ3563.1/3
Engine Shed

ANNFIELD PLAIN

Site NZ1651.1; On the north side of the Hutton Pit Colliery line, west of Annfield Plain Junction.
Annfield Plain (NER)^{NZ1651.1/1A}
A stone built 2TS dead ended shed with a slated hipped roof, located at NZ16785156 and opened on January 1st, 1886. The facilities included a water tank and coal stage. The depot was closed by the LNER on September 9th, 1940 and remained standing until demolition in the 1950s.

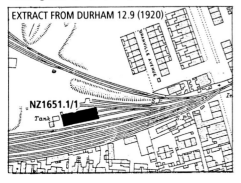
EXTRACT FROM DURHAM 12.9 (1920)
NZ1651.1/1

HAVERTON HILL

Site NZ4822.1; On the south side of the line, west of Haverton Hill Station.
Haverton Hill (NER)^{NZ4822.1/1A}
A brick built 4TS through road shed with a slated gable style roof, located at NZ48292272 and opened in 1899. The facilities included a ramped coaling stage and water tank. The depot was closed by BR on June 13th, 1959 and demolished in June 1965.

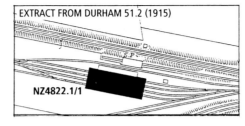
EXTRACT FROM DURHAM 51.2 (1915)
NZ4822.1/1

NANNY MAYER'S INCLINE

Site NZ0646.1; On the east side of the line, at the foot of Nanny Mayer's Incline, north of Waskerley.
Nanny Mayer's Incline (W&DJR)^{NZ0646.1/1A}
A stone built 2TS dead ended shed, located at NZ06204630 and opened by the Wear & Derwent Junction Railway in 1845. No further details are known other than it closed in 1859.

EXTRACT FROM DURHAM 17.12 (1858)
Engine House
NZ0646.1/1

WEAR VALLEY JUNCTION

Site NZ1631.1; On the west side of Wear Valley Junction Station.
Wear Valley Junction (NER)^{NZ1631.1/1A}
A brick built semi-roundhouse shed with a slated continuous pitched roof, located at NZ16653172 and opened in December 1876. Details of the facilities are not known. The depot was closed by the LNER on July 8th, 1935 and subsequently demolished.

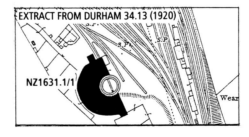
EXTRACT FROM DURHAM 34.13 (1920)
NZ1631.1/1

HOWNES GILL

Site NZ0948.1; On the west side of the line, south of Hownes Gill Junction.
Hownes Gill (S&TR)^{NZ0948.1/1A}
A 1TS dead ended shed, located at NZ09354869 and opened by the Stanhope & Tyne Railway in 1854. No further details are known other than it probably closed on the opening of Hownes Gill Viaduct by the NER on July 1st, 1858

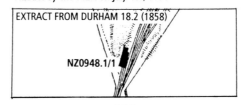
EXTRACT FROM DURHAM 18.2 (1858)
NZ0948.1/1

BYERS GREEN

Site NZ2133.1; On the south side of the line, at the top of Todhills Incline, about one mile west of Burnhouse Junction.
Byers Green* (NER)^{NZ2133.1/1A}
A brick built 3TS dead ended shed with a gable style roof, located at NZ21363395 and opened on June 1st, 1878. The facilities included a turntable, coal stage and water tank. The depot closed on July 17th, 1922 and remained standing in a derelict condition for some years before being sold for use as a brickworks and not suffering demolition until 1994.

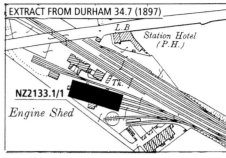
EXTRACT FROM DURHAM 34.7 (1897)
L.B
Station Hotel (P.H.)
NZ2133.1/1
Engine Shed

*The depot was also known as Todhills.

SEAHAM

Site NZ4349.1; On the north side of the North Dock branch, east of Seaham Station.
Seaham (Londonderry)^{NZ4349.1/1A}
A 2TS dead ended shed, located at NZ43124945 and opened by the Londonderry Railway. No further details are known other than it was closed by the NER on October 1st, 1913 and saw further use, until 1960 at least, as a store.

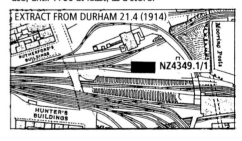
EXTRACT FROM DURHAM 21.4 (1914)
RUTHERFORD'S BUILDINGS
Mooring Posts
NZ4349.1/1
HUNTER'S BUILDINGS

FERRYHILL

Site NZ3032.1; On the west side of the line, at the north end of Ferryhill Station.
Ferryhill (NER)^{NZ3032.1/1A}
A brick built 3TS dead ended shed with a gable style slated roof, located at NZ30273206 and opened in 1881. The facilities included a turntable. The depot was closed by the LNER on November 7th, 1938 and found further use as a store for preserved locomotives evacuated from York during World War II and, in early BR days prior to demolition, for redundant locomotives.

EXTRACT FROM DURHAM 35.10 & 35.14 (1939)
NZ3032.1/1

SPENNYMOOR

Site NZ2533.1; In the vicinity of Spennymoor Station.
Spennymoor (NER)^{NZ2533.1/F1}
A servicing area consisting of some sidings, approximately located at NZ255337 was in existence here in 1870. No further details are known.

SUNDERLAND

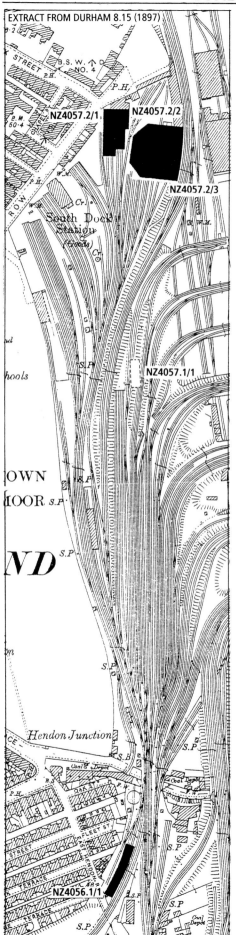

EXTRACT FROM DURHAM 8.15 (1897)

NZ4057.2/1
NZ4057.2/2
NZ4057.2/3

South Dock Station (Goods)

NZ4057.1/1

TOWN MOOR S.P.

ND S.P.

Hendon Junction

NZ4056.1/1

Site NZ4056.1; On the west side of the line, south of South Dock Station at Hendon Junction.
Sunderland Hendon (NER)NZ4056.1/1A
A brick built curved 2TS dead ended shed with a slated gable style roof and located at NZ40865683. The facilities included a turntable. No further details are known other than it was demolished in c1990.

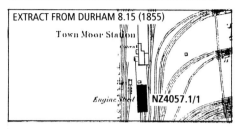

EXTRACT FROM DURHAM 8.15 (1855)

Town Moor Station

Engine Shed   NZ4057.1/1

Site NZ4057.1; On the west side of the line, at the south end of Sunderland Town Moor Station.
Sunderland Moor (D&SR)NZ4057.1/1A
A 2TS dead ended shed, located at NZ40895729 and opened by the Durham & Sunderland Railway at some time prior to 1855.

Replaced by ...
Site NZ4057.2; On the east side of South Dock Station.
Sunderland South Dock (NER)NZ4057.2/1A
A brick built 2TS dead ended shed with a slated gable style roof located at NZ40885752*.

The shed was rebuilt ...
Sunderland South Dock (BR)NZ4057.2/1B
A louvre style roof with brick screen was installed by the North Eastern Region in 1954.

Adjoined by ...
Sunderland South Dock (NER)NZ4057.2/2A
A brick built 2TS shed with a slated gable style roof located at NZ40895752*.

The shed was rebuilt ...
Sunderland South Dock (BR)NZ4057.2/2B
A louvre style roof with brick screen was installed by the North Eastern Region in 1954

*It is not known in which sequence the two buildings were constructed. The first one opened in 1857 with the extension being added in 1861.

Sunderland South Dock (NER)NZ4057.2/3A
A brick built 1RH shed with a slated triple hipped roof, located at NZ40925750 and opened in 1875.

The facilities included a ramped coaling stage and water columns. The depot was closed to steam by BR on September 17th, 1967 and the roundhouse was demolished. The 2TS buildings (NZ4057.2/1B & 2B) were then utilized as a diesel depot until the late 1980s and demolished in 1990.

DUNSTON

Site NZ2362.1; On the east side of the branch to Dunston Staithes.
Dunston (LNER)NZ2362.1/F1
A servicing area located at NZ23366230 and consisting of two sidings, engine pits and a water tank. No further details are known.

EXTRACT FROM DURHAM 6.3 (1940)

NZ2362.1/F1

CONSETT

Site NZ0949.1; In the fork of the Annfield Plain and Bishop Auckland lines, at Consett South Junction.
Consett* (NER)NZ0949.1/1A
A stone built 1TS dead ended shed with a slated gable style roof, located at NZ09734975 and opened in 1875. The facilities included a turntable.

The layout was re-modelled ...
Consett (LNER)NZ0949.1/1B
At some stage access to the building was altered from the north to the southern end. The facilities included a coaling stage and crane sited outside of the shed. The turntable may have been removed at this time.

The depot was enlarged in c1950 ...
Consett (BR)NZ0949.1/1C
A brick built 1TS through road bay with a corrugated asbestos, sheeted gable style roof was built along the western wall of the original building. and the first shed (NZ0949.1/1A) lengthened. The depot closed on May 24th, 1965 and was subsequently demolished. (A corrugated iron 1TS dead ended shed with a corrugated iron pitched roof (NZ0949.1/2A) was subsequently built in the shed yard for the use of an "08" shunter until closure of the steel works)

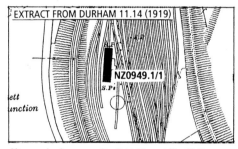

EXTRACT FROM DURHAM 11.14 (1919)

NZ0949.1/1

ett Junction

*It was also known as Benfieldside and Blackhill.

Site NZ1150.1; On the west side of the line at the top of Carr House incline at Consett, Carr House.
Consett, Carr House Engine (NER)NZ1150.1/1A
A 2TS dead ended shed, located at NZ11235083 and converted from a boiler house in 1857. No further details are known other than it closed in 1876.

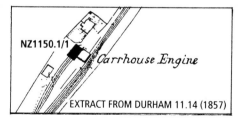

NZ1150.1/1   Carrhouse Engine

EXTRACT FROM DURHAM 11.14 (1857)

WEARHEAD

Site NY8639.1; On the north side of the line, at the east end of Wearhead Station.
Wearhead (WVER) NY8639.1/1A
A stone built 1TS dead ended shed with a slated gable style roof, located at NY86043942 and opened on October 21st, 1895 by the Wear Valley Extension Railway. The facilities included a turntable. The depot was closed by BR on June 29th, 1953 and let out for use as a commercial vehicle garage before demolition in the 1970s.

EXTRACT FROM DURHAM 22.12 (1921)

NY8639.1/1

HARTLEPOOL

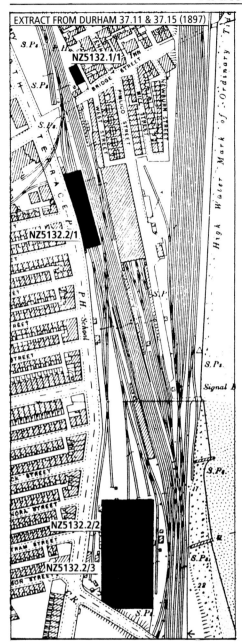

EXTRACT FROM DURHAM 37.11 & 37.15 (1897)

NZ5132.1/1

NZ5132.2/1

NZ5132.2/2

NZ5132.2/3

Site NZ5132.1; On the east side of the line, south of West Hartlepool (1st) Station.
West Hartlepool (HWH&DC) NZ5132.1/1A
A 2TS dead ended shed, located at NZ51613246 and opened on June 1st, 1847 by the Hartlepool West Harbour & Dock Company. The line was absorbed by the NER in 1865 and the depot closed in December 1869. No further details are known other than the building was reputedly blown down in a gale.

Replaced by ...
Site NZ5132.2; On the west side of the line, south of West Hartlepool (1st) Station.
West Hartlepool (NER) NZ5132.2/1A
A brick built 3TS through road shed with a slated gable style roof, located at NZ51623233 and opened in 1867.

West Hartlepool (NER) NZ5132.2/2A
A brick built square 1RH shed with a slated triple hipped roof, located at NZ51663203.

Adjoined by ...
West Hartlepool (NER) NZ5132.2/3A
A brick built square 1RH shed with a slated triple hipped roof, located at NZ51663200.

It is assumed that NZ5132.2/2A was opened in 1871 as the first roundhouse, with the second one, abutting the southern wall, opening in 1875. The facilties included a coal stage and water columns. The depot was closed by BR on September 17th, 1967 and subsequently demolished.

Site NZ5233&4.1; On the south side of Hartlepool East Station.
Hartlepool East (S&HR) NZ5233&4.1/1A
A brick built 3TS shed with two through roads and a gable style slated roof located at NZ52443402.

Hartlepool East (S&HR) NZ5233&4.1/2A
A brick built 2TS dead ended shed with a slated hipped roof located at NZ52513398.

Hartlepool East (S&HR) NZ5233&4.1/3A
A brick built 2TS dead ended shed with a slated hipped roof located at NZ52553398.

The depot was opened at an unknown date by the Stockton & Hartlepool Railway. The facilities included a turntable and water columns. No further details are known other than it was closed by the LNER on April 17th, 1939. Some of the buildings remained standing into the 1960s prior to demolition.

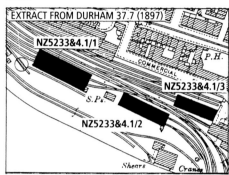

EXTRACT FROM DURHAM 37.7 (1897)

NZ5233&4.1/1

NZ5233&4.1/3

NZ5233&4.1/2

BOWES BRIDGE

Site NZ2057.1; In the fork of the Marley Hill and Tanfield lines, at Bowes Bridge Junction.
Bowes Bridge (NER) NZ2057.1/1A
A stone built 2TS dead ended shed, converted from a winding house and located at NZ20735787. The facilities included a turntable, installed in 1890, and water column. No further details are known except that the roof was destroyed by a fire in January 1943 and locomotives thereafter stabled in the remains of the building.

Replaced, on the same site, by ...
Bowes Bridge (BR) NZ2057.1/1B
A 2TS brick and corrugated sheeting clad dead ended shed with a pitched corrugated sheeting roof and brick screen was erected by the North Eastern Region in 1954. The depot closed in September 1962 and was demolished in c1966.

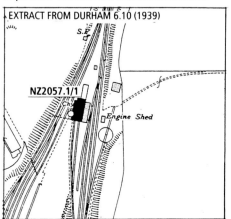

EXTRACT FROM DURHAM 6.10 (1939)

NZ2057.1/1

BARNARD CASTLE

Site NZ0517.1; On the west side of the line, at the north end of Barnard Castle (1st) Station.
Barnard Castle (D&BCR) NZ0517.1/1A
A 1TS dead ended shed, located at NZ05241717 and opened by the Darlington & Barnard Castle Railway on July 8th, 1856. The facilities included a turntable. No further details are known other than it closed in 1865.

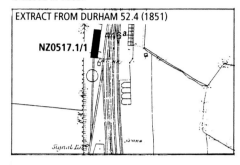

EXTRACT FROM DURHAM 52.4 (1851)

NZ0517.1/1

Replaced by ...
Site NZ0517.2; On the north side of the line, east of Barnard Castle (2nd) Station.
Barnard Castle (NER) NZ0517.2/1A
A 1TS dead ended shed, located at NZ05541758 and opened in 1865. The facilities included a turntable and coal stage.

The building was enlarged ...
Barnard Castle (NER) NZ0517.2/1B
It was rebuilt to a 2TS dead ended shed in 1875 with the addition of another 1TS building at an angle to the original structure. The depot was closed by the LNER on May 3rd, 1937 and subsequently demolished.

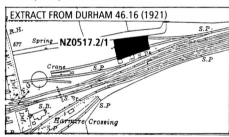

EXTRACT FROM DURHAM 46.16 (1921)

NZ0517.2/1

WASKERLEY

Site NZ0545.1; On the south side of the line, east of Waskeley Station.
Waskerley (S&DR) NZ0545.1/1A
A stone built 2TS dead ended shed with a slated gable style roof, located at NZ05344524 and opened* by the Stockton & Darlington Railway.

Waskerley (S&DR) NZ0545.1/2A
A stone built 2TS shed with one through road and a slated gable style roof, located at NZ05424525 and opened* by the Stockton & Darlington Railway.

*The opening dates of the two buildings were April 1st, 1846 and 1854. At this moment it is not known as to which date applies to which building.

The facilities included water columns. The depot was closed by the LNER on September 9th, 1940 and the buildings were subsequently demolished.

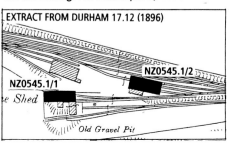

EXTRACT FROM DURHAM 17.12 (1896)

NZ0545.1/2

NZ0545.1/1

SHILDON

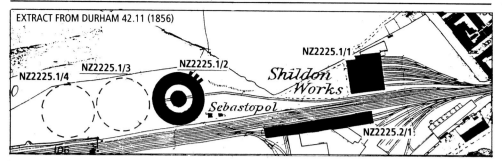

EXTRACT FROM DURHAM 42.11 (1856)

NZ2225.1/4 NZ2225.1/3 NZ2225.1/2 NZ2225.1/1

Shildon Works

Sebastopol

NZ2225.2/1

Site NZ2225.0; In the vicinity of Shildon Station.
Shildon (S&DR) NZ2225.0/1A
A *"shed for 2 engines"* was opened here by the Stockton & Darlington Railway on September 27th, 1825. No further details are known.

Site NZ2225.1; On the north side of the line, west of Shildon Station.
Shildon (S&DR) NZ2225.1/1A
A 9TS dead ended shed, located at NZ22772567 and opened in 1849 by the Stockton & Darlington Railway. The facilities included a coke/coaling shed. The depot was closed by the NER in 1873.

Shildon No.1 (S&DR) NZ2225.1/2A
A brick built circular 1RH shed, located at NZ22582564 and opened in 1854 by the Stockton & Darlington Railway. This building was known as the *"Sebastopol"* shed.

Shildon No.2 (S&DR) NZ2225.1/3A
A brick built circular 1RH shed, located at NZ22522563 and opened in 1856 by the Stockton & Darlington Railway.

Shildon No.3 (S&DR) NZ2225.1/4A
A brick built circular 1RH shed, located at NZ22482562 and opened in 1863 by the Stockton & Darlington Railway.

Neither details of the roundhouses construction or the facilities available are known. Between 1886 and 1892 the three roundhouses were progressively demolished.

Replaced, on the same site, by ...
Shildon (NER) NZ2225.1/2B
A brick built rectangular 3RH shed with a slated triple gable style roof was completed by 1892. In 1915 No.3 shed was modified to accommodate the electric locomotives working the Newport to Shildon line until their withdrawal in 1935. The depot was closed by the LNER on July 8th, 1935 and remained out of use for a short while until conversion to an 8TS wagon works in 1936. It remained standing and in use until the 1990s.

Site NZ2225.2; On the south side of the line, west of Shildon Station.
Shildon (S&DR) NZ2225.2/1A
A 2TS through road shed, located at NZ22712562 and opened in 1852 by the Stockton & Darlington Railway. No further details are known other than it closed in 1873.

Site NZ2125.1; On the south side of the line, at Brusselton Bankfoot, west of Shildon.
Brusselton, Bankfoot (NER) NZ2125.1/1A
A timber built 1TS shed, probably located at NZ21582549 and opened in 1870. No further details are known other than the building had been removed from Slapewath (as NZ6415.1/1A) and re-erected here.

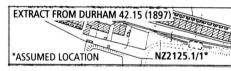

EXTRACT FROM DURHAM 42.15 (1897)
ASSUMED LOCATION NZ2125.1/1

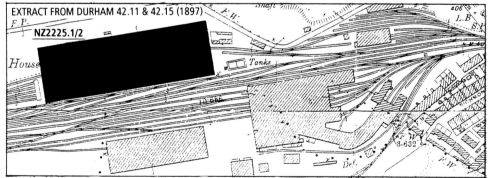

EXTRACT FROM DURHAM 42.11 & 42.15 (1897)
NZ2225.1/2

CASTLE EDEN

Site NZ4237.1; On the north side of Castle Eden (1st) Station.
Castle Eden (NER) NZ4237.1/1A
A 2TS dead ended shed attached to the north side of the station, located at NZ42383765 and opened in 1857. No further details are known.

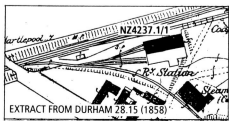

NZ4237.1/1

EXTRACT FROM DURHAM 28.15 (1858)

COLD ROWLEY

Site NZ0847.1; On the south side of the line, at the west end of Cold Rowley Station.
Cold Rowley* (NER) NZ0847.1/1A
A 1TS shed, probably located at NZ08684784 and opened in 1845. No further details are known other than it closed in 1854 when the second shed (NZ0545.1/2A) opened at Waskerley.

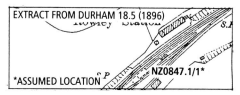

EXTRACT FROM DURHAM 18.5 (1896)
ASSUMED LOCATION NZ0847.1/1

*It was also known as Waskerley Healey Field

DURHAM

Site NZ2743.1; On the west side of the line, north of Durham Station.
Durham (NER) NZ2743.1/1A
A brick built 2TS dead ended shed with a slated gable style roof, located at NZ27124305 and opened in 1864. The facilities included a turntable and water column.

The shed was enlarged ...
Durham (NER) NZ2743.1/1B
At some stage prior to 1893 the building was extended at the rear. The depot was closed by BR on December 8th, 1958 and later demolished.

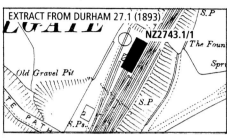

EXTRACT FROM DURHAM 27.1 (1893)
NZ2743.1/1

Site NZ2843.1; On the east side of the line, north of Durham Gilesgate Station.
Durham Gilesgate (N&DJR) NZ2843.1/1A
A 2TS shed with one through road, located at NZ28394300 and opened on April 15th, 1844 by the Newcastle & Darlington Junction Railway. Details of the facilities are not known. The depot closed in 1885 and was demolished.

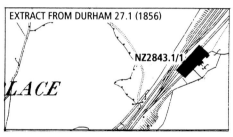

EXTRACT FROM DURHAM 27.1 (1856)
NZ2843.1/1

STANHOPE

Site NZ0038.1; On the east side of the line, south of Stanhope Station.
Stanhope (F&SR) NZ0038.1/1A
A 1TS dead ended shed, located at NZ00073833 and opened in 1865 by the Frosterley & Stanhope Railway. The building may have been a re-erection of the former shed at Frosterley (NZ0238.1/1A).

The shed was rebuilt ..
Stanhope (NER) NZ0038.1/1B
A stone built 3TS dead ended shed with a slated gable style roof was constructed on the same site in 1876. The facilities included a turntable and water tank.

The shed was rebuilt again ...
Stanhope (LNER) NZ0038.1/1C
At some stage the building over the two easternmost tracks was demolished and the remaining portion was re-modelled as a 1TS shed. The depot was closed on May 1st, 1930 and saw further use as a store for *Locomotion No.1* and *Derwent* during World War II. It was demolished during the 1960s.

Engine Shed NZ0038.1/1

EXTRACT FROM DURHAM 24.14 (1896)

STOCKTON

Site NZ4419.1; On the west side of Stockton (Leeds Northern) Station.
Stockton (LNR)[NZ4419.1/1A]
A 3TS dead ended shed, located at NZ44111966 and opened on May 15th, 1852 by the Leeds Northern Railway. No further details are known.

The building was enlarged ...
Stockton (LNR)[NZ4419.1/1B]
At some stage the shed was enlarged to a 6TS dead ended structure. The facilities included a turntable and the depot closed in 1891 upon the opening of NZ4420.1/2A.

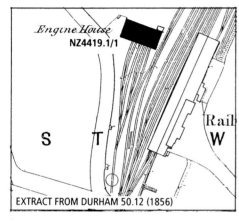

EXTRACT FROM DURHAM 50.12 (1856)

Site NZ4420.1; On the east side of the line, north of Stockton Station.
Stockton, Clarence Jct (Clarence)[NZ4420.1/1A]
A 2TS dead ended shed, located at NZ44382035 and opened in 1835 by the Clarence Railway. Details of the facilities are not known. The depot was probably closed by the NER in 1891*.

*It is reputed that this shed was removed in 1882 and re-erected at Port Clarence as NZ4921.1/1A. However, in view of the size of the building installed at the latter site it is more likely that a part of the adjacent Engine Works, located at NZ49432034, was utilized.

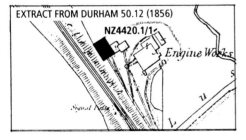

EXTRACT FROM DURHAM 50.12 (1856)

Replaced by ...
Stockton (NER)[NZ4420.1/2A]
A brick built 8TS dead ended shed with a twin slated gable style roof, located slightly north east of its predecessor (NZ4420.1/1A) at NZ44482038 and opened in 1891. The facilities included a ramped coaling stage, turntable and water columns. The depot was closed by BR on June 13th, 1959 and sold for private use. The building was demolished in 1998.

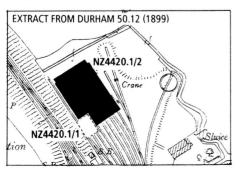

EXTRACT FROM DURHAM 50.12 (1899)

Site NZ4418.1; In the Goods Yard at Stockton Stanley Lane Station.
Stockton (S&DR)[NZ4418.1/1A]
A 1TS dead ended shed, located at NZ44631840 was opened here by the Stockton & Darlington Railway. No further details are known.

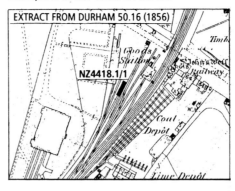

EXTRACT FROM DURHAM 50.16 (1856)

STELLA GILL

Site NZ2552.1; On the north side of Stella Gill Sidings at Pelton Fell.
Stella Gill (NER)[NZ2552.1/1A]
A 4TS dead ended shed, located at NZ25675201 and opened in 1858. The facilities included a turntable. No further details are known.

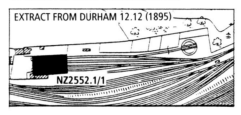

EXTRACT FROM DURHAM 12.12 (1895)

At some stage, replaced by ...
Site NZ2652.1; On the north side of the line, at the east end of Stella Gill Sidings.
Stella Gill (LNER)[NZ2652.1/F1]
A servicing area consisting of a turntable, located at NZ26045217, water tank, engine pit and coal stage. No further details are known other than it was utilized into BR days.

Site NZ2652.2; On the south side of the line, at the east end of Stella Gill Sidings.
Stella Gill (LNER)[NZ2652.2/F1]
A servicing area consisting of a turntable, located at NZ26215217, water tank, siding and engine pit. No further details are known.

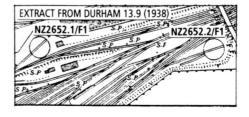

EXTRACT FROM DURHAM 13.9 (1938)

WASHINGTON

Site NZ3255.1; On the east side of the line, at the north end of Washington Station.
Washington (LNER)[NZ3255.1/F1]
A servicing area located at NZ32025581 and consisting of two sidings, engine pit and a coal stage. No further details are known.

EXTRACT FROM DURHAM 13.3 (1932)

BLAYDON

Site NZ1963.2; In the vicinity of Blaydon Station.
Blaydon (NER)[NZ1963.2/F1]
Some form of facility was established here on March 9th, 1835. No further details are known.

Replaced by ...
Site NZ1963.1; On the south side of the line, east of Blaydon Station.
Blaydon (NER)[NZ1963.1/1A]
A brick built 2RH shed, located at NZ19326355 and opened in April 1900. Further details of the construction are not known. The facilities included a ramped coal stage and water tank.

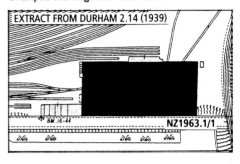

EXTRACT FROM DURHAM 2.14 (1939)

The shed was re-roofed ...
Blaydon (BR)[NZ1963.1/1B]
At some stage a corrugated steel single pitched gable style roof was installed by the North Eastern Region. The depot closed to steam on June 16th, 1963, and totally on March 15th, 1965 with demolition following in May 1966.

MARSDEN

Site NZ4063.1; In the vicinity of Whitburn Colliery, east of the line, south of Marsden Station.
Marsden (SSM&WCR)[NZ4063.1/1A]
A shed, approximately located at NZ407637, was opened here by the South Shields, Marsden & Whitburn Colliery Railway. No further details are known.

SOUTH SHIELDS

Site NZ3666.1; In the vicinity of South Shields (1st) Station.
South Shields (BJR)[NZ3666.1/F1]
Some sort of facility, approximately located at NZ361668, was opened here by the Brandling Junction Railway. No further details are known.

Site NZ3666.2; On the north side of the line, west of Westoe Lane Station.
South Shields (SSM&WCR)[NZ3666.2/1A]
A 1TS through road building, located at NZ36546632 may have been utilized by the South Shields, Marsden & Whitburn Colliery Railway as an engine shed. No further details are known.

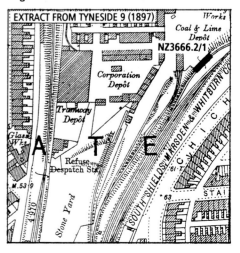

EXTRACT FROM TYNESIDE 9 (1897)

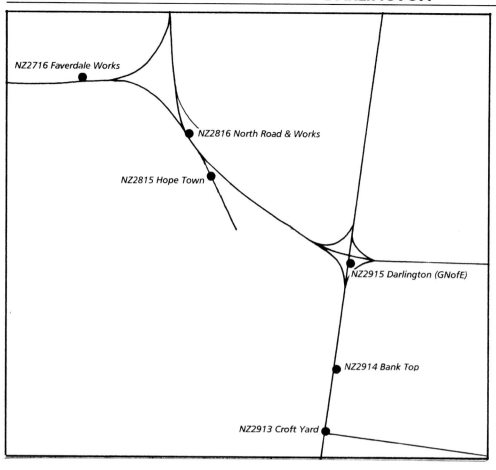

NZ2716 Faverdale Works

NZ2816 North Road & Works

NZ2815 Hope Town

NZ2915 Darlington (GNofE)

NZ2914 Bank Top

NZ2913 Croft Yard

Site NZ2815.1; On the south side of Darlington North Road Station.

Hope Town (D&BCR) NZ2815.1/1A

A 2TS through road shed located at NZ28831563 and opened on July 8th, 1856 by the Darlington & Barnard Castle Railway. The shed was closed by the NER in 1877 and remained standing until c1900. No further details are known.

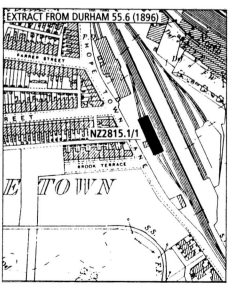

EXTRACT FROM DURHAM 55.6 (1896)

NZ2815.1/1

Site NZ2913.1; On the east side of the line, south of Darlington Bank Top Station.

Croft Yard Engineers Depot (NER) NZ2913.1/1A

A timber built 1TS dead ended shed located at NZ29411314. The facilities included a coal stage, sited outside of the shed entrance. No further details are known.

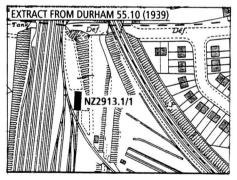

EXTRACT FROM DURHAM 55.10 (1939)

NZ2913.1/1

Site NZ2716.1; In Faverdale Wagon Works, on the north side of the Barnard Castle line, west of Darlington North Road Station.

Faverdale Works (LNER) NZ2716.1/1A

A 1TS through road shed located at NZ27921651 and built to house the works Sentinel shunter. It opened in 1923 and was closed by BR in 1962. No further details are known.

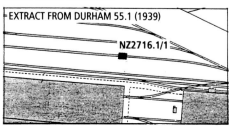

EXTRACT FROM DURHAM 55.1 (1939)

NZ2716.1/1

Site NZ2914.1; On the east side of the line, north of Darlington Bank Top Station.

Darlington (NER) NZ2914.1/3A

A 1TS through road shed located at NZ29621447. The facilities included a turntable. No further details are known.

Replaced by ...

Darlington (NER) NZ2914.1/1A

A brick built circular 1RH shed with a slated radiating multi-pitched roof surmounted by a central conical section, located at NZ29711465 and opened in 1866. Following the rebuilding of the adjacent shed (NZ2914.1/2) in 1939 the building was mainly utilized for its turntable and the stabling of tank engines.

Darlington (NER) NZ2914.1/2A

A brick built 9TS shed with five through roads and hipped roofs, it was located at NZ29631461 and converted from a wagon repair shop in 1885. The facilities included a water tank and coal stage. The depot was closed by the LNER in 1938.

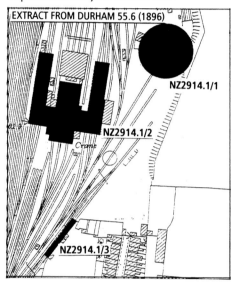

EXTRACT FROM DURHAM 55.6 (1896)

NZ2914.1/1

NZ2914.1/2

NZ2914.1/3

Replaced, on the same site, by ...

Darlington (LNER) NZ2914.1/2B

A brick built 7TS through road shed with a shallow multi-pitched roof and brick screen, it opened in 1940. The additional facilities included a mechanical coaling plant and a 2TS repair shed.

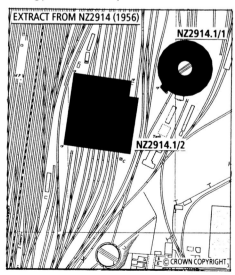

EXTRACT FROM NZ2914 (1956)

NZ2914.1/1

NZ2914.1/2

© CROWN COPYRIGHT

The depot was closed by BR on March 27th, 1966 and the buildings were subsequently demolished.

Continued ...

EXTRACT FROM DURHAM 55.1 & 55.2 (1896)

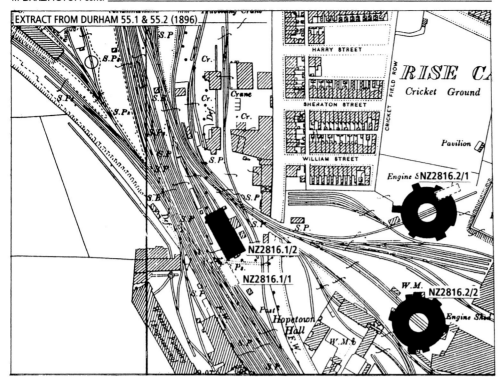

FROSTERLEY

Site NZ0238.1; On the south side of the line, east of Frosterley Station.
Frosterley (WVR) NZ0238.1/1A
A 1TS dead ended shed located at NZ02563881 and opened on August 3rd, 1847 by the Wear Valley Railway. The line was worked by the Stockton & Darlington Railway which was absorbed by the NER on July 31st, 1863. No further details are known except that it closed on November 29th, 1865 and may have been removed and re-erected at Stanhope (as NZ0038.1/1A).

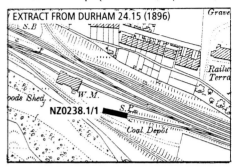

EXTRACT FROM DURHAM 24.15 (1896)

Site NZ2816.1; On the east side of the line, north of Darlington North Road Station.
North Road (S&DR) NZ2816.1/1A
A 1TS shed located at NZ28631606 and opened on September 27th, 1825 by the Stockton & Darlington Railway. No further details are known.

The shed was enlarged ...
North Road (S&DR) NZ2816.1/1B
At some stage the shed was rebuilt as 2TS through road shed. No further details are known other than it closed in 1856 and saw brief use as part of the works until demolished to make way for track widening.

Replaced by ...
North Road (S&DR) NZ2816.1/2A
A brick built 4TS dead ended shed with a slated gable style roof, located at NZ28621610 and opened in 1861 by the Stockton & Darlington Railway. The depot closed in 1877 and the building was converted for works use, surviving until the 1970s.

Site NZ2816.2; In North Road Works on the east side of the line, north of Darlington North Road Station.
North Road (NER) NZ2816.2/1A
A brick built circular 1RH shed with a continuous pitched slated roof, located at NZ28811612 and opened in 1862.

North Road (NER) NZ2816.2/2A
A brick built circular 1RH shed with a radiating multi-pitched slated roof, located at NZ28801602 and opened in 1877.

Details of the facilities are not known. The roundhouses closed on April 4th, 1903 and were utilized for the storage of locomotives passing through the works. They were demolished in 1933 to accommodate re-modelling of the works yard with the site of the first building (NZ2816.2/1A) being partially utilized for the Works engine shed (NZ2816.2/1B).

NB. The location of a 2TS building identified as a "former S&DR shed" on an official photograph dated c1920 has yet to be established.

North Road Works (LNER) NZ2816.2/1B
A 1TS through road shed located at NZ28831614 and opened in c1935. No further details are known other than it saw use into BR days.

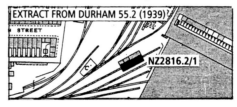

EXTRACT FROM DURHAM 55.2 (1939)

Site NZ2915.1; On the east side of the line, north of Darlington Bank Top Station, at Parkgate Junction.
Darlington (GNofER) NZ2915.1/1A
A brick built 2TS dead ended shed with a slated hipped roof, located at NZ29671527 and opened in c1841 by the Great North of England Railway. No further details are known other than it still stood in the 1990s.

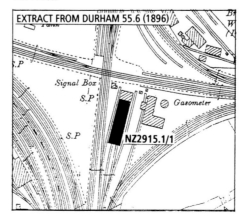

EXTRACT FROM DURHAM 55.6 (1896)

MONKWEARMOUTH

Site NZ3957.1; In the vicinity of Monkwearmouth Station.
Monkwearmouth (BJR) NZ3957.1/1A
A shed, approximately located at NZ396576, was opened here by the Brandling Junction Railway on June 19th, 1839 and closed by the NER in 1879. No further details are known.

CRAWLEYSIDE

Site NY9941.1; On the west side of the Stanhope line at Crawley Engine.
Crawleyside Engine (S&TR) NY9941.1/1A
A 1TS dead ended shed, located at NY99324164 and opened by the Stanhope & Tyne Railway on May 15th, 1834. The shed either formed part of the Crawley Engine House or was converted from the boiler house. No further details are known.

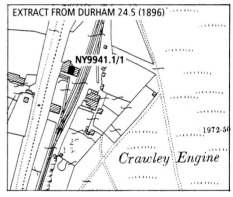

EXTRACT FROM DURHAM 24.5 (1896)

SHINCLIFFE

Site NZ2840.1; On the south side of Shincliffe Station.
Shincliffe (D&SR) NZ2840.1/1A
A 1TS dead ended shed, located at NZ28914089 and opened in 1860 by the Durham & Sunderland Railway. The depot, which probably formed an integral part of the station building, closed in 1893.

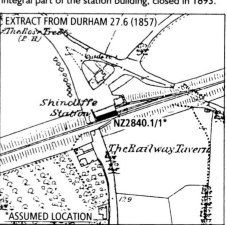

EXTRACT FROM DURHAM 27.6 (1857)

*ASSUMED LOCATION

NEWCASTLE & GATESHEAD

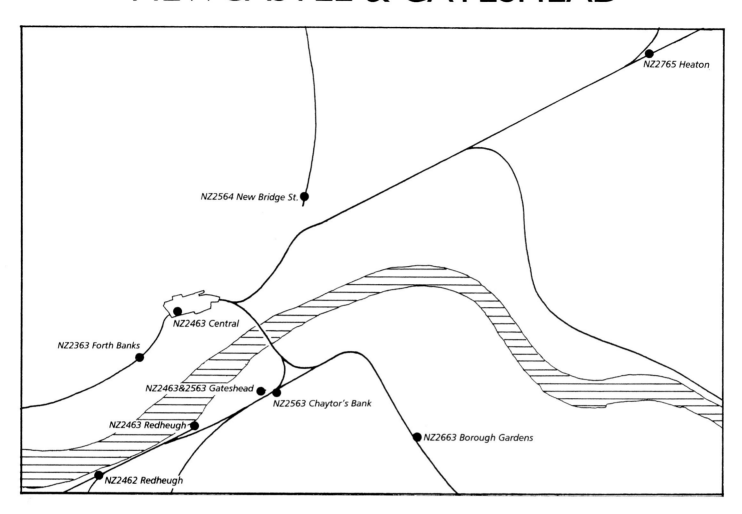

NZ2765 Heaton

NZ2564 New Bridge St.

NZ2463 Central

NZ2363 Forth Banks

NZ2463&2563 Gateshead

NZ2563 Chaytor's Bank

NZ2463 Redheugh

NZ2663 Borough Gardens

NZ2462 Redheugh

NEW BRIDGE STREET

Site NZ2564.1; On the west side of the line, north of New Bridge Street Station.
New Bridge Street (B&TR) NZ2564.1/F1
A servicing area consisting of a turntable, located at NZ25366405, siding and engine pit was established here by the Blyth & Tyne Railway. No further details are known.

Replaced by ...
New Bridge Street (B&TR) NZ2564.1/1A
A 2TS dead ended shed located at NZ25366465. No further details are known other than it closed on December 19th, 1902 and was subsequently demolished to accommodate track alterations.

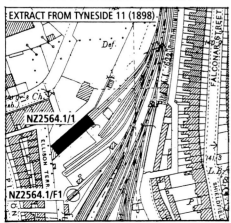

EXTRACT FROM TYNESIDE 11 (1898)

NZ2564.1/1

NZ2564.1/F1

CENTRAL STATION

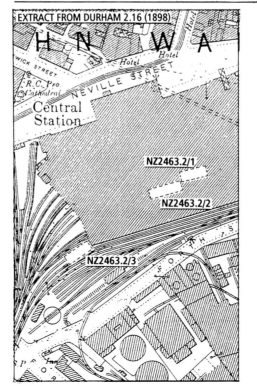

EXTRACT FROM DURHAM 2.16 (1898)

NZ2463.2/1

NZ2463.2/2

NZ2463.2/3

Site NZ2463.2; On the south side of Newcastle Central Station.
Central (YN&BR) NZ2463.2/1A
A 2TS through road shed located at NZ24666382 and opened on August 29th, 1850 by the York, Newcastle & Berwick Railway.

Adjoined by ...
Central (YN&BR) NZ2463.2/2A
A 2TS through road shed located at NZ24636380 and opened on August 29th, 1850 by the York, Newcastle & Berwick Railway.

The facilities included a turntable. The depot was closed prior to 1859 and demolished to make way for the enlargement of the station.

Replaced by ...
Central (NER) NZ2463.2/3A
A 2TS dead ended shed located at NZ24556374 and opened prior to 1859. The facilities included a turntable. The depot closed in c1890 and was subsequently demolished.

FORTH BANKS

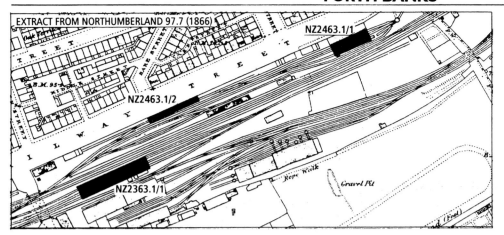

EXTRACT FROM NORTHUMBERLAND 97.7 (1866)

NZ2463.1/1
NZ2463.1/2
NZ2363.1/1

Site NZ2363.1; On the south side of the line, west of Newcastle Central Station.
Forth Banks (N&CR) NZ2363.1/1A
A 3TS through road shed, located at NZ23966326 and opened by the Newcastle & Carlisle Railway on March 1st, 1847. No further details are known other than the depot was demolished in c1872.

Site NZ2463.1; On the north side of the line, west of Newcastle Central Station.
Forth Banks (N&CR) NZ2463.1/1A
A 3TS shed with two through roads, located at NZ24196338 and opened by the Newcastle & Carlisle Railway on March 1st, 1847. The facilities included a turntable.

Forth Banks (N&CR) NZ2463.1/2A
A 1TS through road shed located at NZ24026333 and opened by the Newcastle & Carlisle Railway on March 1st, 1847.

BOROUGH GARDENS

Site NZ2663.1; On the east side of the line, south of Gateshead East Station.
Borough Gardens (NER) NZ2663.1/1A
A brick built 2RH shed* with a slated multi-pitched gable style roof, located at NZ26296312 and opened in 1875.

The building was enlarged ...
Borough Gardens (NER) NZ2663.1/1B
At some stage prior to 1898 a brick built 2RH extension* with a slated multi-pitched gable style roof was added. The facilities included a ramped coaling stage and water tank. The depot was closed by BR on June 13th, 1959 and subsequently demolished, the site later being utilized as a Freightliner depot.

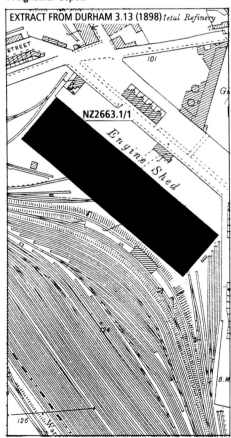

EXTRACT FROM DURHAM 3.13 (1898)

NZ2663.1/1

*In its original state the depot may have been composed of two adjacent but separate circular roundhouse buildings (NZ2663.1/1A & 2A) with the "extension" then involving the construction of a new 4RH shed (NZ2663.1/1B) embracing the same site.

HEATON

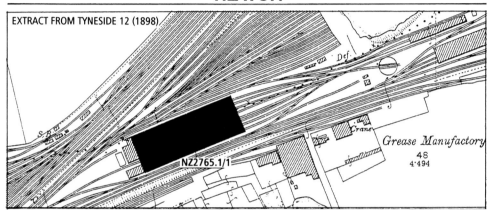

EXTRACT FROM TYNESIDE 12 (1898)

NZ2765.1/1

Grease Manufactory

Site NZ2765.1; In the fork of the North Shields and Edinburgh lines, east of Heaton Station.
Heaton (NER) NZ2765.1/1A
A brick built 3TS dead ended shed, located at NZ27606554 and opened on August 31st, 1875.

The shed was enlarged ..
Heaton (NER) NZ2765.1/1B
In 1889 the depot was enlarged to a brick built 8TS dead ended shed. The facilities included a turntable, water columns and ramped coal stage.

The shed was modified ...
Heaton (LNER) NZ2765.1/1C
In 1931 the five northernmost tracks were extended through the back of the shed.

The shed was re-roofed ...
Heaton (BR) NZ2765.1/1D
At some stage, probably in BR days, a louvre style roof with brick screen was installed. The depot closed on June 17th, 1963 and, apart from officially housing the two Quayside electric locomotives Nos 26500 and 26501 until September 14th, 1964, was then utilized for the storage and repair of steam locomotives. The shed was demolished in the 1970s.

REDHEUGH

Site NZ2463.3; At the west end of Redheugh Station.
Redheugh (N&CR) NZ2463.3/1A
A 1TS dead ended shed, located at NZ24566302 and opened by the Newcastle & Carlisle Railway on March 1st, 1837. No further details are known other than it closed on March 1st, 1847.

Possibly replaced by ...
Site NZ2462.1; In the fork of the lines at Redheugh Junction, west of Redheugh Station.
Redheugh (N&CR) NZ2462.1/1A
A 2TS dead ended shed, located at NZ24126275. No further details are known.

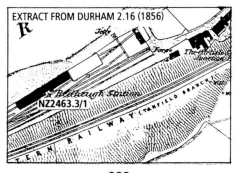

EXTRACT FROM DURHAM 2.16 (1856)

NZ2463.3/1

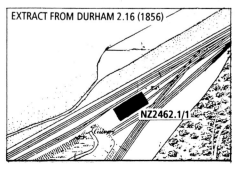

EXTRACT FROM DURHAM 2.16 (1856)

NZ2462.1/1

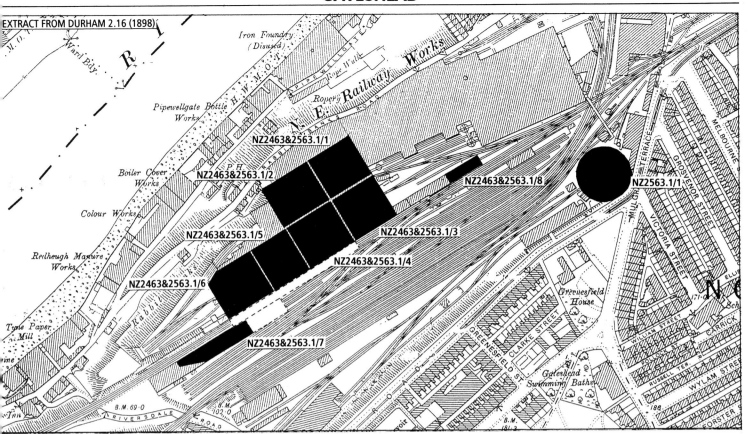

EXTRACT FROM DURHAM 2.16 (1898)

Site NZ2463&2563.1; On the north side of the line, west of Gateshead Station.

Gateshead (YN&BR) NZ2463&2563.1/1A
A brick built 1RH shed* located at NZ25006330 and opened in 1854. At some time prior to 1902 the turntable was removed and the building absorbed into the works.

Adjoined by ...
Gateshead (YN&BR) NZ2463&2563.1/2A
A brick built 1RH shed* located at NZ24976328 and opened in 1854. At some time prior to 1902 the turntable was removed and the building absorbed into the works.

Adjoined by ...
Gateshead (YN&BR) NZ2463&2563.1/3A
A brick built 1RH shed* located at NZ25026325 and opened in 1854.

The shed was re-roofed ...
Gateshead (BR) NZ2463&2563.1/3B
A louvre style roof with raised central arch and brick screen was installed by the North Eastern Region in 1956.

Adjoined by ...
Gateshead (YN&BR) NZ2463&2563.1/4A
A brick built 1RH shed* located at NZ25006323 and opened in 1854.

The shed was extended ...
Gateshead (NER) NZ2463&2563.1/4B
A wooden lean-to structure was added to the south side of the building in 1902.

The shed was re-roofed ...
Gateshead (BR) NZ2463&2563.1/4C
A louvre style roof with raised central arch and brick screen was installed by the North Eastern Region in 1956.

The first four roundhouses, built in the form of a square by the York, Newcastle & Berwick Railway were probably provided with a slated multi-hipped roof.

Adjoined by ...
Gateshead (NER) NZ2463&2563.1/5A
A brick built square 1RH shed with a slated multiple hipped roof was added to the western end of NZ2463&2563.1/4A. It opened in c1867 and was located at NZ24966321.

The shed was extended ...
Gateshead (NER) NZ2463&2563.1/5B
A wooden lean-to structure was added to the south side of the shed in 1902. The building was abandoned when BR removed the roof in 1956, locomotives thereafter utilizing the turntable and stalls just for stabling until closure of the depot to steam.

Adjoined by ...
Gateshead (NER) NZ2463&2563.1/6A
A brick built square 1RH shed with a slated multiple hipped roof was added to the western end of NZ2463&2563.1/5A. It opened in c1877 and was located at NZ24916318.

The shed was extended ...
Gateshead (NER) NZ2463&2563.1/6B
A wooden lean-to structure was added to the south side of the shed in 1902. The building was abandoned when BR removed the roof in 1956, locomotives thereafter utilizing the turntable and stalls just for stabling until closure of the depot to steam.

Gateshead (NER) NZ2463&2563.1/7A
A brick built 3TS dead ended shed with a slated gable style roof, located at NZ24906313 and converted from a tender shop in c1920. The building was known as the *"Pacific"* shed.

The shed was extended ...
Gateshead (LNER) NZ2463&2563.1/7B
The building was lengthened at the eastern end in 1924.

Gateshead (BJR) NZ2463&2563.1/8A
A brick built 2TS dead ended shed located at NZ25136339 and opened in 1839 by the Brandling Junction Railway. The building adjoined the winding house and after closure it was incorporated into the works complex and remained standing, and in use, until the 1960s.

The depot, sited alongside the main works, had use of all facilities. The wooden extension added to the roundhouses (4B, 5B and 6B) was built on the trackbed of the former Redheugh branch, and the tender shop, which later became the Pacific Shed, was partially demolished to accommodate the north to east curve off the King Edward Bridge.

The easternmost roundhouse (3B) was converted by the North Eastern Region in 1964 to a 9TS shed (as NZ2463&2563.1/3C) for the maintenance of diesel locomotives.

Although the depot officially closed to steam on March 20th, 1965 it continued to service the locomotives until October of the same year. The other remaining roundhouse (4C) was similarly converted to a 9TS shed (as NZ2463&2563.1/4D) creating a through road diesel depot. The Pacific Shed (7B) was demolished in October 1969 and the diesel depot closed on July 8th, 1991. It saw brief use as a wagon works prior to abandonment.

Site NZ2563.1; On the south side of the line, west of Gateshead Station.
Gateshead Chaytor's Bank (NER) NZ2563.1/1A
A brick built circular 1RH shed with a slated radiating multi-pitched roof surmounted by a central conical section, located at NZ25266338 and opened in c1862. The facilities included a water tank.

The building was modified ...
Gateshead Chaytor's Bank (NER) NZ2563.1/1B
At some stage after 1899 the north west side of the building was cut back to accommodate track widening and the shed subsequently closed, finding further use as a Paint Shop for Gateshead Works. The building was demolished in the 1960s.

NORTHUMBERLAND

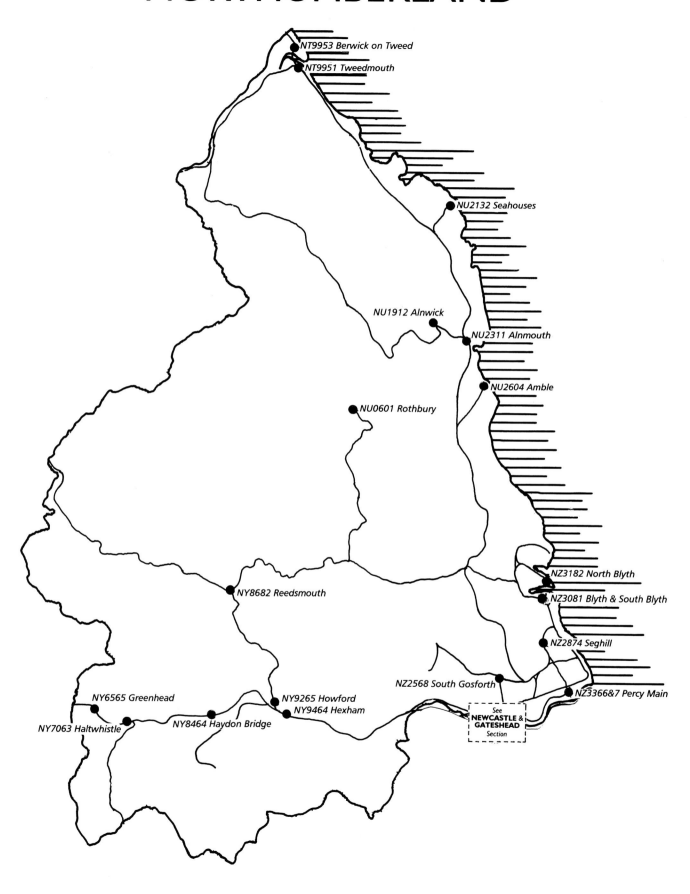

NT9953 Berwick on Tweed

NT9951 Tweedmouth

NU2132 Seahouses

NU1912 Alnwick

NU2311 Alnmouth

NU2604 Amble

NU0601 Rothbury

NY8682 Reedsmouth

NZ3182 North Blyth

NZ3081 Blyth & South Blyth

NZ2874 Seghill

NZ2568 South Gosforth

NY6565 Greenhead

NY9265 Howford

NY9464 Hexham

NY7063 Haltwhistle

NY8464 Haydon Bridge

NZ3366&7 Percy Main

See
NEWCASTLE &
GATESHEAD
Section

BLYTH

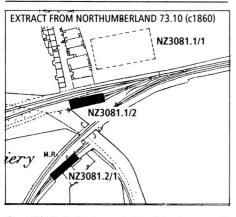

EXTRACT FROM NORTHUMBERLAND 73.10 (c1860)

NZ3081.1/1
NZ3081.1/2
NZ3081.2/1

Site NZ3081.2; On the south side of the line, west of Blyth Station.
Blyth (BS&PMR) NZ3081.2/1A
A 2TS building, with one through road and which was located at NZ30838151, may have been an engine shed that was opened in March 1847 by the Blyth, Seghill & Percy Main Railway. No further details are known other than it may have closed in 1855.

Site NZ3081.1; On the north side of the line, west of Blyth Station.
Blyth (BS&PMR) NZ3081.1/2A
A 2TS dead ended building which was located at NZ30848156 may have been an engine shed that was opened in March 1847 by the Blyth, Seghill & Percy Main Railway. No further details are known other than it may have closed in 1855.

Blyth South (NER) NZ3081.1/1A
A brick built 3TS dead ended shed with a slated gable style roof, located at NZ30888160 and opened in 1880.

The shed was enlarged ...
Blyth South (NER) NZ3081.1/1B
A brick built 3TS dead ended extension with a slated gable style roof was added to the original building, NZ3081.1/1A, in 1894. It was probably constructed along the northern side and created a 6TS dead ended structure. The facilities included a turntable, water columns and ramped coaling stage. The depot was closed by BR on May 28th, 1967 and subsequently demolished.

EXTRACT FROM NORTHUMBERLAND 78.3 (1922)

Iron Foundry
White Row
NZ3081.1/1

Site NZ3182.1; Amongst sidings at the end of the branch to North Blyth Docks.
Blyth North (NER) NZ3182.1/1A
A brick built square 1RH shed with a slated triple gable style roof, located at NZ31228255 and opened in 1897. The facilities included a water tank and ramped coaling stage. The depot was closed by BR on September 9th, 1967 and subsequently demolished.

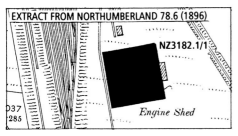

EXTRACT FROM NORTHUMBERLAND 78.6 (1896)

NZ3182.1/1
Engine Shed

HEXHAM

Site NY9464.1; On the south side of the line, at the east end of Hexham Station.
Hexham (NER) NY9464.1/1A
A 2TS shed located at NY94176422. No further details are known.

The shed was extended ...
Hexham (NER) NY9464.1/1B
An extension was added in 1869.

The shed was extended ...
Hexham (NER) NY9464.1/1C
An extension was added in 1878. The shed, by now, was a 2TS through road building and the facilities included a water tank and turntable. The depot was destroyed by a fire in 1929.

The shed was rebuilt ...
Hexham (LNER) NY9464.1/1D
The building was reconstructed in c1929 and again destroyed by fire, this time from a World War II incendiary bomb in c1942.

The shed was rebuilt ...
Hexham (LNER) NY9464.1/1E
A brick built 2TS through road shed with a louvre style roof and brick screen was constructed on the same site, possibly in c1946. The depot was closed by BR on April 6th, 1959 and stood in a derelict condition until the 1970s.

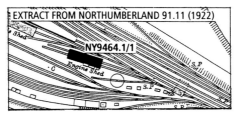

EXTRACT FROM NORTHUMBERLAND 91.11 (1922)

Shed
NY9464.1/1
Engine Shed

TWEEDMOUTH

Site NT9951.1; On the south side of the line, at the east end of Tweedmouth Station.
Tweedmouth (NER) NT9951.1/1A
A brick built square 1RH shed with a slated triple gable style roof, located at NT99885174 and opened in 1877.

Tweedmouth (N&BR) NT9951.1/2A
A stone built 4TS dead ended shed, located at NT999835178 and opened on July 1st, 1847 by the Newcastle & Berwick Railway.

The shed was re-roofed ...
Tweedmouth (NER) NT9951.1/2B
After re-roofing in 1881 the building possesssed a gable style single pitched roof.

The facilities included an external turntable, coal stage and water tank. The depot was closed by BR on June 19th, 1966, and the four road straight shed (NU9951.1/2B) was demolished in 1968. The roundhouse (NU9951.1/1A) was sold for private use and still stood in 1997.

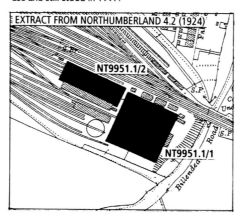

EXTRACT FROM NORTHUMBERLAND 4.2 (1924)

NT9951.1/2
NT9951.1/1
Billendea Road

PERCY MAIN

Site NZ3366&7.1; On the east side of the Blyth and Tyne Colliery line, south of Percy Main Junction.
Percy Main (B&TR) NZ3366&7.1/1A
A stone built 2TS dead ended shed located at NZ33546697.

The shed was probably re-roofed ..
Percy Main (B&TR) NZ3366&7.1/1B
At some stage a slated single pitched roof with a brick gable was installed.

Adjoined by ...
Percy Main (B&TR) NZ3366&7.1/2A
A brick built 3TS dead ended shed with a slated gable style roof located at NZ33526697.

Percy Main (B&TR) NZ3366&7.1/3A
A stone built 3TS through road shed with a slated triple gable style roof located at NZ33496704.

The shed was partially re-roofed ...
Percy Main (BR) NZ3366&7.1/3B
A corrugated steel sheeted lean-to type roof was installed over part of the easternmost track by the North Eastern Region in c1960.

Adjoined by . . .
Percy Main (B&TR) NZ3366&7.1/4A
A stone built 1TS dead ended shed with a slated gable style roof located at NZ33506704.

The opening dates for the various buildings of Blyth & Tyne Railway origin are not known but most of them were in existence in 1855. The facilities included a water tank, coal stage and a turntable installed later by the NER. The depot was closed to steam by BR on February 28th, 1965 and totally on February 27th, 1966 with demolition of sheds 3B & 4A following in the same year.

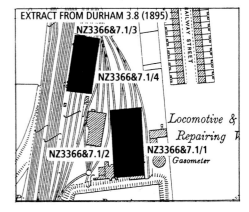

EXTRACT FROM DURHAM 3.8 (1895)

NZ3366&7.1/3
NZ3366&7.1/4
NZ3366&7.1/2
NZ3366&7.1/1
Locomotive & Repairing
Gasometer

GREENHEAD

Site NY6565.1; On the east side of the line, at the south end of Greenhead Station.
Greenhead (N&CR) NY6565.1/1A
A 2TS dead ended shed, located at NY65936544 and opened on July 19th, 1836 by the Newcastle & Carlisle Railway. No further details are known other than, possibly after closure to locomotive use, one track was removed and it may have seen further use as a goods shed. The building was still standing in 1999.

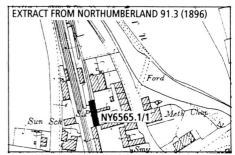

EXTRACT FROM NORTHUMBERLAND 91.3 (1896)

Ford
NY6565.1/1
Sun Sch

ALNMOUTH

Site NU2311.1; On the west side of Alnmouth Station.
Alnmouth* (NER)^{NU2311.1/1A}
A brick built 2TS dead ended shed with a slated gable style roof, located at NU23071104 and opened in 1875.

The shed was enlarged ...
Alnmouth* (NER)^{NU2311.1/1B}
The building was extended in 1887. The facilities included a coaling stage, water tank and turntable. The depot was closed by BR on June 19th, 1966 and subsequently demolished.

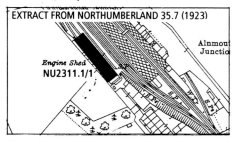
EXTRACT FROM NORTHUMBERLAND 35.7 (1923)

*It was known as Bilton Junction until 1892.

ALNWICK

Site NU1912.1; On the south side of Alnwick Station.
Alnwick (NER)^{NU1912.1/1A}
A 1TS dead ended shed located at NU19171290 and opened on August 5th, 1850. No further details are known other than it was closed in 1875 and subsequently demolished.

EXTRACT FROM NORTHUMBERLAND 32.13 (c1860)

REEDSMOUTH

Site NY8682.1; On the east side of the Riccarton Junction line at Reedsmouth Junction.
Reedsmouth (BCR)^{NY8682.1/1A}
A brick built 2TS through road shed with a slated gable style roof, it was located at NZ86418219 and was opened on July 1st, 1862 by the Border Counties Railway. The facilities included a turntable.

The shed was enlarged ...
Reedsmouth (BCR)^{NY8682.1/1B}
The building was extended in the 1870s and modified to a one through road shed. The depot was closed by BR on September 15th, 1952 and the building still stood in 1998, in use as a barn for the adjacent farm.

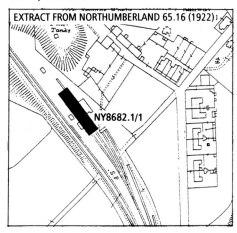
EXTRACT FROM NORTHUMBERLAND 65.16 (1922)

HAYDON BRIDGE

Site NY8464.1; On the south side of the line, at the west end of Haydon Bridge Station.
Haydon Bridge (NER)^{NY8464.1/1A}
A 1TS shed was in existence here until 1875. It was probably the dead ended building located at NY84246450 and at right angles to the main line. No further details are known.

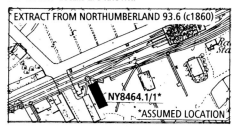
EXTRACT FROM NORTHUMBERLAND 93.6 (c1860)

*ASSUMED LOCATION

HOWFORD

Site NY9265.1; On the east side of the Reedsmouth line, north of the Tyne Bridge and west of Hexham.
Howford (NBR)^{NY9265.1/1A}
A stone built 2TS through road shed located at NY92226550 and opened in 1859. The facilities included a turntable and the depot closed in 1865. No further details are known.

EXTRACT FROM NORTHUMBERLAND 94.2 (c1860)

SEGHILL

Site NZ2874.1; On the west side of the Seghill Colliery branch, north of Seghill Station.
Seghill (Seghill)^{NZ2874.1/1A}
A shed was opened here on June 1st, 1840 by the Seghill Railway. It was probably the building located at NZ28927477 and may have been a 3TS dead ended structure. No further details are known other than it closed in 1855.

EXTRACT FROM NORTHUMBERLAND 81.9 (1896)

BERWICK ON TWEED

Site NT9953.1; On the west side of the line, north of Berwick on Tweed Station.
Berwick on Tweed (NBR)^{NT9953.1/1A}
A stone built semi-roundhouse shed with a slated continuous pitched roof, located at NT99505362 and opened on June 18th, 1846. The facilities, apart from the turntable, included a water tank and coal stage. The depot was closed by the LNER in August 1924 and demolished to accommodate track re-alignments for the enlarged station.

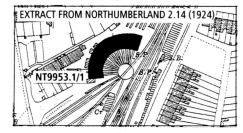
EXTRACT FROM NORTHUMBERLAND 2.14 (1924)

ROTHBURY

Site NU0601.1; On the south side of Rothbury Station.
Rothbury (NBR)^{NU0601.1/1A}
A brick built 1TS dead ended shed with a slated pitched roof and timber gable, located at NU06220161 and opened in 1870. The facilities included a water tank and turntable sited outside of the shed entrance. The depot was closed by BR on September 15th, 1952 and remained standing in a derelict condition until the 1960s.

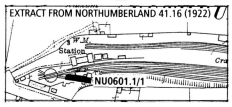
EXTRACT FROM NORTHUMBERLAND 41.16 (1922)

SEAHOUSES

Site NU2132.1; At the north end of Seahouses Station.
Seahouses (NSLR)^{NU2132.1/1A}
A corrugated iron 1TS dead ended shed with a slated gable style roof, located at NU21913210 and opened by the North Sunderland Light Railway on December 14th, 1898. Details of the facilities are not known. The depot was closed by BR on October 29th, 1951 and remained standing until the 1960s before being demolished.

EXTRACT FROM NORTHUMBERLAND 18.3 (1924)

SOUTH GOSFORTH

Site NZ2568.1; In the triangle of lines at the north end of South Gosforth Station.
South Gosforth (NER)^{NZ2568.1/1A}
A corrugated iron 2TS shed with a dutch barn style corrugated iron roof opened on December 19th, 1902. The building was probably located at NZ25436845 and the facilities included a water column. The depot only lasted a short period of time and closed on August 1st, 1904.

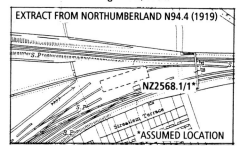
EXTRACT FROM NORTHUMBERLAND N94.4 (1919)

*ASSUMED LOCATION

AMBLE

Site NU2604.1; In the vicinity of Amble Station.
Amble (NER)^{NU2604.1/F1}
Some form of facility, approximately located at NU267045, was established here. No further details are known.

HALTWHISTLE

Site NY7063.1; In the vicinity of Haltwhistle Station.
Haltwhistle (NER)^{NY7063.1/1A}
A 1TS shed, approximately located at NY703638, was opened here in 1875. No further details are known.

CUMBERLAND

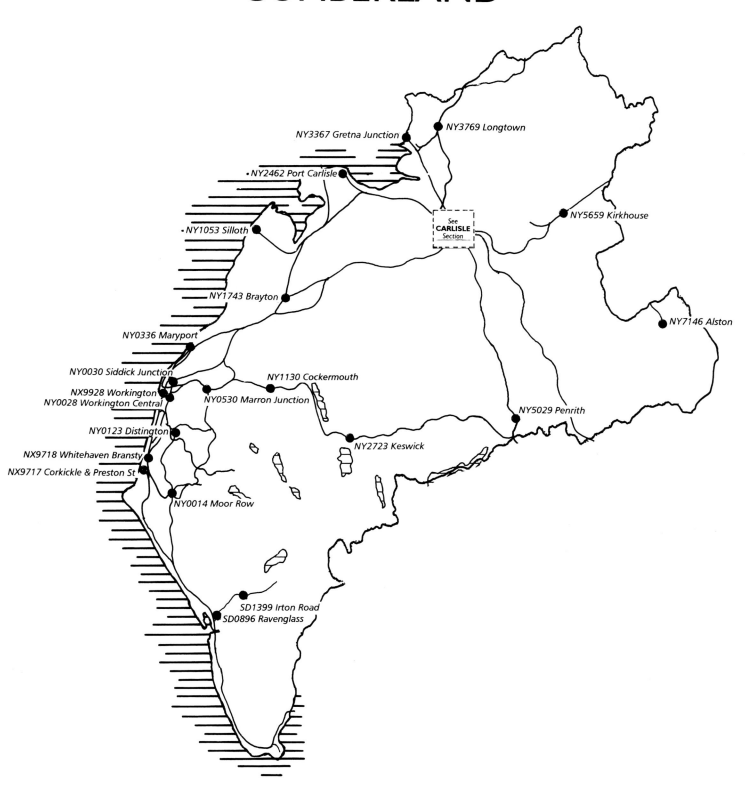

NY3367 Gretna Junction
NY3769 Longtown

• NY2462 Port Carlisle

NY5659 Kirkhouse

• NY1053 Silloth

See
CARLISLE
Section

NY1743 Brayton

NY7146 Alston

NY0336 Maryport

NY0030 Siddick Junction

NY1130 Cockermouth

NX9928 Workington
NY0028 Workington Central
NY0530 Marron Junction

NY5029 Penrith

NY0123 Distington

NY2723 Keswick

NX9718 Whitehaven Bransty
NX9717 Corkickle & Preston St

NY0014 Moor Row

SD1399 Irton Road
SD0896 Ravenglass

RAVENGLASS

Site SD0896.1; On the east side of the line, north of Ravenglass (R&ER) Station.
Ravenglass (R&ER) SD0896.1/1A
A 3ft 0in gauge 2TS dead ended shed located at SD08579660 and opened on May 24th, 1875 by the Ravenglass & Eskdale Railway. No further details are known. The depot was closed, along with the line on April 30th, 1913.

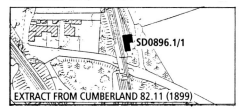

EXTRACT FROM CUMBERLAND 82.11 (1899)
SD0896.1/1

The line was re-gauged ...
Ravenglass (R&ER) SD0896.1/1B
The track was re-gauged to 1ft 3in and the depot re-opened, as a 4TS dead ended shed, along with the line on August 28th, 1915.

The depot was rebuilt ...
Ravenglass (R&ER) SD0896.1/1C
At some stage the building was extended and re-modelled as a 3TS dead ended shed. No further details are known.

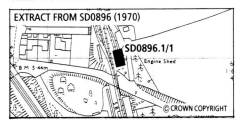

EXTRACT FROM SD0896 (1970)
SD0896.1/1
Engine Shed
© CROWN COPYRIGHT

IRTON ROAD

Site SD1399.1; On the north side of the line at the east end of Irton Road Station.
Irton Road (R&ER) SD1399.1/1A
A 1ft 3in gauge 1TS dead ended shed, located at SD13779997 and opened on October 10th, 1915 by the Ravenglass & Eskdale Railway. No further details are known other than it closed in 1930.

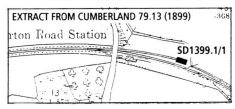

EXTRACT FROM CUMBERLAND 79.13 (1899)
Irton Road Station
SD1399.1/1

KIRKHOUSE

Site NY5659.1; On the south side of the line, east of Brampton Junction.
Kirkhouse (Brampton) NY5659.1/1A
A 1TS dead ended shed, probably the building located at NY56525996, opened in 1881 by the Brampton Railway. The depot closed in 1890 and re-opened on August 1st 1913 following the takeover of the line by the NER. It closed again in 1917, re-opened on March 1st, 1920 and was finally closed by the LNER on October 29th, 1923. No further details are known.

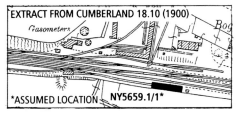

EXTRACT FROM CUMBERLAND 18.10 (1900)
Gasometers
Bog
ASSUMED LOCATION NY5659.1/1

KESWICK

Site NY2723.1; On the north side of Keswick Station.
Keswick (CK&PR) NY2723.1/F1
A servicing area consisting of a turntable, located at NY27082384 and siding. It was opened on October 26th, 1864 by the Cockermouth, Keswick & Penrith Railway. No further details are known.

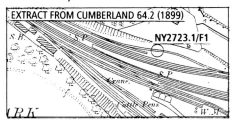

EXTRACT FROM CUMBERLAND 64.2 (1899)
NY2723.1/F1

DISTINGTON

Site NY0123.1; On the west side of the Moor Row line, south of Distington Station.
Distington (C&WJR) NY0123.1/1A
A stone built 1TS dead ended shed with a slated gable style roof, located at NY01212377 and opened by the Cleator & Workington Joint Railway in July 1879. No further details are known other than the LMS closed it in April 1931.

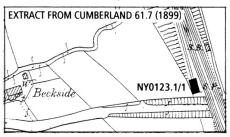

EXTRACT FROM CUMBERLAND 61.7 (1899)
Beckside
NY0123.1/1

MARRON JUNCTION

Site NY0530.1; In the triangle of lines at the east end of Marron Junction Station.
Marron Junction (WC&ER) NY0530.1/1A
A brick built 1TS dead ended shed located at NY05753006 and opened on January 15th, 1866 by the Workington, Cleator & Egremont Railway. The facilities included a water tank. The depot closed in 1898.

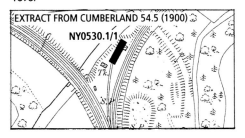

EXTRACT FROM CUMBERLAND 54.5 (1900)
NY0530.1/1

LONGTOWN

Site NY3769.1; On the west side of the line, north of Longtown Station.
Longtown (NBR) NY3769.1/1A
A 2TS dead ended shed located at NY37606925 and opened by the NB (Border Union) Railway on October 15th, 1861. No further details are known other than it was closed by the LNER in 1924.

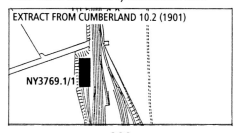

EXTRACT FROM CUMBERLAND 10.2 (1901)
NY3769.1/1

GRETNA JUNCTION

Site NY3367.1; On the west side of Gretna Junction, east of Gretna Green Station.
Gretna Junction (NBR) NY3367.1/1A
A 2TS dead ended shed located at NY33166759 and opened by the NB (Border Union Railway) on October 15th, 1861. No further details are known.

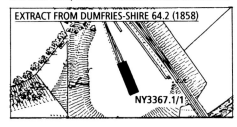

EXTRACT FROM DUMFRIES-SHIRE 64.2 (1858)
NY3367.1/1

SILLOTH

Site NY1053.1; On the south side of Silloth Station.
Silloth (C&SR&DC) NY1053.1/1A
A stone built 2TS dead ended shed with a slated gable style roof, located at NY10965328 and opened on August 28th, 1856 by the Carlisle & Silloth Railway & Dock Company. The facilities included a water tank and turntable. The depot was closed by BR on July 6th, 1953 and demolished between 1967 and 1971.

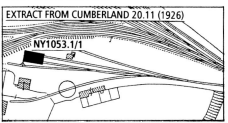

EXTRACT FROM CUMBERLAND 20.11 (1926)
NY1053.1/1

ALSTON

Site NY7146.1; On the west side of Alston Station.
Alston (N&CR) NY7146.1/1A
A stone built 1TS through road shed with a slated gable style roof, located at NY71684673 and opened by the Newcastle & Carlisle Railway on November 17th, 1852. The building was unusual in that one wall supported the adjacent station canopy and the other was common to the goods depot. The facilities included a water column, turntable and coal stage. The depot was closed by BR on September 27th, 1959 and subsequently demolished.

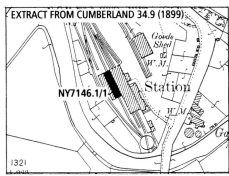

EXTRACT FROM CUMBERLAND 34.9 (1899)
Goods Shed
Station
NY7146.1/1

MARYPORT

EXTRACT FROM CUMBERLAND 44.8 (1900)

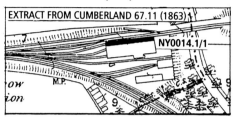

Site NY0336.0; In the vicinity of Maryport Station.
Maryport (M&CR) NY0336.0/1A
A shed was opened here on July 15th, 1840 by the Maryport & Carlisle Railway and closed on June 4th, 1860. No further details are known.

Replaced by ...
Site NY0336.1; On the north side of the line, at the west end of Maryport Station.
Maryport (M&CR) NY0336.1/1A
A stone built 2TS dead ended shed located at NY03703611 and opened on June 4th, 1860 by the Maryport & Carlisle Railway. The facilities included a turntable. It is believed that after the M&CR locos moved to the new depot (NY0336.2/1A) the building was then occupied by L&NWR engines that had been formerly housed at Whitehaven Bransty shed (NX9718.1/1A). No further details are known.

Replaced by ...
Site NY0336.2; On the north side of the line, west of Maryport Station.
Maryport (M&CR) NY0336.2/1A
A timber built 4TS dead ended shed with a twin slated gable style roof, located at NY03453604 and opened at some time prior to 1900 by the Maryport & Carlisle Railway. The facilities included a turntable later enlarged to 60ft. The depot was closed by the LMS on September 14th, 1931 and later demolished.

BRAYTON

Site NY1743.1; In the fork of the lines, at Brayton Junction, east of Brayton Station.
Brayton (SJR) NY1743.1/1A
A 2TS through road shed located at NY17014390 and opened by the Solway Junction Railway on September 13th, 1869. The facilities included a water tank and turntable. The depot was closed in 1896 by the Caledonian Railway with the building being demolished in c1904.

A servicing area was then established ...
Brayton (CR) NY1743.1/F1
The turntable (located at NY17074394), siding and water tank were then utilized until LMS days. No further details are known.

EXTRACT FROM CUMBERLAND 36.2 (1900)

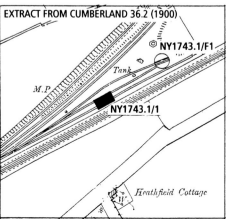

COCKERMOUTH

Site NY1130.1; On the north side of the line, at the west end of Cockermouth (1st) Station.
Cockermouth (C&WR) NY1130.1/1A
A 2TS dead ended shed located at NY11333080 and opened by the Cockermouth & Workington Railway on April 28th, 1847. The facilities included a turntable.

The shed was enlarged ...
Cockermouth (C&WR) NY1130.1/1B
The building was extended in 1858 and closed in 1876, finding further use as a goods shed. It was demolished in the mid-1990s.

EXTRACT FROM CUMBERLAND 54.4 (1863)

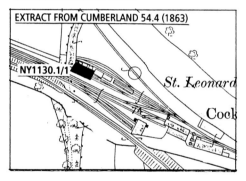

SIDDICK JUNCTION

Site NY0030.1; On the west side of the line, south of Siddick Dock Junction.
Siddick Junction (C&WJR) NY0030.1/1A
A brick built 2TS dead ended shed with an unusual slated transverse multiple hipped roof, located at NY00023022 and opened in July 1879 by the Cleator & Workington Junction Railway. The facilities included a turntable and a coal stage, with water tank over. The building was severely damaged by a fire on February 17th, 1923 so the LMS closed it on May 23rd of the same year; the shed then stood in a derelict condition for some years prior to demolition.

EXTRACT FROM CUMBERLAND 53.7 (1925)

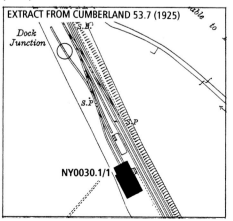

MOOR ROW

Site NY0014.1; On the south side of the line, east of Moor Row Station.
Moor Row (WC&ER) NY0014.1/1A
A 1TS dead ended shed located at NY00771459 and opened by the Workington, Cleator and Egremont Railway on January 11th, 1856. No further details are known other than it was sited within the locomotive works and was partially destroyed by a fire in 1857.

The shed was rebuilt ...
Moor Row (WC&ER) NY0014.1/1B
The depot was rebuilt, and possibly extended, in 1857. The facilities included a water tank. It closed in 1884 and was subsequently demolished.

EXTRACT FROM CUMBERLAND 67.11 (1863)

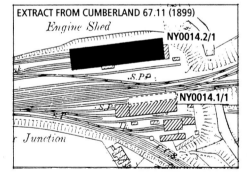

Replaced by ...
Site NY0014.2; On the north side of the line, east of Moor Row Station.
Moor Row (FR/L&NWR) NY0014.2/1A
A stone built 4TS dead ended shed with a slated gable style roof, located at NY00751463 and opened in 1884. The facilities included a coal stage and water column. The building over the years suffered from the effects of mining subsidence and the building was partially demolished in 1940.

The shed was rebuilt ...
Moor Row (LMS) NY0014.2/1B
The northern 2TS bay was totally demolished and the stone from this section utilized to build a new buttressed wall for the remaining 2TS shed. A timber clad single pitched roof with timber gable was also installed over the remainder of the building. The depot was closed by BR on July 31st, 1954 and subsequently demolished.

EXTRACT FROM CUMBERLAND 67.11 (1899)

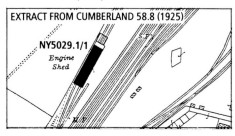

PENRITH

Site NY5029.1; On the west side of the line, south of Penrith Station.
Penrith (L&NWR) NY5029.1/1A
A stone built 2TS dead ended shed with a slated gable style roof, located at NY50962961 and opened in 1865. The facilities included a water column. The depot was closed by BR on June 18th, 1962 and subsequently demolished.

EXTRACT FROM CUMBERLAND 58.8 (1925)

WHITEHAVEN

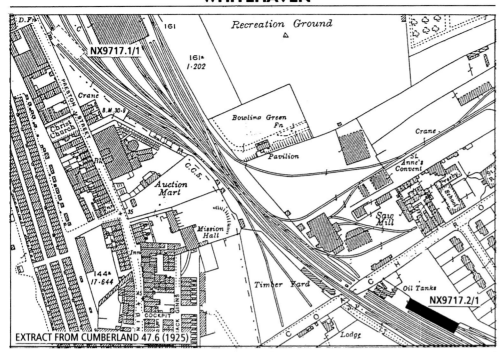

EXTRACT FROM CUMBERLAND 47.6 (1925)

Site NX9717.1; On the west side of the Preston Street Goods Branch, south of Corkickle Station.
Preston Street (W&FJR) NX9717.1/1A
A 2TS through road shed, located at NX97211768 and opened by the Workington & Furness Junction Railway on July 8th, 1850. The facilities included a coal stage and two water tanks. The line was absorbed on July 16th, 1866 by the Furness Railway and the depot was closed in 1898. The building was subsequently demolished and the site incorporated into a goods depot.

EXTRACT FROM CUMBERLAND 67.6 (1862)

Replaced by ...
Site NX9717.2; On the east side of the Preston Street Goods Branch, south of Corkickle Station.
Corkickle (FR) NX9717.2/1
A stone built 2TS dead ended shed with a slated gable style roof, located at NX97541741 and opened in 1898. The facilities included a coaling shed and turntable. The depot was closed by the LMS on January 4th, 1932 but saw further use as a carriage shed into BR days, and still stood into the 1960s.

Site NX9718.1; On the east side of Bransty Station.
Bransty (WJR) NX9718.1/1A
A 2TS dead ended shed, located at NX97441859 and opened in 1858 by the Whitehaven Junction Railway. The facilities included a coal stage and turntable. No further details are known other than it closed in c1870 and was demolished to accommodate station improvements.

Probably replaced by ...
Site NX9718.2; On the west side of the line, at the north end of Bransty Station.
Bransty (L&NWR) NX9718.2/F1
A servicing area consisting of a turntable, located at NX97391877, siding and water tank. Although officially closed by the LMS in 1924 it may well have been utilized until the end of steam in the area in c1964.

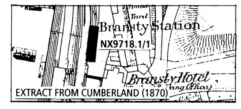

EXTRACT FROM CUMBERLAND (1870)

PORT CARLISLE

Site NY2462.1; On the east side of the line, at the north end of Port Carlisle Station.
Port Carlisle (PCD&RC) NY2462.1/1A
A 1TS through road shed, probably built in timber and located at NY24006228. It was opened on May 22nd, 1854 by the Port Carlisle Dock & Railway Company and the line was worked by the Newcastle & Carlisle Railway until the arrival of its own locomotive in 1855. The depot closed on January 1st, 1899 when the line was switched to horse traction.

Replaced, on the same site, by ...
Port Carlisle (NBR) NY2462.1/1B
A timber built 1TS through road shed with a slated gable style roof, it opened on April 4th, 1914 upon the reinstatement of steam locomotion. No further details are known other than the facilities included a turntable and the depot was closed by the LNER in July 1928.

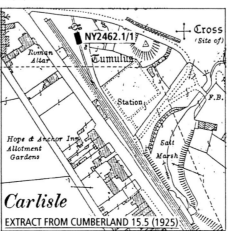

EXTRACT FROM CUMBERLAND 15.5 (1925)

WORKINGTON

Site NX9928.1; On the east side of the line, south of Workington Station.
Workington (L&NWR) NX9928.1/1A
A brick built 3TS dead ended shed with a northlight pattern roof located at NX99352854 and opened in 1890.

The shed was enlarged ...
Workington (L&NWR) NX9928.1/1B
The building was quadrupled in size to a 12TS dead ended shed in 1891. The facilities included a coal stage, with water tank over, and a turntable.

The shed was modified ...
Workington (BR) NX9928.1/1C
In 1955 the London Midland Region reduced the length of the building and installed a louvre style roof with brick screen. The shed closed to steam on January 1st, 1968 and, after a brief period as a diesel depot, found further use as a wagon repair shop. The building was abandoned in the 1980s but survived until at least 1998.

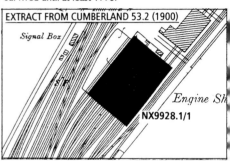

EXTRACT FROM CUMBERLAND 53.2 (1900)

Site NY0028.1; On the west side of the line, at the south end of Workington Central Station.
Workington Central (C&WJR) NY0028.1/1A
A brick and stone built 2TS dead ended shed with a slated gable style roof, located at NY00182838 and opened in July 1879 by the Cleator & Workington Junction Railway. Details of the facilities are not known.

The shed was modified ...
Workington Central (FR) NY0028.1/1B
At some stage in the early 1900s the building was lengthened and the easternmost track extended through the back wall. The depot was closed by the LMS in May 1923 and later demolished.

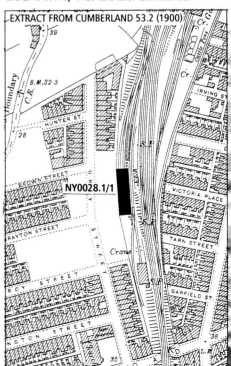

EXTRACT FROM CUMBERLAND 53.2 (1900)

CARLISLE

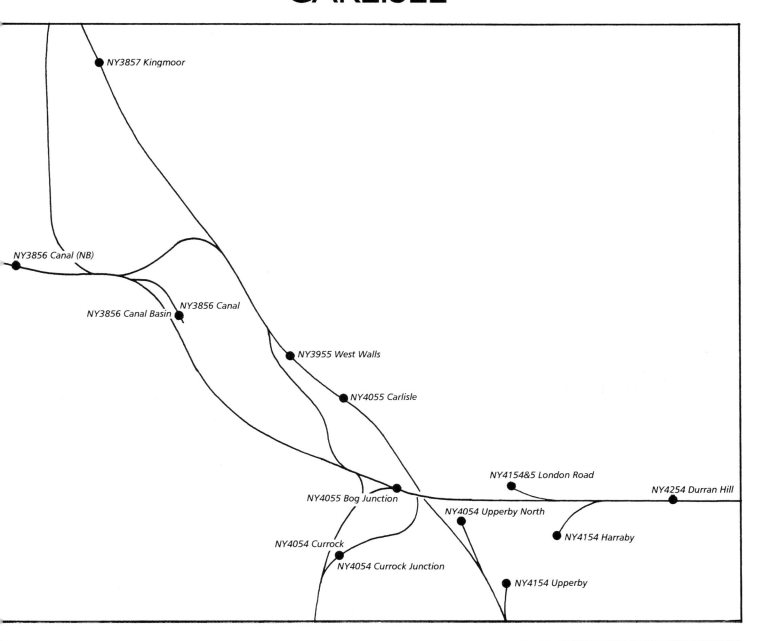

- NY3857 Kingmoor
- NY3856 Canal (NB)
- NY3856 Canal Basin
- NY3856 Canal
- NY3955 West Walls
- NY4055 Carlisle
- NY4154&5 London Road
- NY4254 Durran Hill
- NY4055 Bog Junction
- NY4054 Upperby North
- NY4154 Harraby
- NY4054 Currock
- NY4054 Currock Junction
- NY4154 Upperby

CURROCK JUNCTION

Site NY4054.2; On the west side of the Workington line, south of Carlisle Citadel Station.
Currock (M&CR) NY4054.2/1A
A stone built 3TS dead ended shed with a slated gable style roof, located at NY40185467 and opened in January 1876 by the Maryport & Carlisle Railway. The facilities included a water tank and turntable. The depot was closed by the LMS on July 1st, 1923 and saw further use as a wagon works until demolition in the 1930s.

Site NY4054.3; On the east side of the Workington line, south of Carlisle Citadel Station.
Currock Junction (G&SWR) NY4054.3/1A
A brick built 6TS through road shed with a slated northlight roof, located at NY40175456 and opened in 1895 by the Glasgow & South Western Railway. The facilities included a ramped coaling stage, water tank and turntable. The depot was closed by the LMS on June 24th, 1924 and converted into a wagon works. In the 1980s it was partially reinstated as an engine shed, housing the last remaining locomotives in the Carlisle area, Class 08 shunters, until closure in 1999.

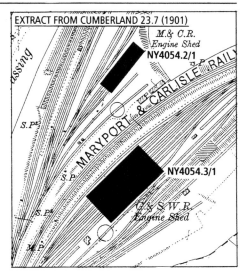

EXTRACT FROM CUMBERLAND 23.7 (1901)

M.& C.R. Engine Shed
NY4054.2/1

NY4054.3/1

G.S.&W.R. Engine Shed

BOG JUNCTION

Site NY4055.1; On the south side of Bog Junction.
Bog Junction (M&CR) NY4055.1/1A
A 2TS dead ended shed located at NY40485501 and opened on May 10th, 1843 by the Maryport & Carlisle Railway.

The shed was enlarged or rebuilt ...
Bog Junction (M&CR) NY4055.1/1B
A 3TS dead ended shed was established on the site in 1863. The facilities included a turntable and coaling crane. The depot was closed in 1875 and demolished to accommodate new track work.

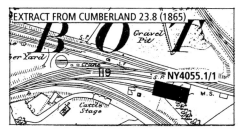

EXTRACT FROM CUMBERLAND 23.8 (1865)

NY4055.1/1

UPPERBY

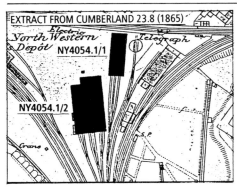

EXTRACT FROM CUMBERLAND 23.8 (1865)

Site NY4054.1; On the east side of the Lancaster line, south of Carlisle Citadel Station.
Upperby North (L&C) NY4054.1/1A
A 1TS shed, located at NY40965492 and opened on December 17th, 1846 by the Lancaster & Carlisle Railway. No further details are known.

The shed was enlarged ...
Upperby North (L&C/L&NWR) NY4054.1/1B
A 3TS dead ended shed was in use here in 1865.

The shed was enlarged ...
Upperby North (L&C/L&NWR) NY4054.1/2A
A 6TS dead ended shed, composed of three 2TS buildings and located at NY40955488 was in use here in 1865.

The facilities included a turntable and coaling shed. The depot closed in 1875 and the buildings were briefly utilized as a carriage works prior to demolition.

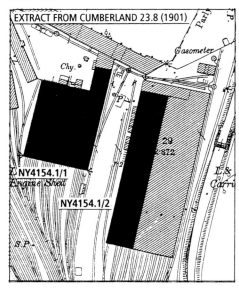

EXTRACT FROM CUMBERLAND 23.8 (1901)

Site NY4154.1; On the east side of the Lancaster line, south of Carlisle Citadel Station.
Upperby South (L&NWR) NY4154.1/1A
A brick built 11TS dead ended shed with a slated triple hipped roof, located at NY41075457 and opened in 1875. The facilities included a repair shop, turntable and coal stage with water tank over. By 1948 the building was derelict.

Replaced, on the same site, by ...
Upperby (BR) NY4154.1/1B
A concrete built 1RH polygonal shed with a flat roof was constructed by the London Midland Region in 1948.

Upperby (BR) NY4154.1/2A
One bay of the adjacent carriage shed was utilized as a 5TS dead ended shed with a slated single gable style hipped roof. The building was opened by the London Midland Region in 1948 and was located at NY41125449.

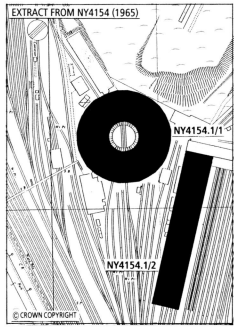

EXTRACT FROM NY4154 (1965)
© CROWN COPYRIGHT

At the same time the facilities were improved with the provision of a new coaling plant. The modernization of the depot was completed in 1958 and it closed to steam on December 12th, 1966. Diesel locomotives were then serviced for a brief period of time before the roundhouse was given over to the Civil Engineering Department, which utilized it until demolition in 1978. The 5TS shed (NY4154.1/2A) continued in use as a carriage shed until 1995 and still stood in 1999.

KINGMOOR

Site NY3857.1; On the east side of the Glasgow line, about 1.5 miles north of Carlisle Citadel Station.
Kingmoor* (CR) NY3857.1/1A
A timber built 8TS through road shed with a slated gable style multiple pitched roof, it was located at NY38585770 and opened in 1876. The facilities included a ramped coaling stage, turntable, water tank and repair shop.

The depot was rebuilt ...
Kingmoor (CR) NY3857.1/1B
A brick built 8TS through road shed with a slated gable style multiple pitched roof was constructed on the same site in 1916/17. Amongst other improvements a mechanical coaling plant was installed by the LMS in 1937. The depot was closed by BR on January 1st, 1968 and subsequently demolished.

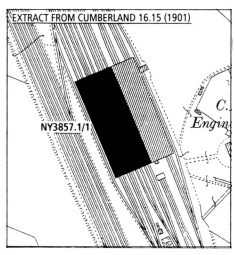

EXTRACT FROM CUMBERLAND 16.15 (1901)

*The depot was originally known as Etterby

CANAL

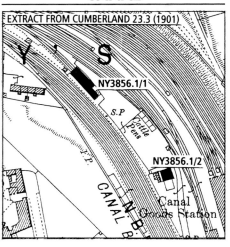

EXTRACT FROM CUMBERLAND 23.3 (1901)

Site NY3856.1; In Canal Goods Station, east of Canal Junction.
Carlisle Canal Basin (N&CR) NY3856.1/2A
A 1TS dead ended shed located at NY38995615 and opened on March 9th, 1837 by the Newcastle & Carlisle Railway. The facilities included a turntable sited outside of the shed entrance. No further details are known.

Carlisle Canal (PC&SR) NY3856.1/1A
A 2TS dead ended shed located at NY38925624 and opened in July 1856 by the Port Carlisle and Silloth Railway. The line was absorbed by the NBR and no further details are known other than it probably closed in 1862

Replaced by ...
Site NY3856.2; On the north side of the Silloth line, west of Canal Junction.
Carlisle Canal (NBR) NY3856.2/1A
A stone built square 1RH shed with a slated triple gable style roof, located at NY38055641 and opened on July 1st, 1862. The facilities included a ramped coaling stage and water tank.

The shed was re-modelled in 1910 ...
Carlisle Canal (NBR) NY3856.2/1B
Two tracks were extended from the yard into the north side of the building and the turntable serving the remaining stalls in the southern portion of the building was enlarged.

The shed was extended in 1933 ...
Carlisle Canal (LNER) NY3856.2/2A
A brick built 3TS dead ended shed with a slated gable style roof sited along the northern wall of NY3856.2/1B and located at NY38055644. It had been utilized as a wagon works and was converted for locomotive use in 1933. By this time an additional and larger turntable and mechanical coaling plant had been installed in the yard by the LNER.

The depot was closed by BR on June 17th, 1963 and demolished in the following year.

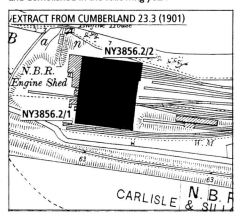

EXTRACT FROM CUMBERLAND 23.3 (1901)

LONDON ROAD

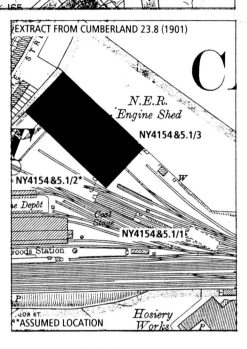

EXTRACT FROM CUMBERLAND 23.8 (1865)

Site NY4154&5.1; On the north side of the Newcastle line, east of Carlisle Citadel Station.
London Road (N&CR) NY4154&5.1/1A
A 2TS dead ended shed, located at NY41305499 and opened on July 19th, 1836 by the Newcastle & Carlisle Railway. The facilities included a coal stage and turntable. No further details are known other than the building was destroyed by a fire on April 30th, 1864.

Replaced by ...
London Road (NER) NY4154&5.1/2A
A shed opened here in 1865. The precise location is not known but it may have occupied the same site as the later external turntable at NY41135507. No further details are known.

Replaced by ...
London Road (NER) NY4154&5.1/3A
A brick built 1RH shed with a slated triple gable style roof located at NY41205510. The opening date is not known but may have been 1881.

The shed was extended ...
London Road (NER) NY4154&5.1/3B
It was enlarged to a 2RH shed with a slated triple gable style roof in 1890. The facilities included a ramped coal stage, water tank and external turntable by which access could be gained to the rear portion of the shed. The depot was closed by the LNER in 1933 and saw further use a wagon repair shop before being sold off for private use. The building still stood in 1998.

DURRAN HILL

Site NY4254.1; On the south side of the Leeds line, east of Carlisle Citadel Station.
Durran Hill (MR) NY4254.1/1A
A brick built square 1RH shed with a slated triple gable style roof located at NY42175489 and opened on August 2nd, 1875. The facilities included a repair shop, ramped coal stage and water tank.

The building was modified in 1912 ...
Durran Hill (MR) NY4254.1/1B
Two tracks were extended from the yard into the north side of the building, replacing the stalls in that section of the shed. The depot was closed by the LMS on February 16th, 1936 and, as it had not been immediately demolished, it was re-opened as a wartime measure in 1943. It was finally closed by BR on November 2nd, 1959 and demolished in the 1960s.

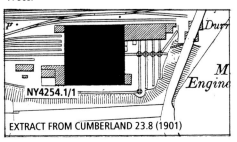

EXTRACT FROM CUMBERLAND 23.8 (1901)

EXTRACT FROM CUMBERLAND 23.8 (1901)

**ASSUMED LOCATION

WEST WALLS

Site NY3955.1; On the east side of the Glasgow line, north of Carlisle Citadel Station.
West Walls (CR/G&SWR) NY3955.1/1A
A brick built 6TS dead ended shed located at NY39825589 and opened in 1849 by the Caledonian Railway. The Glasgow & South Western Railway moved in to share the building in 1850, occupying the two easternmost tracks. The facilities included a repair shop, turntable, water tank and coal stage. The G&SWR moved out on April 7th, 1874 to Harraby shed (NY4154.1/1A) and the depot closed in 1877 with demolition following in 1886.

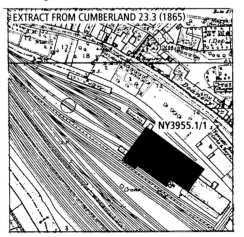

EXTRACT FROM CUMBERLAND 23.3 (1865)

HARRABY

Site NY4154.1; On the south side of the Newcastle line, east of Carlisle Citadel Station.
Harraby (G&SWR) NY4154.1/1A
A timber built 2TS through road shed located at NY41435474 and opened on January 1st, 1875 by the Glasgow & South Western Railway. No further details are known other than it blew down on January 20th of the same year.

Replaced, on the same site, by ...
Harraby (G&SWR) NY4154.1/1B
A timber built 2TS through road shed was opened here on March 2nd, 1875. The facilities included a turntable and use of the adjacent coaling stage at Durran Hill shed (NY4254.1/1). The depot closed in 1895 upon the opening of Currock Junction shed (NY4054.3/1A) and was subsequently demolished.

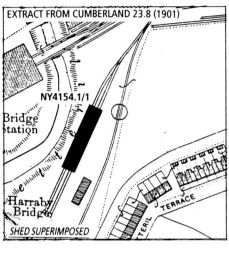

EXTRACT FROM CUMBERLAND 23.8 (1901)

SHED SUPERIMPOSED

CITADEL STATION

Site NY4055.0; At the north end of Citadel Station.
Carlisle (CR) NY4055.0/1A
A temporary timber built 1TS shed was opened here on September 10th, 1847 and closed in 1849. No further details are known.

WESTMORLAND

NY5426 Clifton

NY6820 Appleby West

NY6004 Tebay Loups Fell

SD4198 Windermere

NY6103 Tebay

NY7707 Kirkby Stephen

SD5390 Kendal Junction

SD5389 Oxenholme

WINDERMERE

Site SD4198.1; On the west side of Windermere Station.
Windermere (L&NWR)^{SD4198.1/1A}
A stone built ITS dead ended shed with a slated gable style roof, located at SD41389863 and opened in 1895. The facilities included a coal stage and turntable sited outside of the shed entrance. The depot was closed by the LMS in 1931.

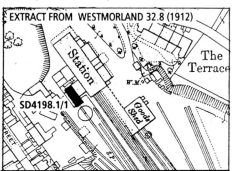

EXTRACT FROM WESTMORLAND 32.8 (1912)

SD4198.1/1

APPLEBY

Site NY6820.1; On the north side of the line, at the east end of Appleby West Station.
Appleby West (MR)^{NY6820.1/1A}
A ITS dead ended shed located at NY68722063 and opened on August 2nd, 1875. No further details are known other than it was demolished in the early 1900s.

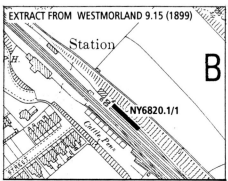

EXTRACT FROM WESTMORLAND 9.15 (1899)

B

NY6820.1/1

CLIFTON

Site NY5426.1; In the vicinity of Clifton Station.
Clifton (EVR)^{NY5426.1/1A}
A ITS shed, approximately located at NY541262, was opened here by the Eden Valley Railway on April 8th, 1862 and closed on August 1st, 1863. No further details are known.

Site NY6004.1; On the west side of the Carlisle line, north of Tebay Station.

Loups Fell (L&CR) NY6004.1/1A

A 2TS dead ended shed, located at NY60820498 and opened by the Lancaster & Carlisle Railway on December 17th, 1846. The facilities included a water tank and small turntable sited outside of the shed entrance. The depot was closed by the L&NWR in 1861.

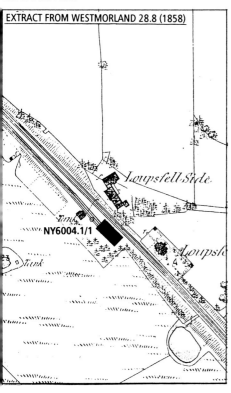

EXTRACT FROM WESTMORLAND 28.8 (1858)

NY6004.1/1

Replaced by ...

Site NY6103.1; On the west side of Tebay Station.

Tebay (L&NWR) NY6103.1/1A

A stone built 5TS dead ended shed with a slated twin hipped roof and a 1TS dead ended lean-to style building* attached to the eastern wall. It was located at NY61240354 and opened in 1861. The facilities included a turntable, water tank and, added later, a coal stage. By the mid-1930s the shed was roofless and it was demolished in 1947.

The shed was rebuilt ...

Tebay (LMS) NY6103.1/1B

A brick built 4TS dead ended shed with a louvre style roof and brick screen was constructed on the same site in 1947. A new coal plant and 60ft turntable were installed by BR in 1956 and the depot was closed on January 1st, 1968 and demolished the same year.

*This section may have been a later addition

Site NY6103.2; On the east side of the Barnard Castle line, north of Tebay Station.

Tebay (SD&LUR) NY6103.2/1A

A 1TS shed was opened here by the South Durham & Lancashire Union Railway on July 4th, 1861. It is assumed to have been located at NY61420393 and was closed by the NER in 1867.

Replaced, on the same site, by ...

Tebay (NER) NY6103.2/1B

A stone built 4TS dead ended shed with a slated twin gable style roof, it was opened in 1867. The facilities included a turntable and water tank. The depot closed in 1872, re-opened in 1878 and finally closed on October 30th, 1902. After closure locomotives continued to utilize the shed yard until the end of steam on the line in the 1960s. The building remained standing in a derelict condition until demolished in September 1942.

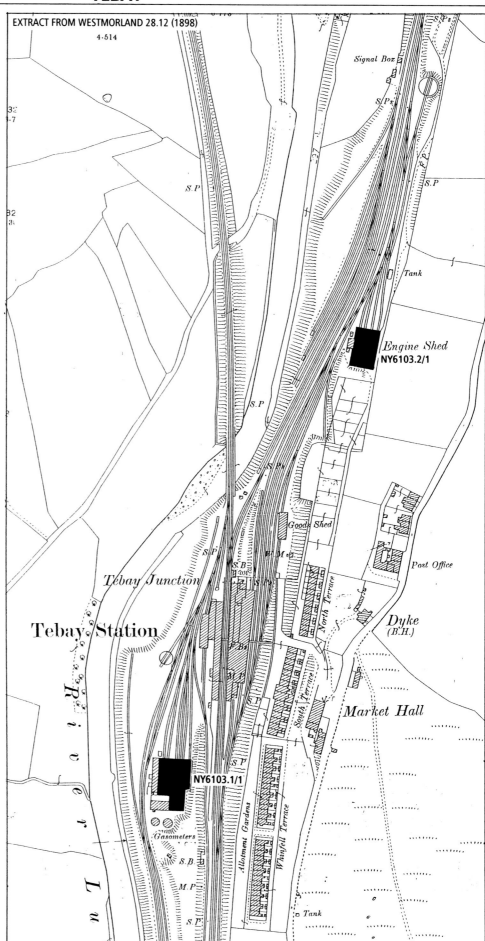

EXTRACT FROM WESTMORLAND 28.12 (1898)

Engine Shed NY6103.2/1

Tebay Junction

Tebay Station

NY6103.1/1

Site SD5390.1; On the east side of the Carlisle line, north of Oxenholme Station.
Kendal Junction* (K&WR) SD5390.1/1A
A 1TS dead ended shed located at SD53219040.

Site SD5390.2; On the east side of the line, at the south end of Oxenholme Station.
Kendal Junction* (K&WR) SD5390.2/1A
A 1TS dead ended shed located at SD53149016.

*It is not known if either, or indeed any, of these buildings were used for locomotive purposes. They were probably built by the Kendal & Windermere Railway and were in existence in 1858. No further details are known other than SD5390.1/1A was still standing in 1898, having been extended, and the other depot (SD5390.2/1A) was demolished to accommodate station enlargements.

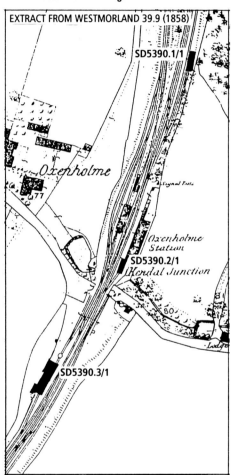

EXTRACT FROM WESTMORLAND 39.9 (1858)
SD5390.1/1
Oxenholme
77
Oxenholme Station
SD5390.2/1
Kendal Junction
80
SD5390.3/1
Lodge

Site SD5390.3; On the west side of the line, at the south end of Oxenholme Station.
Kendal Junction (K&WR) SD5390.3/1A
A 1TS through road shed located at SD53069007 and opened by the Kendal & Windermere Railway on September 21st, 1846. The facilities included a small turntable outside of the shed entrance. No further details are known other than it closed in 1880.

Replaced by ...
Site SD5389.1; On the west side of the line, at the south end of Oxenholme Station.
Oxenholme (L&NWR) SD5389.1/1A
A brick built 4TS dead ended shed with a northlight pattern roof, located at SD53008999 and opened in 1880. The facilities included a 42ft turntable and coal stage with water tank over.

The shed was re-roofed ...
Oxenholme (LMS) SD5389.1/1B
A slated multi-pitched roof was installed in 1938. The depot was closed by BR on June 18th, 1962 and demolished in 1966.

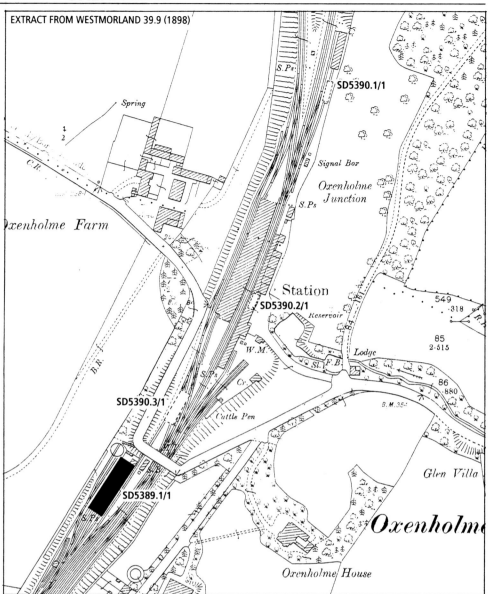

EXTRACT FROM WESTMORLAND 39.9 (1898)
Spring
Oxenholme Farm
SD5390.1/1
Signal Box
Oxenholme Junction
Station
SD5390.2/1
Reservoir
549
.318
85
2.515
W.M.
Lodge
86
.880
SD5390.3/1
Cattle Pen
SD5389.1/1
Glen Villa
Oxenholme
Oxenholme House

Site NY7707.1; On the north side of Kirkby Stephen (East) Station.
Kirkby Stephen (SD&LUR) NY7707.1/1A
A 1TS shed located at NY77000755 and opened on August 7th, 1861 by the South Durham & Lancashire Union Railway. The line was worked by the Stockton & Darlington Railway. No further details are known.

The shed was enlarged ...
Kirkby Stephen (NER) NY7707.1/1B
A stone built 2TS dead ended shed with a slated gable style roof was constructed on the same site in 1865.

The shed was enlarged again in 1866 ...
Kirkby Stephen (NER) NY7707.1/2A
A stone built 2TS dead ended shed with a slated gable style roof and located at NY77000754 was constructed on the south side. It was built at an angle, with the entrances adjoining and the back walls some distance apart. The gap between the two was walled and roofed creating a 4TS dead ended shed in the style of a semi-roundhouse. The facilities, by now, included a turntable, coal stage and water tank. The depot was closed by BR on November 20th, 1961 and, after standing derelict for some years, demolished.

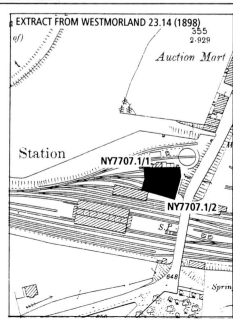

EXTRACT FROM WESTMORLAND 23.14 (1898)
355
2.929
Auction Mart
Station
NY7707.1/1
NY7707.1/2

GLASGOW

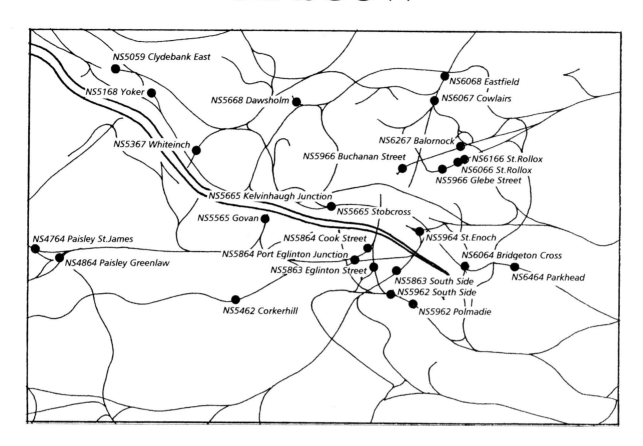

SOUTH SIDE

Site NS5863.1; In the fork of the Pollokshaws and Cathcart lines at the south end of South Side Station.

South Side (GB&KJR) NS5863.1/1A

A timber built 2TS dead ended shed located at NS58686356 and opened on September 27th, 1848 by the Glasgow, Barrhead & Kilmarnock Joint Railway. The facilities included a 15ft turntable. No further details are known.

South Side (CR) NS5863.1/2A

A 1TS dead ended shed located at NS58636350 and opened by the Clydesdale Junction Railway (CR). No further details are known.

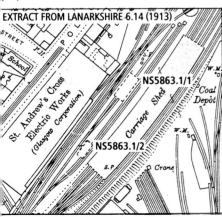

EXTRACT FROM LANARKSHIRE 6.14 (1913)

Replaced by ...

Site NS5962.2; On the north side of the line, east of Gushetfaulds Junction.

South Side (CR) NS5962.2/1A

A brick built 3TS dead ended shed, located at NS59186291 and opened in 1857. No further details are known.

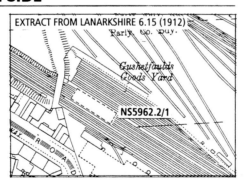

EXTRACT FROM LANARKSHIRE 6.15 (1912)

COOK STREET

Site NS5864.1; On the east side of the line, north of Eglinton Street Goods Station.

Cook Street (GPK&AR) NS5864.1/1A

An irregularly shaped 4TS dead ended shed consisting of a 2TS section with two shorter 1TS bays built along the western side. It was located at NS58526421 and was opened on July 13th, 1840 by the Glasgow, Paisley, Kilmarnock, & Ayrshire Railway. The depot incorporated the locomotive works and other facilities included a 42ft turntable. The line was absorbed by the G&SWR in 1851 and the works were moved out in 1856, all the accommodation then being utilized for the running shed. The depot closed in 1920.

EXTRACT FROM LANARKSHIRE 6.14 (1913)

EGLINTON STREET

Site NS5863.2; On the west side of Eglinton Street Station.

Eglinton Street (CR) NS5863.2/1A

A stone built 4TS dead ended shed with a single gable style slated roof, located at NS58446377 and opened in 1878. The facilities included a ramped coaling stage, water columns and a 42ft turntable, later enlarged to 51ft. The depot closed in 1885 and the shed building was later let out for private use.

The yard was re-opened ...

Eglinton Street (CR) NS5863.2/F1

A servicing area utilizing the turntable, sidings, pits and coal stage was established here in 1902 and closed by BR in 1960.

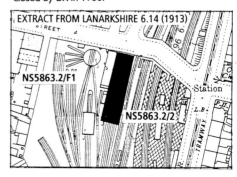

EXTRACT FROM LANARKSHIRE 6.14 (1913)

PORT EGLINTON JCT

Site NS5864.2; In the vicinity of Port Eglinton Junction, west of Eglinton Street (G&SWR) Station.

Port Eglinton Junction (G&SWR) NS5864.2/1A

Some sort of facility, approximately located at NS585640, was opened here. No further details are known.

POLMADIE

Site NS5962.1; On the north side of the Carstairs line, west of Rutherglen Station.
Polmadie (CR) NS5962.1/1A
A timber built 14TS shed with 7 through roads and a multi-pitched roof, it was located at NS59786266 and opened in September 1875. The facilities included a coal stage, water tank, repair shop and turntable.

The shed was rebuilt ...
Polmadie (LMS) NS5962.1/1B
A new 14TS structure in brick, with 7 through roads and a slated multi-pitched transverse roof was constructed on the same site in 1925. At the same time a mechanical coaling stage was installed and the repair shop rebuilt in brick.

The shed was rebuilt ...
Polmadie (BR) NS5962.1/1C
The roof was re-clad in corrugated sheeting by the Scottish Region and the shed yard remodelled. The shed closed to steam on May 1st, 1967 and saw use as a diesel depot for a number of years. In c1975 the shed buildings were demolished and only the 2TS repair shop, on the north side of the depot, was then utilized for locomotive servicing.

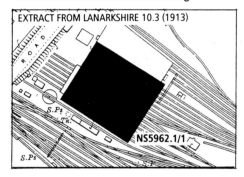
EXTRACT FROM LANARKSHIRE 10.3 (1913)
NS5962.1/1

EASTFIELD

Site NS6068.1; On the east side of the line, north of Cowlairs Station.
Eastfield (NB) NS6068.1/1A
A brick built 14TS through road shed with a transverse slated multi-pitched roof located at NS60036868 and opened in September 1904. The facilities originally included a ramped coal stage, replaced later with a mechanical coaling plant, water tank, and two turntables.

The shed was re-roofed ...
Eastfield (LNER) NS6068.1/1B
At some stage, possibly in the 1940s, the roof was re-clad. The depot was closed to steam by BR in November 1966 and a diesel depot constructed on the same site. This closed in 1992 and the whole site was cleared in 1995.

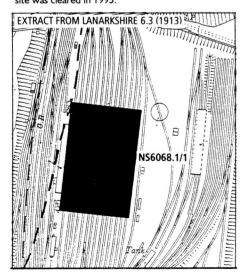
EXTRACT FROM LANARKSHIRE 6.3 (1913)
NS6068.1/1

PAISLEY

Site NS4764.1; In the vicinity of Paisley St.James Station.
Paisley St.James (CR) NS4764.1/1A
A timber built 1TS dead ended shed, approximately located at NS743643 and opened in 1913. There were no facilities. The depot was closed by the LMS in 1923 and demolished.

A servicing point was then established ...
Site NS4764.2; In the goods yard on the east side of Paisley St.James Station.
Paisley St.James (LMS) NS4764.2/F1
Locomotives utilized the water tower, engine pit and siding located at NS47346473 until the facility was closed by BR on January 3rd, 1953.

Site NS4864.1; At the west end of Paisley Station.
Paisley (P&RR) NS4864.1/1A
A shed, approximately located at NS480642 and *"on the left going north towards Renfrew"* was opened here by the Paisley & Renfrew Railway. No further details are known.

Site NS4864.2; In Greenlaw Goods Yard, on the north side of the line, east of Paisley Station.
Paisley Greenlaw (G&PJR) NS4864.2/1A
A 1TS dead ended shed, located at NS48966451 and opened in 1848 by the Glasgow & Paisley Joint Railway. The facilities included a water tank. The depot was closed by the LMS in 1924 and demolished in c1927. No further details are known.

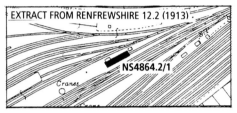
EXTRACT FROM RENFREWSHIRE 12.2 (1913)
NS4864.2/1

KELVINHAUGH JUNCTION

Site NS5665.2; In the vicinity of Kelvinhaugh Junction, between Charing Cross and Partick Stations.
Kelvinhaugh Junction (GC&DR) NS5665.2/1A
Some sort of facility, approximately located at NS565657, was opened here by the Glasgow City & District Railway. No further details are known.

STOBCROSS

Site NS5665.1; On the north side of the line, between Charing Cross and Partick Stations.
Stobcross (NB) NS5665.1/1A
A brick built 2TS dead ended shed with a slated gable style roof, located at NS56686574 and opened on October 20th, 1874. The facilities included a water tank and turntable. The depot was closed by BR in October 1950, let out for private use and subsequently demolished at some time in the 1960s.

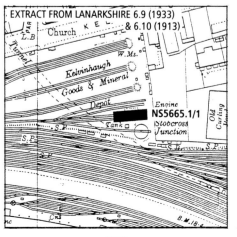
EXTRACT FROM LANARKSHIRE 6.9 (1933) & 6.10 (1913)
NS5665.1/1

PARKHEAD

Site NS6464.1; On the south side of the line, east of Parkhead Station.
Parkhead (NB) NS6464.1/1A
A brick built 6TS through road shed with a slated triple gable style roof, located at NS64806458 and opened on February 2nd, 1871. The facilities included a water tank, coal stage and turntable.

The shed was re-roofed ...
Parkhead (BR) NS6464.1/1B
A new triple pitched roof, probably clad in corrugated sheeting, with an unusual castellated style brick screen was installed by the Scottish Region shortly after nationalization. The depot closed on October 18th, 1965 and was subsequently demolished.

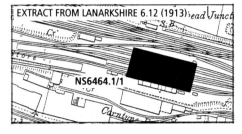
EXTRACT FROM LANARKSHIRE 6.12 (1913)
NS6464.1/1

DAWSHOLM

Site NS5668.1; On the east side of the goods branch, north of Maryhill Station.
Dawsholm (CR) NS5668.1/1A
A brick built 6TS dead ended shed with a northlight pattern roof, located at NS56456859 and opened on August 10th, 1896. The facilities included a ramped coal stage, water tank, turntable and repair shop.

The shed was re-roofed ...
Dawsholm (BR) NS5668.1/1B
A louvre style roof with brick screen was installed by the Scottish Region in 1949. The depot closed on October 5th, 1964 and was subsequently demolished.

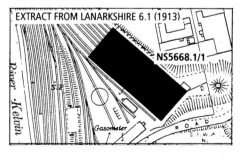
EXTRACT FROM LANARKSHIRE 6.1 (1913)
NS5668.1/1

GLEBE STREET

Site NS5966.1; On the north side of the St.Rollox Goods Branch.
Glebe Street (G&GR) NS5966.1/1A
A stone built 2TS dead ended shed located at NS59846633 and opened by the Glasgow & Garnkirk Railway in 1835. Details of the facilities are not known. The depot closed in 1847 and the building was utilized for a while by the Permanent Way Department. A unique feature of the building was that it was constructed in two storeys with living accommodation occupying the first floor and it is believed that this was utilized as a private dwelling for many years after the shed had closed.

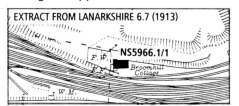
EXTRACT FROM LANARKSHIRE 6.7 (1913)
NS5966.1/1

CLYDEBANK EAST

Site NS5069.1; On the south side of the line, at the east end of Clydebank East Station.
Clydebank East (GY&CR) NS5069.1/1A
A brick built 1TS dead ended shed with a slated gable style roof, located at NS50176975 and opened on December 1st, 1882 by the Glasgow, Yoker and Clydebank Railway. The facilities included a turntable, sited outside of the shed entrance. Although the depot was closed by the LNER in 1925 the building remained standing until at least 1950.

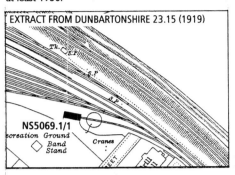

WHITEINCH

Site NS5367.1; On the west side of the line, at the north end of Whiteinch Station.
Whiteinch (NB) NS5367.1/1A
A brick built 1TS dead ended shed with a slated gable style roof, located at NS5367651 and opened on December 1st, 1897. There were no facilities. The depot was closed by the LNER in 1939 but locomotives continued to be serviced on the shed road until about 1951. The building was let out for private use and demolished in the 1960s.

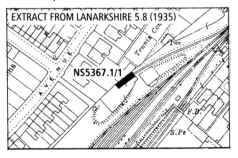

ST.ENOCH

Site NS5964.1; In the triangle of lines at the east end of St.Enoch Station.
St.Enoch (G&SWR) NS5964.1/1A
A brick built 12TS dead ended shed with a slated transverse multi-hipped roof, it was located at NS59416477 and opened in 1884. The facilities included a coal stage, water tank and 50ft turntable. An unusual feature was that the depot was built on brick arches and this gave rise to an assumed limit as to the size and weight of locomotives that it could accommodate. The depot was closed by the LMS on April 13th, 1935 and saw further use for engine storage and, later, as a materials store. It lasted into the 1970s before demolition took place.

BUCHANAN STREET

Site NS5966.1; On the north side of the line, at the east end of Buchanan Street Station.
Buchanan Street (CR) NS5966.1/1A
A brick built 2TS dead ended shed with a slated gable style roof, located at NS59336621 and opened on November 1st, 1849. The facilities included a coke/coal stage, water column and 20ft turntable, enlarged to 48ft in 1862 and to 60ft in 1905. Although the depot closed in 1916, upon the opening of Balornock shed (NS6267.1/1), the building remained standing until the early 1950s.

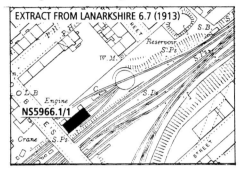

GOVAN

Site NS5565.1; On the west side of the line, south of Govan Station.
Govan (CR/G&SWR) NS5565.1/F1
A servicing area consisting of a turntable and siding was opened here in 1868 and closed in c1899. No further details are known.

Replaced by ...
Govan (CR/G&SWR) NS5565.1/1A
A 2TS dead ended shed, located at NS55296513 and opened in c1899. It was closed by the LMS in 1923. No further details are known.

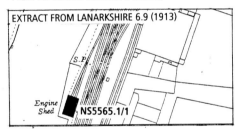

COWLAIRS

Site NS6067.1; On the west side of Cowlairs Station.
Cowlairs (NB) NS6067.1/1A
A stone built 15TS dead ended shed with a gable style slated multi-pitched roof, it was located at NS60006775. Being sited adjacently to the main locomotive works the depot had use of all facilities. The opening date is not known but it closed upon the opening of Eastfield shed (NS6068.1/1) in September 1904 with the buildings being absorbed into the works complex.

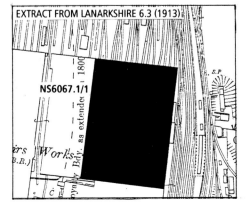

YOKER

Site NS5168.1; On the north side of the goods line between Scotstoun West and Clydebank Dock West Junctions.
Yoker* (CR) NS5168.1/1A
A brick built 2TS dead ended shed with a slated gable style roof, located at NS51696866 and opened in March 1907. The facilities included a water tank, ramped coaling stage and turntable. The depot was closed to steam by BR in March 1961 and totally in January 1964, but continued in use as a diesel depot until demolition.

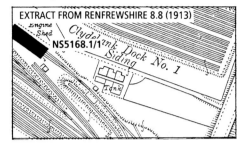

*It was also known as Rothesay Dock.

CORKERHILL

Site NS5462.1; On the south side of the line, east of Corkerhill Station.
Corkerhill (G&SWR) NS5462.1/1A
A brick built 6TS through road shed with a northlight pattern roof, located at NS54536278 and opened in 1896. The facilities included a ramped coal stage with water tank over, turntable and repair shop.

The shed was partially re-roofed ...
Corkerhill (BR) NS5462.1/1B
The eastern end of the building was rebuilt by the Scottish Region with a triple gable style roof in corrugated sheeting. The depot closed to steam on May 1st, 1967 and was then utilized for diesel servicing prior to demolition in the 1970s. An emu servicing facility was later established on the site.

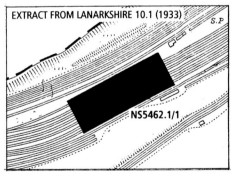

BRIDGETON CROSS

Site NS6064.1; On the west side of Bridgeton Cross (NBR) Station.
Bridgeton Cross (NB) NS6064.1/F1
A facility consisting of a water column, turntable, located at NS60636414, siding and coal stage opened here on June 1st, 1892. No further details are known other than it probably was still in use in BR days.

ST.ROLLOX

Site NS6066.1; On the south side of St.Rollox Works.
St.Rollox (CR) NS6066.1/1A
A shed, located at NS60476650, opened here in June 1856. No further details are known

The shed was enlarged ...
St.Rollox (CR) NS6066.1/1B
The building was extended in 1864. No further details are known

The shed was enlarged again ...
St.Rollox (CR) NS6066.1/1C
The building was extended in 1870 to a 5TS dead ended structure. No further details are known. The depot closed in December 1880 and the site was absorbed into the works complex.

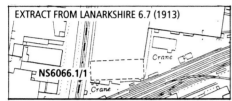
EXTRACT FROM LANARKSHIRE 6.7 (1913)
NS6066.1/1

Replaced by ...
Site NS6166.1; In St.Rollox Works Yard.
St.Rollox (CR) NS6166.1/1A
A brick built 4TS shed with two through roads, it was located at NS61136678 and opened in December 1880. The facilities included a water tank, coal stage and turntable. The depot closed in 1916 and was immediately demolished, the shed roads subsequently being utilized for the storage of rolling stock.

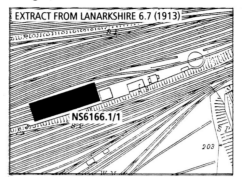
EXTRACT FROM LANARKSHIRE 6.7 (1913)
NS6166.1/1

Replaced by ...
Site NS6267.1; On the north side of the line, east of Buchanan Street Station.
Balornock (CR) NS6267.1/1A
A brick built 12TS through road shed with a transverse slated multi-pitched roof, located at NS62216729 and opened in 1916. The facilities included a water tank, ramped coaling stage, repair shop and turntable. The depot was closed by BR on November 7th, 1966 and later demolished.

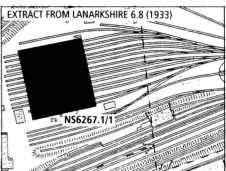
EXTRACT FROM LANARKSHIRE 6.8 (1933)
NS6267.1/1

KIRKCUDBRIGHT

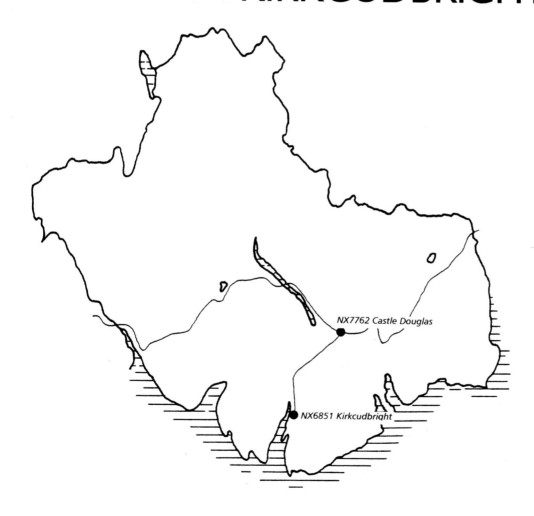

NX7762 Castle Douglas

NX6851 Kirkcudbright

CASTLE DOUGLAS

Site NX7762.1; On the north side of the line, at the east end of Castle Douglas Station.
Castle Douglas (CD&DR) NX7762.1/1A
A 2TS through road shed, possibly located at NX77036285 and opened on November 7th, 1859 by the Castle Douglas & Dumfries Railway. The facilities included a 40ft turntable. No further details are known. The line was taken over by the Portpatrick & Wigtownshire Joint in 1884 and the depot was closed shortly after.

Replaced by ...
Castle Douglas (G&SWR) NX7762.1/2A
A 1TS through road shed with a slated gable style roof located at NX77036285. The facilities included a water tank and the turntable of its predecessor. The opening date is not known but the depot closed in 1921.

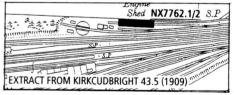
NX7762.1/2
EXTRACT FROM KIRKCUDBRIGHT 43.5 (1909)

KIRKCUDBRIGHT

Site NX6851.1; On the east side of the line, at the north end of Kirkcudbright Station.
Kirkcudbright (Kirkcudbright) NX6851.1/1A
A stone built 1TS through road shed with a slated gable style roof, located at NX68635125 and opened by the Kirkcudbright Railway on February 17th, 1864. The facilities included a water tank and 42ft turntable, later enlarged to 44ft 6ins. The depot was closed by BR in 1955 and the building let out for private use. It was later demolished.

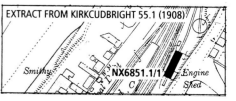
EXTRACT FROM KIRKCUDBRIGHT 55.1 (1908)
NX6851.1/1

DUMFRIES-SHIRE

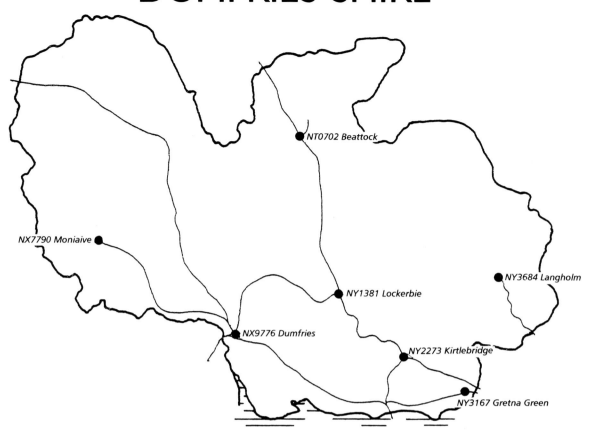

NT0702 Beattock

NX7790 Moniaive

NY3684 Langholm

NY1381 Lockerbie

NX9776 Dumfries

NY2273 Kirtlebridge

NY3167 Gretna Green

BEATTOCK

Site NT0702.1; On the west side of the line, at the north end of Beattock Station.
Beattock (CR) NT0702.1/1A
A stone built 2TS shed with a slated gable style roof located at NT07670249 and opened on September 10th, 1847. No further details are known.

The shed was enlarged ...
Beattock (CR) NT0702.1/1B
The building was extended in 1857.

The shed was enlarged again ...
Beattock (CR) NT0702.1/1C
The building was extended in 1869. By this time the shed had two through roads and the facilities included a 42ft turntable and coal stage. The depot was closed to steam by BR on May 1st, 1967 and then housed the diesel locomotives utilized for banking duties until demolished in 1978.

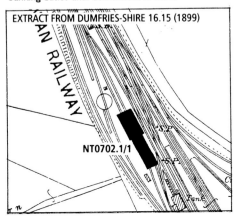

EXTRACT FROM DUMFRIES-SHIRE 16.15 (1899)

AN RAILWAY

NT0702.1/1

KIRTLEBRIDGE

Site NY2273.1; On the west side of the line, at the north end of Kirtlebridge Station.
Kirtlebridge (SJR) NY2273.1/1A
A 2TS shed, probably located at NY22577367 and opened on September 13th, 1869 by the Solway Junction Railway. The facilities included a 42ft turntable and water column. The building was demolished under a local order dated July 16th, 1895.

Replaced, on the same site, by ...
Kirtlebridge (CR) NY2273.1/1B
A timber built 2TS through road shed with a gable style roof it opened in 1895 and was closed by the LMS on April 27th, 1931.

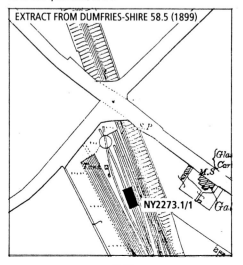

EXTRACT FROM DUMFRIES-SHIRE 58.5 (1899)

NY2273.1/1

LOCKERBIE

Site NY1381.1; On the east side of Lockerbie Station.
Lockerbie (DL&LJR) NY1381.1/1A
A stone built 2TS dead ended shed with a slated gable style roof, located at NY13778184 and opened on September 1st, 1863 by the Dumfries, Lochmaben & Lockerbie Junction Railway. The facilities included a 42ft turntable, water tank and, installed in c1901, a coal stage. The depot was closed by the LMS in April 1931 and the building remained standing until the 1960s.

A stabling point was then established ...
Lockerbie (LMS) NY1381.1/F1
Locomotives utilized the siding, turntable, coal stage and water tank until closure by BR on February 5th, 1951.

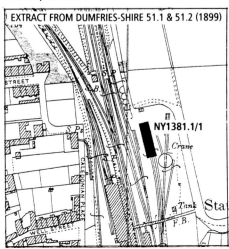

EXTRACT FROM DUMFRIES-SHIRE 51.1 & 51.2 (1899)

NY1381.1/1

DUMFRIES

Site NX9776.1; On the north side of the Kilmarnock line, at the east end of Dumfries (GD&CR) Station.
Dumfries (GD&CR) NX9776.1/1A
A 1TS dead ended shed located at NX97937618 and opened on August 23rd, 1848 by the Glasgow, Dumfries & Carlisle Railway. The facilities included a turntable sited outside of the shed entrance. No further details are known other than it closed on October 15th, 1849.

Replaced by ...
Site NX9776.2; On the north side of Dumfries (GD&CR) Station.
Dumfries (GD&CR) NX9776.2/1A
A 3TS dead ended shed located at NX97877620 and opened on October 15th, 1849 by the Glasgow, Dumfries & Carlisle Railway. The facilities included a water column, the turntable of its predecessor (NX9776.1/1A) and a coke/coal stage. The line merged with the Glasgow, Paisley, Kilmarnock & Ayr Railway in 1850 to form the G&SWR, and the depot closed in 1878.

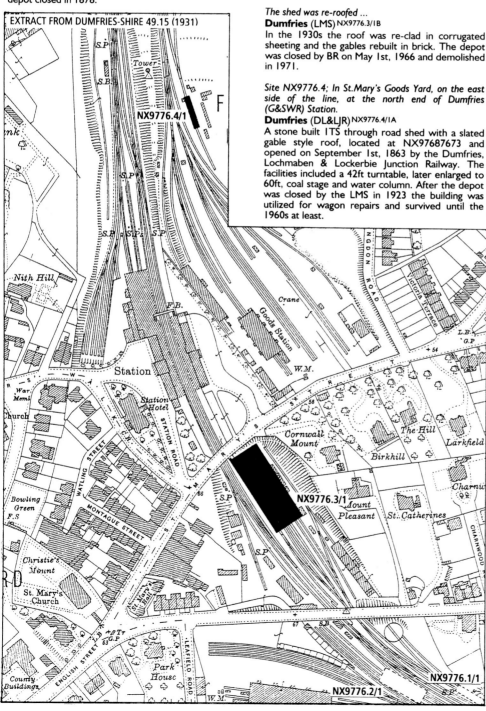

EXTRACT FROM DUMFRIES-SHIRE 49.15 (1931)

NX9776.4/1

NX9776.3/1

NX9776.1/1

NX9776.2/1

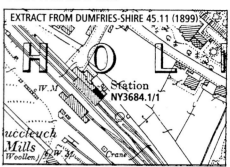

EXTRACT FROM DUMFRIES-SHIRE 49.15 & 55.3 (1858)

NX9776.2/1

NX9776.1/1

Replaced by ...
Site NX9776.3; On the east side of the line, south of Dumfries (G&SWR) Station.
Dumfries (G&SWR) NX9776.3/1A
A stone built 6TS dead ended shed with a twin slated gable style roof, located at NX97747638 and opened in 1878. The facilities included a turntable, water columns and, installed in 1893, a ramped coaling stage.

The shed was re-roofed ...
Dumfries (LMS) NX9776.3/1B
In the 1930s the roof was re-clad in corrugated sheeting and the gables rebuilt in brick. The depot was closed by BR on May 1st, 1966 and demolished in 1971.

Site NX9776.4; In St.Mary's Goods Yard, on the east side of the line, at the north end of Dumfries (G&SWR) Station.
Dumfries (DL&LJR) NX9776.4/1A
A stone built 1TS through road shed with a slated gable style roof, located at NX97687673 and opened on September 1st, 1863 by the Dumfries, Lochmaben & Lockerbie Junction Railway. The facilities included a 42ft turntable, later enlarged to 60ft, coal stage and water column. After the depot was closed by the LMS in 1923 the building was utilized for wagon repairs and survived until the 1960s at least.

LANGHOLM

Site NY3684.1; On the east side of Langholm Station.
Langholm (NB/BUR) NY3684.1/1A
A stone built 1TS dead ended shed with a slated gable style roof located at NY36598425 and opened on April 18th, 1864. The facilities included a turntable sited outside of the shed entrance. The depot was closed by the LNER in May 1932 and later de-roofed with the remains, being an integral part of the station buildings, surviving until the closure of the line in 1967.

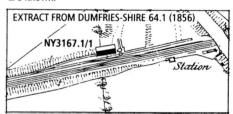

EXTRACT FROM DUMFRIES-SHIRE 45.11 (1899)

NY3684.1/1

GRETNA GREEN

Site NY3167.1; On the north side of the line, at the west end of Gretna Green Station.
Gretna Green (GD&CR) NY3167.1/1A
A goods shed, located at NY31956788 was utilized as a 1TS through road engine shed by the Glasgow, Dumfries & Carlisle Railway between August 23rd, 1848 and October 28th, 1850. No further details are known.

EXTRACT FROM DUMFRIES-SHIRE 64.1 (1856)

NY3167.1/1

MONIAIVE

Site NX7790.1; In the vicinity of Moniaive Station.
Moniaive (CVLR) NX7790.1/1A
A 1TS shed, approximately located at NX77959073 was opened here on March 1st, 1905 by the Cairn Valley Light Railway. No further details are known. The line was worked from the outset by the G&SWR and the depot closed in 1921.

LANARKSHIRE

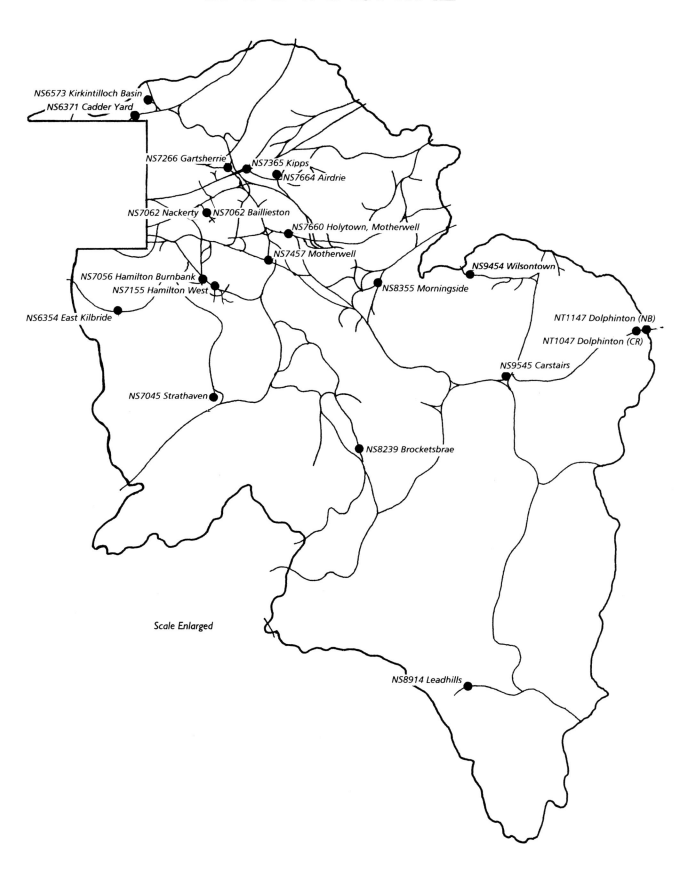

NS6573 Kirkintilloch Basin
NS6371 Cadder Yard

NS7266 Gartsherrie
NS7365 Kipps
NS7664 Airdrie

NS7062 Nackerty
NS7062 Baillieston

NS7660 Holytown, Motherwell

NS7457 Motherwell

NS9454 Wilsontown

NS7056 Hamilton Burnbank
NS7155 Hamilton West

NS8355 Morningside

NS6354 East Kilbride

NT1147 Dolphinton (NB)

NT1047 Dolphinton (CR)

NS9545 Carstairs

NS7045 Strathaven

NS8239 Brocketsbrae

Scale Enlarged

NS8914 Leadhills

343

MORNINGSIDE

Site NS8355.2; In the vicinity of Chapel sidings.
Morningside (W&CR) NS8355.2/1A
A shed was opened here in 1842 by the Wishaw & Coltness Railway. No further details are known other than it closed in 1855.

Site NS8355.3; In the goods yard on the east side of Morningside (CR) Station.
Morningside (CR) NS8355.3/F1
By about 1880 the locomotives were stabling in the sidings which were located at NS83235503. In c1900 this practice ceased when an agreement was reached with the NB to enable them to utilize the depot at Morningside (NS8355.1/1).

Site NS8355.1; On the west side of Morningside (NB) Station.
Morningside (NB) NS8355.1/1A
A 2TS dead ended shed, located at NS83335522 and opened at some time prior to 1859. No further details are known other than it had been closed and demolished by 1912.

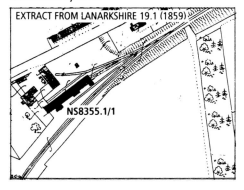

EXTRACT FROM LANARKSHIRE 19.1 (1859)
NS8355.1/1

Replaced, on the same site, by ...
Morningside (NB) NS8355.1/1B
A servicing area consisting of a turntable, sidings, coal stage, engine pit and water tower was established here. The facility was officially closed by BR in November 1954 but saw further use until c1960.

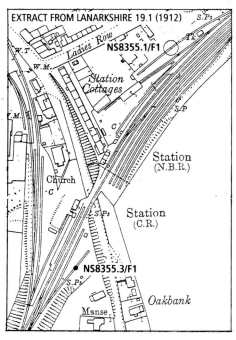

EXTRACT FROM LANARKSHIRE 19.1 (1912)
NS8355.1/F1
NS8355.3/F1

EAST KILBRIDE

Site NS6354.1; In the vicinity of East Kilbride Station.
East Kilbride (CR) NS6354.1/1A
A shed, approximately located at NS633547, was opened here in May 1878. No further details are known other than it had been removed by 1896.

AIRDRIE

Site NS7664.1; On the east side of the line, south of Airdrie (CR) Station.
Airdrie (CR) NS7664.1/1A
A timber built 2TS shed, located at NS76246477 and opened on April 19th, 1886. The facilities included a 42ft turntable and coal stage. No further details are known.

The shed was extended ...
Airdrie (CR) NS7664.1/1B
The building was enlarged in 1897 but was destroyed by a fire on November 21st, 1899.

Replaced, on the same site, by ...
Airdrie (CR) NS7664.1/1C
A timber built 3TS dead ended shed with a slated and glazed northlight pattern roof, it opened in November 1900. The facilities now included a ramped coaling stage and water tank, but the turntable had been removed. The depot was closed by the LMS on September 11th, 1939 and subsequently demolished.

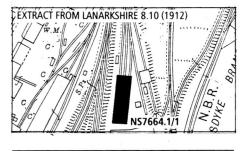

EXTRACT FROM LANARKSHIRE 8.10 (1912)
NS7664.1/1

BAILLIESTON

Site NS7062.0; In the vicinity of Bredisholm Collieries.
Nackerty (F&CN) NS7062.0/1A
A shed, opened by the Forth & Clyde Navigation, was in existence here in 1860. No further details are known.

Site NS7062.1; On the west side of the Tannochside Branch and adjacent to Bredisholm Collieries Pit No.3.
Baillieston (CR) NS7062.1/1A
A brick built 3TS dead ended shed, located at NS70626244 and opened in 1877. No further details are known other than it was closed by the LMS in 1935 and demolished in 1936.

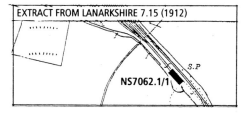

EXTRACT FROM LANARKSHIRE 7.15 (1912)
NS7062.1/1

LEADHILLS

Site NS8914.1; On the south side of the line, east of Wanlockhead Station.
Leadhills (CR) NS8914.1/1A
A timber built 1TS dead ended shed with a slated gable style roof, located at NS89201462 and opened on October 1st, 1901. The facilities included a water tank. The depot was closed by the LMS on January 2nd, 1939 and subsequently demolished.

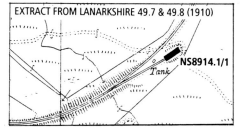

EXTRACT FROM LANARKSHIRE 49.7 & 49.8 (1910)
NS8914.1/1

HAMILTON

Site NS7155.0; In the vicinity of Hamilton West (CR) Station.
Hamilton (CR) NS7155.0/1A
A 1TS shed was opened here on September 17th, 1849 and possibly closed and removed in the following year. No further details are known.

Replaced by ...
Hamilton West (CR) NS7155.0/2A
A shed was opened here in 1861 and, upon closure in 1884, removed to Bridgeton for further use as a goods shed. No further details are known.

Replaced by ...
Site NS7155.1; On the west side of the line, at the north end of Hamilton West (CR) Station.
Hamilton West (CR) NS7155.1/1A
A timber built 10TS dead ended shed with a gable style multi-pitched roof, located at NS71065595 and opened in 1884. The facilities included a ramped coaling stage, with water tank over, 50ft turntable and repair shop.

The shed was partially demolished ...
Hamilton West (LMS) NS7155.1/1B
As a result of subsidence due to coal workings, part of the northern end of the building was removed.

The shed was re-roofed ...
Hamilton West (LMS) NS7155.1/1C
At some stage the remaining part of the depot was re-roofed in a simple shallow multi-pitched style with corrugated sheeting. The shed was closed to steam by BR in November 1962 and a new dmu depot (NS7155.1/1D) constructed on the site in c1968. It closed completely in July 1982.

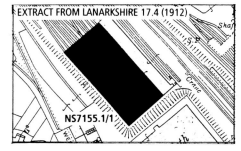

EXTRACT FROM LANARKSHIRE 17.4 (1912)
NS7155.1/1

Site NS7056.1; On the east side of the line, north of Hamilton Burnbank Station.
Hamilton Burnbank (GHB&CR) NS7056.1/1A
A brick built 3TS dead ended shed with a slated gable style roof located at NS70125684 and opened in 1890 by the Glasgow, Hamilton, Bothwell & Coatbridge Railway. The facilities included a coal stage and 50ft turntable. The building suffered from the effects of subsidence and as a result the depot was closed by the LNER in April 1933 and subsequently demolished.

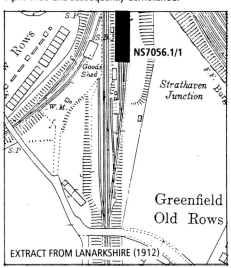

NS7056.1/1
EXTRACT FROM LANARKSHIRE (1912)

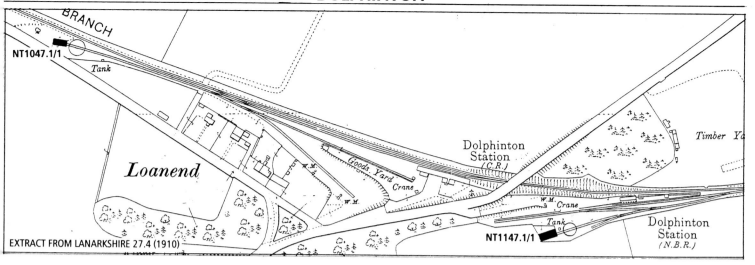

EXTRACT FROM LANARKSHIRE 27.4 (1910)

Site NT1047.1; On the south side of the line, west of Dolphinton (CR) Station.
Dolphinton (CR) NT1047.1/1A
A ITS dead ended shed, probably built in timber with a gable style roof, located at NT10864799 and opened in 1869. The building was originally the engine shed at Dunblane (as NN7701.1/1A) and the facilities included a turntable, sited outside of the shed entrance, and water tank. The depot closed on December 31st, 1915 and was demolished in 1933.

Site NT1147.1; On the south side of the line, at the west end of Dolphinton (NB) Station.
Dolphinton (LL&DR) NT1147.1/1A
A stone built ITS dead ended shed with a slated gable style roof, located at NT1314780 and opened on July 4th, 1864 by the Leadburn, Linton & Dolphinton Railway. The facilities included a turntable, sited outside of the shed entrance, and water tank. The line was worked by the NBR which absorbed it on July 31st, 1865. The depot was closed by the LNER on April 1st, 1933 and let out to private use, surviving until at least 1996 as a store for farm machinery.

KIRKINTILLOCH

Site NS6573.1; In the vicinity of Kirkintilloch Basin.
Kirkintilloch Basin (M&KR) NS6573.1/1A
A 4ft 6in gauge ITS shed was opened here by the Monklands & Kirkintilloch Railway in May 1831. No further details are known.

The line was re-gauged ...
Kirkintilloch Basin (M&KR) NS6573.1/1B
The track was altered to standard gauge on July 26th, 1847. No further details are known.

Replaced by ...
Site NS6573.2; In the works at Kirkintilloch Basin.
Kirkintilloch Basin (NB) NS6573.2/1A
At some stage, possibly in NB days, locomotives then utilized the ITS through road works building at NS65007320. The depot was closed by the LNER in 1947.

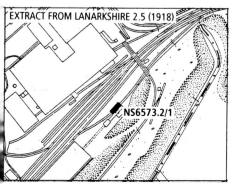

EXTRACT FROM LANARKSHIRE 2.5 (1918)
NS6573.2/1

CARSTAIRS

Site NS9545.1; On the north side of Carstairs Station.
Carstairs (CR) NS9545.1/1A
A timber built shed, converted from a store, was opened here on December 15th, 1848 and closed in 1853. No further details are known.

Replaced, probably not on the same site, by ...
Carstairs (CR) NS9545.1/2A
A timber built 4TS through road shed with a Dutch barn style roof, located at NS95354543 and opened in 1853. The facilities included a water tank, coal stage, replaced with a ramped coaling stage in 1860, and a turntable which was enlarged to 50ft in 1896.

The shed was rebuilt in 1935 ...
Carstairs (LMS) NS9545.1/2B
A brick built 4TS through road shed with a corrugated sheeting multi-pitched gable style roof was constructed on the same site. The facilities included a mechanical coaling plant. The depot was closed to steam by BR on February 2nd, 1967 and utilized as a diesel depot into the 1970s when it was demolished, locomotives thereafter stabling in the open.

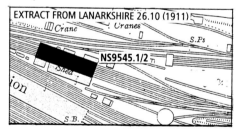

EXTRACT FROM LANARKSHIRE 26.10 (1911)
NS9545.1/2

BROCKETSBRAE

Site NS8239.1; On the east side of the line, at the south end of Brocketsbrae Station.
Brocketsbrae (CR) NS8239.1/1A
A ITS through road shed located at NS82393965 and opened in 1877. No further details are known other than it was closed by the LMS in 1924 and demolished in 1929.

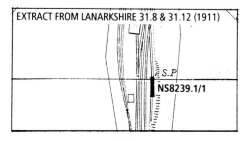

EXTRACT FROM LANARKSHIRE 31.8 & 31.12 (1911)
NS8239.1/1

MOTHERWELL

Site NS7660.1; In the vicinity of Holytown Station.
Holytown (W&CR) NS7660.1/1A
A shed was opened here in 1840 by the Wishaw & Coltness Railway and closed in 1842. No further details are known.

Site NS7457.1; On the west side of the Coatbridge line, north of Motherwell Station.
Motherwell (CR) NS7457.1/1A
A stone built 8TS through road shed with a slated gable style quadruple-pitched roof, located at NS74915795 and opened in 1866. The facilities included a water tank, ramped coal stage and turntable.

The shed was re-roofed ...
Motherwell (BR) NS7457.1/1B
At some stage in the early 1950s the gables at one end were replaced and the roof reclad in corrugated sheeting by the Scottish Region. The depot closed to steam on July 1st, 1967 and it was subsequently utilized as a diesel depot and wagon repair shop. By 1996 it had become Scotland's main loco depot.

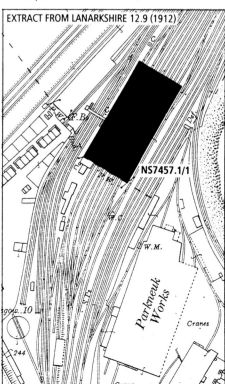

EXTRACT FROM LANARKSHIRE 12.9 (1912)
NS7457.1/1

STRATHAVEN

Site NS7045.1; On the east side of the line, at the north end of Strathaven (1st) Station.
Strathaven (H&SR) NS7045.1/1A
A 1TS through road shed located at NS70834514 and opened in October 1871 by the Hamilton & Strathaven Railway. The facilities included a water tank and a 40ft turntable sited outside of the shed entrance. The line was worked by the CR and absorbed by them on July 25th, 1864. No further details are known other than by 1907 the building had become semi-derelict.

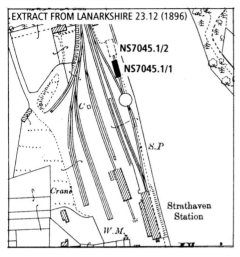
EXTRACT FROM LANARKSHIRE 23.12 (1896)

Replaced by ...
Strathaven (CR) NS7045.1/2A
A 1TS through road shed constructed at the rear of its predecessor (NS7045.1/1A) in 1907 and sited at NS70824516. The depot was closed by the LMS in 1931 and demolished in 1934.

EXTRACT FROM LANARKSHIRE 23.12 (1912)

GARTSHERRIE

Site NS7266.1; On the east side of the line, at the south end of Gartsherrie Station.
Gartsherrie (G&GR) NS7266.1/1A
A 4ft 6in gauge 2TS through road shed, located at NS72206672 and opened on September 27th, 1831 by the Glasgow & Garnkirk Railway. No further details are known.

The line was re-gauged ...
Gartsherrie (G&GR) NS7266.1/1B
The track was altered to standard gauge in c1840 and the depot closed in March 1866. No further details are known.

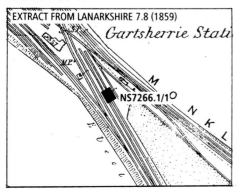
EXTRACT FROM LANARKSHIRE 7.8 (1859)

KIPPS

Site NS7365.1; On the north side of the line, east of Coatbridge Sunnyside Station.
Kipps (M&KR) NS7365.1/1A
A 1TS through road shed, probably located at NS73956580, and opened in 1837 by the Monklands & Kirkintilloch Railway. No further details are known other than it was destroyed by a fire in 1890.

Replaced by ...
Kipps (NB) NS7365.1/2A
A brick built 3TS through road shed with a slated pitched roof with wooden gables, it was sited slightly west of its predecessor, NS7365.1/1A, at NS73856577 and opened on March 18th, 1890. The building had originally been utilized as a contractors' shed during the building of the Forth Bridge and the facilities included a turntable, water tank and coal stage, later replaced by a mechanical coaling plant. The depot was closed to steam by BR in January 1963 and stabled diesels until at least 1966.

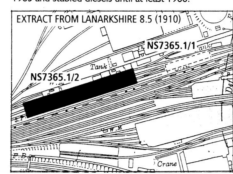
EXTRACT FROM LANARKSHIRE 8.5 (1910)

CADDER YARD

Site NS6371.1; On the north side of the Edinburgh line, west of Lenzie Station.
Cadder Yard (CR) NS6371.1/F1
A servicing area consisting of a turntable, located at NS63767131, water tank, coal stage and siding. No further details are known other than it was in existence in 1909 and was still utilized in BR days.

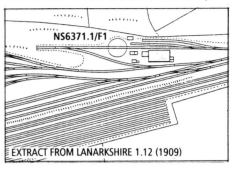
EXTRACT FROM LANARKSHIRE 1.12 (1909)

WILSONTOWN

Site NS9454.1; On the north side of Wilsontown Station.
Wilsontown (CR) NS9454.1/F1
A servicing area consisting of a siding located at NS94885492. No further details are known.

EXTRACT FROM LANARKSHIRE 20.1 (1911)

An end-to-end junction was made at **Dolphinton** between the CR and the Leadburn Linton & Dolphinton Railway, later NBR. Each company had a single road engine shed in the village with the CR building (NT1047.1/1A) closing as early as 1915 with demolition in 1933, the same year in which the NBR shed (NT1147.1/1A) closed.

The latter building remained in other use for many years, as seen here on June 1st, 1958. Note the ramp up to the right hand window - it seems the shed could have been a very large chicken coop!
WT Stubbs

AYRSHIRE

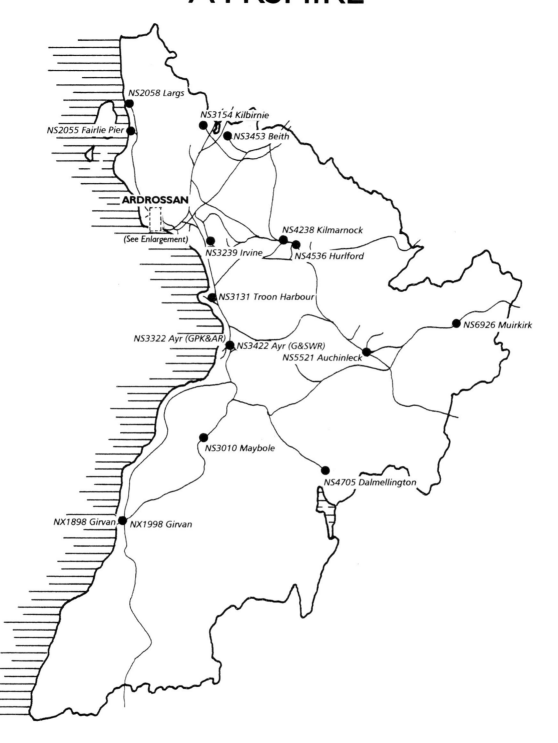

NS2058 Largs

NS3154 Kilbirnie

NS2055 Fairlie Pier

NS3453 Beith

ARDROSSAN

(See Enlargement)

NS4238 Kilmarnock

NS3239 Irvine

NS4536 Hurlford

NS3131 Troon Harbour

NS6926 Muirkirk

NS3322 Ayr (GPK&AR)

NS3422 Ayr (G&SWR)

NS5521 Auchinleck

NS3010 Maybole

NS4705 Dalmellington

NX1898 Girvan

NX1998 Girvan

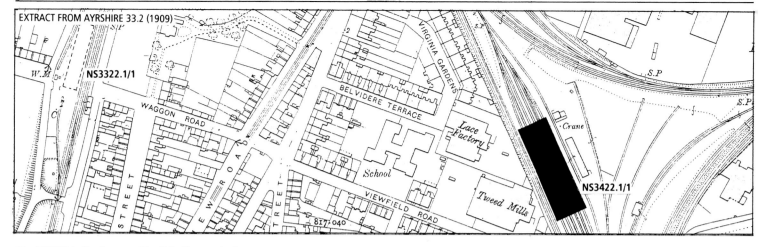

EXTRACT FROM AYRSHIRE 33.2 (1909)

NS3322.1/1

NS3422.1/1

Site NS3322.1; On the west side of the line, north of Ayr Station.
Ayr (GKP&AR) NS3322.1/1A
A 3TS dead ended shed, located at NS33852287 and opened on August 5th, 1839 by the Glasgow, Kilmarnock, Paisley & Ayr Railway. The facilities included a turntable, sited outside of the shed entrance, coal stage and water column. The line was absorbed by the G&SWR on October 28th, 1850 and the depot closed in 1879.

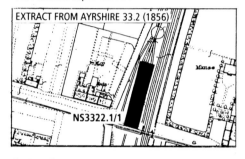

EXTRACT FROM AYRSHIRE 33.2 (1856)

NS3322.1/1

Replaced by ...
Site NS3422.1: In the triangle of Ayr to Newton on Ayr to Auchincruive lines, north of Ayr Station.
Ayr (G&SWR) NS3422.1/1A
A brick built 6TS through road shed with a slated twin gable style roof, located at NS34302275 and opened in 1879. The facilities originally included a coal stage and water tank. By 1913 a 60ft turntable had been installed and a ramped coaling stage constructed.

The shed was re-roofed ...
Ayr (LMS) NS3422.1/1B
At some stage the roofs were re-clad in timber and felt and at least one of the gables rebuilt in timber.

The shed was extended ...
Ayr (BR) NS3422.1/1C
In 1959, to accommodate an allocation of dmus the westernmost three roads of the shed were lengthened at each end with a steel and corrugated sheeting extension, the steam locomotives then occupying the remaining three roads. The depot closed to steam on October 3rd 1966 and the eastern section, which had not been extended, was demolished in the 1970s. Parts of the steam shed still remained in 1994, with the former diesel depot in use as a wagon works.

TROON

Site NS3131.1; On the north side of the Harbour Branch, west of Troon Station.
Troon Harbour (G&SWR) NS3131.1/1A
A stone built 2TS dead ended shed with a slated gable style roof, located at NS31533111 and opened in 1846. The facilities included a water tank. The depot was closed by the LMS in 1935 and the building subsequently demolished.

A servicing point was then established ...
Troon Harbour (LMS) NS3131.1/F1
The siding and water tank were utilized by visiting locomotives until the 1960s.

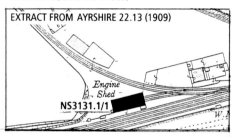

EXTRACT FROM AYRSHIRE 22.13 (1909)

NS3131.1/1

BEITH

Site NS3453.1; On the west side of the line, south of Beith Station.
Beith (GB&KR) NS3453.1/1A
A stone built 1TS dead ended shed with a slated gable style roof, located at NS34555338 and opened on June 26th, 1873 by the Glasgow, Barrhead and Kilmarnock Railway. The facilities included a turntable. The depot was closed by BR on November 5th, 1962 and subsequently demolished.

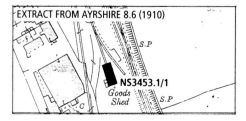

EXTRACT FROM AYRSHIRE 8.6 (1910)

NS3453.1/1

GIRVAN

Site NX1998.1; On the east side of the line, north of Girvan Station.
Girvan, Bridgemill (A&WR) NX1998.1/1A
A corrugated iron built shed, approximately located at NX19049865 and opened in August 1887 by the Ayrshire & Wigtownshire Railway. Details of the facilities are not known. The line was taken over by the G&SWR in 1892 and the depot closed in the same year.

Site NX1898.1; In the goods yard, on the south side of the Girvan Goods & Harbour Branch.
Girvan (M&GR) NX1898.1/1A
A brick built 2TS dead ended shed with a slated twin hipped roof, located at NX18629837 and opened on May 24th, 1860 by the Maybole & Girvan Railway. The facilities included a 44ft turntable and, installed later, a coal stage. The line was worked from the outset by the G&SWR and the depot was closed by the LMS in November 1940.

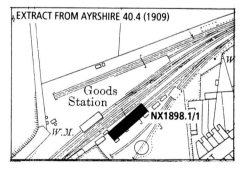

EXTRACT FROM AYRSHIRE 40.4 (1909)

NX1898.1/1

AUCHINLECK

Site NS5521.1; In the fork of the lines, east of Auchinleck Station.
Auchinleck (GKP&AR) NS5521.1/1A
A 2TS dead ended shed, located at NS55332190 and opened on August 9th, 1848 by the Glasgow, Kilmarnock, Paisley & Ayr Railway. The facilities included a turntable sited outside of the shed entrance. No further details are known. The line was absorbed by the G&SWR on October 28th, 1850 and the depot closed in 1879.

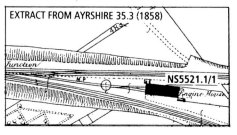

EXTRACT FROM AYRSHIRE 35.3 (1858)

NS5521.1/1

MAYBOLE

Site NS3010.1; On the east side of Maybole (1st) Station.
Maybole (G&SWR) NS3010.1/1A
A 2TS dead ended shed, located at NS30521038 and opened prior to 1856. The facilities included a turntable. No further details are known. The depot probably closed upon the line's extension and closure of the station on May 24th, 1860.

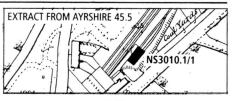

EXTRACT FROM AYRSHIRE 45.5

NS3010.1/1

ARDROSSAN

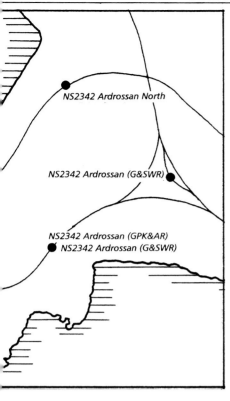

NS2342 Ardrossan North

NS2342 Ardrossan (G&SWR)

NS2342 Ardrossan (GPK&AR)
NS2342 Ardrossan (G&SWR)

Site NS2342.1; On the west side of Ardrossan Town Station.

Ardrossan (GKP&AR) NS2342.1/1A

A 2TS dead ended shed, located at NS23174281 and opened on July 27th, 1840 by the Glasgow, Kilmarnock, Paisley & Ayr Railway. The facilities included a small turntable. No further details are known. The line was absorbed by the G&SWR in 1851 and the depot was closed in 1869 and removed to make way for station enlargements.

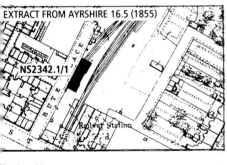

EXTRACT FROM AYRSHIRE 16.5 (1855)

NS2342.1/1

Replaced by ...
Site NS2342.2; On the east side of Ardrossan Town Station.

Ardrossan (G&SWR) NS2342.2/1A

A timber built 3TS through road shed, located at NS23134211 and opened in 1869. The facilities included a turntable. No further details are known other than it closed in 1895 and was subsequently demolished.

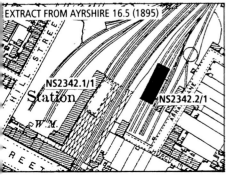

EXTRACT FROM AYRSHIRE 16.5 (1895)

NS2342.1/1
NS2342.2/1
Station

Replaced by ...
Site NS2342.3; In the triangle of lines at Parkhouse Junction, east of Ardrossan Town Station

Ardrossan (G&SWR) NS2342.3/1A

A brick built 4TS through road shed with a slated twin gable style roof, located at NS23594239 and opened in 1895. The facilities included a ramped coal stage, water tank and turntable. The depot was closed to steam by BR in February 1965 and it saw brief use as a diesel stabling point until total closure came in September 1969. The building subsequently housed a number of redundant D8500 Class 17 locomotives awaiting disposal, prior to being demolished in 1975.

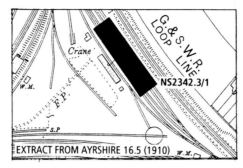

G.&S.W.R. LOOP LINE

Crane

NS2342.3/1

EXTRACT FROM AYRSHIRE 16.5 (1910)

Site NS2342.4; On the west side of the line, north of Ardrossan (L&AR) Station.

Ardrossan North (L&AR) NS2342.4/1A

A brick built 4TS dead ended shed with a slated northlight pattern roof, located at NS23174281 and opened on September 4th, 1888 by the Lanarkshire & Ayrshire Railway. The facilities included a water tank, coal stage and 42ft turntable, later enlarged to 51ft 4ins. The depot was closed by the LMS in July 1931 and the building was utilized for locomotive storage prior to demolition.

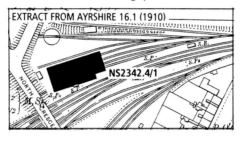

EXTRACT FROM AYRSHIRE 16.1 (1910)

NS2342.4/1

FAIRLIE PIER

Site NS2055.1; On the north side of the line, at the east end of Fairlie Pier Station.

Fairlie Pier (G&SWR) NS2055.1/1A

A timber built 2TS through road shed with a slated gable style roof, located at NS20835591 and opened on July 1st, 1882. The facilities included a water tank. No further details are known other than it was destroyed by a fire on July 3rd, 1917.

Replaced, on the same site, by ...
Fairlie Pier (G&SWR) NS2055.1/1B

A brick built 2TS through road shed with a slated gable style roof, it was opened in 1918. The depot was closed by the LMS in 1930 and let out for private use, not being demolished until 1987.

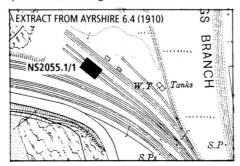

EXTRACT FROM AYRSHIRE 6.4 (1910)

NS2055.1/1

BRANCH

Tanks

DALMELLINGTON

Site NS4705.1; On the east side of Dalmellington Station.

Dalmellington (A&DR) NS4705.1/1A

A stone built 2TS through road shed with a slated twin gable style roof, located at NS47830595 and opened in 1856 by the Ayr & Dalmellington Railway. The facilities included a water tank and, installed later, a 44ft turntable. The depot was closed by the LMS in 1935 and later demolished.

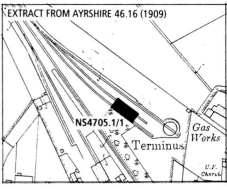

EXTRACT FROM AYRSHIRE 46.16 (1909)

NS4705.1/1

Terminus

Gas Works

KILBIRNIE

Site NS3154.1; On the east side of Kilbirnie Station.

Kilbirnie (L&AR) NS3154.1/1A

A timber built 2TS dead ended shed with a slated gable style roof, located at NS31815472 and opened on November 1st, 1889 by the Lanarkshire & Ayrshire Railway. The facilities included a 50ft turntable. The depot was closed by the LMS on December 1st, 1930 and later demolished.

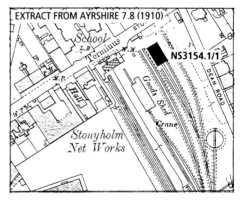

EXTRACT FROM AYRSHIRE 7.8 (1910)

School

Terminus

NS3154.1/1

Goods Shed

DEAN ROAD

Hall

Stonyholm Net Works

Crane

IRVINE

Site NS3239.1; On the west side of the line, north of Irvine Station.

Irvine (L&AR) NS3239.1/1A

A timber built 1TS dead ended shed with a slated gable style roof, located at NS32213949 and opened on June 2nd, 1890 by the Lanarkshire & Ayrshire Railway. The facilities included a 50ft turntable and water tank. The depot was closed by the LMS in 1925 and subsequently demolished.

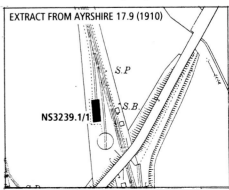

EXTRACT FROM AYRSHIRE 17.9 (1910)

NS3239.1/1

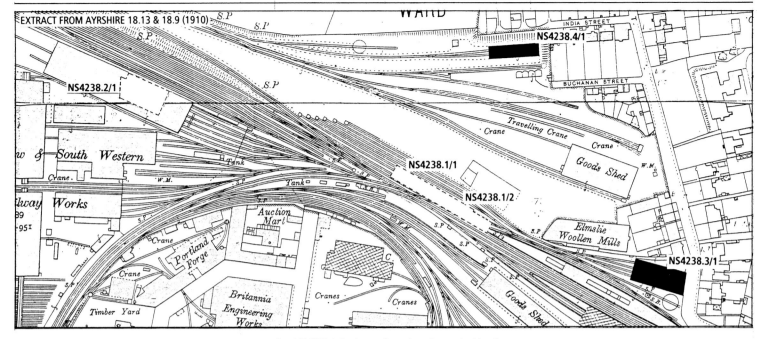

EXTRACT FROM AYRSHIRE 18.13 & 18.9 (1910)

NS4238.2/1

NS4238.4/1

NS4238.1/1

NS4238.1/2

NS4238.3/1

Site NS4238.1; On the north side of the line, west of Kilmarnock Station.
Kilmarnock (GKP&AR) NS4238.1/1A
A 2TS dead ended shed, located at NS42483839.

Adjoined, at its eastern end, by ...
Kilmarnock (GKP&AR) NS4238.1/2A
A 2TS through road shed, located at NS42523836.

The sheds were opened on July 16th, 1846 by the Glasgow, Paisley, Kilmarnock & Ayr Railway. The facilities included a water column and coke/coal stage. No further details are known other than they closed in 1860 upon the opening of NS4238.3/1.

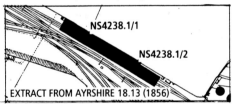

NS4238.1/1

NS4238.1/2

EXTRACT FROM AYRSHIRE 18.13 (1856)

Site NS4238.2; On the south side of the line, west of Kilmarnock Station.
Kilmarnock (G&SWR) NS4238.2/1A
A 4TS dead ended shed, located at NS42223850 and opened in 1855. The facilities included a turntable, sited outside of the shed entrance. No further details are known other than it closed in 1860 upon the opening of NS4238.3/1.

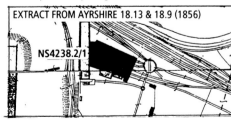

EXTRACT FROM AYRSHIRE 18.13 & 18.9 (1856)

NS4238.2/1

Site NS4238.3; On the north side of Kilmarnock Station.
Kilmarnock (G&SWR) NS4238.3/1A
A stone built 4TS dead ended shed with a slated twin gable style roof, located at NS42723831 and opened in 1860. The facilities included a turntable. Although the depot closed in 1877 upon the opening of Hurlford shed (NS4536.1/1) it was utilized as a stabling point and servicing area until BR days. The shed building was let out for private use and still stood in 1998.

Site NS4238.4; In the goods yard on the north side of Kilmarnock Station.
Kilmarnock (GB&KR) NS4238.4/1A
A stone built 2TS dead ended shed with a slated gable style roof, located at NS42593852 and opened on June 26th, 1873 by the Glasgow, Barrhead & Kilmarnock Railway. The facilities included a water tank and turntable. Although the depot fell out of use when the G&SWR took over the line in 1910, it was not until 1923 that the depot was officially closed, by the LMS.

HURLFORD

Site NS4536.1; On the south side of the line, at the west end of Barleith Station.
Hurlford (G&SWR) NS4536.1/1A
A stone built 6TS dead ended shed with a slated twin gable style roof, located at NS45463605 and opened in 1877. The facilities included a ramped coaling stage, water tank and a turntable which was re-sited and enlarged to 60ft in 1918. The depot was closed by BR on October 6th, 1966 and subsequently demolished.

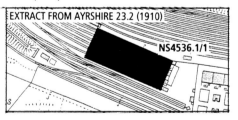

EXTRACT FROM AYRSHIRE 23.2 (1910)

NS4536.1/1

LARGS

Site NS2058.1; On the west side of the line, south of Largs Station.
Largs (G&SWR) NS2058.1/F1
A servicing area consisting of a turntable (located at NS20475888), water tank and siding. No further details are known.

EXTRACT FROM AYRSHIRE 3.12 (1910)

NS2058.1/F1

MUIRKIRK

Site NS6926.1; On the south side of the line, at the east end of Muirkirk Station.
Muirkirk (GKP&AR) NS6926.1/1A
A 2TS dead ended shed, located at NS69552648 and opened on August 9th, 1848 by the Glasgow, Kilmarnock, Paisley & Ayr Railway. The facilities included a turntable. The depot closed in 1879 and was immediately demolished.

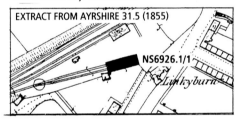

EXTRACT FROM AYRSHIRE 31.5 (1855)

NS6926.1/1

Replaced by ...
Muirkirk (CR/G&SWR) NS6926.1/2A
A stone built 4TS dead ended shed with a slated twin gable style roof, sited slightly south of its predecessor at NS69532646 and opened in 1879. The facilities included a 50ft turntable, water tank and coal stage.

The shed was rebuilt ...
Muirkirk (BR) NS6926.1/2B
In 1955 the northernmost 2TS bay was demolished and the remaining portion re-roofed in corrugated sheeting. The gable was also clad in corrugated sheeting and a brick and corrugated sheeting wall erected along the northern side. The depot closed on October 5th, 1964 and was subsequently demolished.

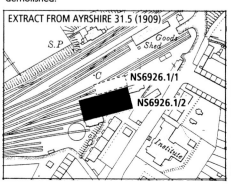

EXTRACT FROM AYRSHIRE 31.5 (1909)

NS6926.1/1

NS6926.1/2

WIGTOWNSHIRE

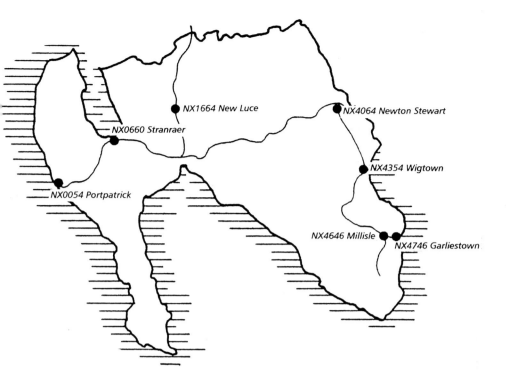

STRANRAER

Site NX0660.1; On the north side of Stranraer Town Station.
Stranraer (Portpatrick) NX0660.1/1A
A stone built 1TS through road shed with a slated gable style roof, located at NX06806049, and opened on March 12th, 1861. It was known as the "Girvan" shed and was utilized by the G&SWR.

The shed was rebuilt ...
Stranraer (BR) NX0660.1/1B
The gables were rebuilt in brick, the entrances enlarged and steel lintels were installed by the Scottish Region in 1950. At the same time the roof was renewed.

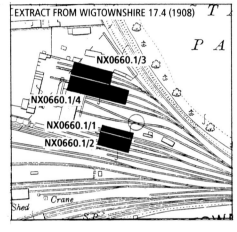

Adjoined by ...
Stranraer (Portpatrick) NX0660.1/2A
A stone built 2TS through road shed with a slated gable style roof, located at NX06796048, and opened in 1877. It was known as the "Joint Line" shed, being utilized by both the G&SWR and CR.

The shed was rebuilt ...
Stranraer (BR) NX0660.1/2B
The gables were rebuilt in brick, the entrances enlarged and steel lintels were installed by the Scottish Region in 1950. At the same time the roof was renewed.

Stranraer (Portpatrick) NX0660.1/3A
A stone built 2TS through road shed with a gable style slated roof, located at NX06776054 and opened in 1875. It was known as the "Caledonian" shed and went out of use at some time during LMS days, finding further use as a Joiners' Shop and store.

Adjoined by ...
Stranraer (Portpatrick) NX0660.1/4A
A stone built 2TS shed with one through road and a very high gable style slated roof, it was located at NX06786053. Although the building had originally been constructed as an erecting shop in c1870 over the years it gradually became integrated as part of the running sheds.

The shed was rebuilt ...
Stranraer (BR) NX0660.1/4B
The gables were rebuilt in brick and steel lintels were installed by the Scottish Region in 1950. At the same time the roof was renewed.

The facilities included a repair shop, 40ft turntable (enlarged to 50ft in 1892 and 60ft in 1939), coal stage (replaced with a mechanical coaler in 1937) and two water tanks. The depot was closed by BR in October 1966 and the whole site let out for private use as a scrapyard. All but NX0660.1/2B were demolished in 1996.

PORTPATRICK

Site NX0054.1; On the east side of the line, at the north end of Portpatrick Station.
Portpatrick (P&WJR) NX0054.1/1A
A stone built 1TS dead ended shed with a slated gable style roof, located at NX00385453 and opened on August 28th, 1862 by the Portpatrick & Wigtownshire Joint Railway. The facilities included a water tank and turntable. Although the depot closed in 1895 visiting locomotives continued to utilize the facilities in the yard until the line was closed by BR in 1950.

GARLIESTOWN

Site NX4746.1; On the south side of the line, at the east end of Garliestown Station.
Garliestown (Wigtown) NX4746.1/F1
A stabling point consisting of a siding, located at NX47764617, and water tank, it was opened on April 3rd, 1876 by the Wigtownshire Railway and closed by the G&SWR on March 1st, 1903. No further details are known.

MILLISLE

Site NX4646.1; On the north side of Millisle Station.
Millisle (Wigtown) NX4646.1/1A
A timber built 2TS shed with one through road and a hipped roof, located at NX46444636 and opened in June 1877 by the Wigtownshire Railway. One road of the shed was utilized by the Goods Department and there were no facilities. The depot was closed by the LMS in 1943 and subsequently demolished.

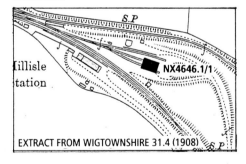

NEW LUCE

Site NX1664.1; On the east side of the line, at the south end of New Luce Station.
New Luce (G&PR) NX1664.1/1A
The goods shed located at NX16966448 was utilized as a temporary 1TS through road engine shed by the Girvan & Portpatrick Railway between February 7th, 1882 and August 1st, 1883*.

*G&SWR 2-4-0 No.59 was stabled here between these dates for two daily return trips to Girvan.

WIGTOWN

Site NX4354.1; On the east side of Wigtown Station.
Wigtown (Wigtown) NX4354.1/1A
A 1TS through road shed, located at NX43465479 and opened by the Wigtownshire Railway on April 3rd, 1875.

Adjoined by ...
Wigtown (Wigtown) NX4354.1/2A
A goods shed, located at NX43485480, and utilized as a temporary 1TS through road engine shed for stabling locomotives as required. It was opened by the Wigtownshire Railway on April 3rd, 1875.

There were no facilities. The line was absorbed into the Portpatrick & Wigtownshire Joint in 1885 and the depot closed in the same year, with the goods shed (NX4354.1/2A) reverting to its original use. The demolition date is not known.

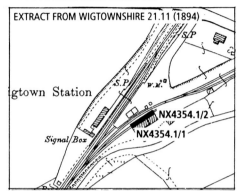

EXTRACT FROM WIGTOWNSHIRE 21.11 (1894)

NEWTON STEWART

Site NX4064.1; In the fork of the Stranraer and Whithorn lines, west of Newton Stewart Station.
Newton Stewart (P&WJR) NX4064.1/1A
A timber built 1TS dead ended shed, located at NX40286491 and opened by the Portpatrick & Wigtownshire Joint Railway in 1895. The facilities included a coal stage. No further details are known other than it was destroyed by a fire on March 24th, 1919.

Replaced by ...
Newton Stewart (P&WJR) NX4064.1/2A
A brick built 2TS shed with one through road and a slated gable style roof it was constructed slightly west of its predecessor at NX40256489 and opened in 1921. The facilities included a coal stage, water tank and turntable. The depot was closed by BR in 1959 and leased out for private use. The building still stood in 1998.

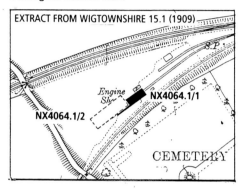

EXTRACT FROM WIGTOWNSHIRE 15.1 (1909)

RENFREWSHIRE

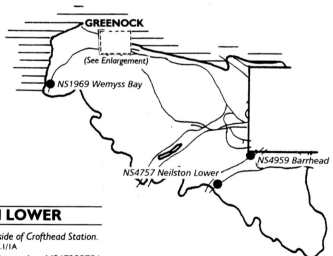

NEILSTON LOWER

Site NS4757.1; On the south side of Crofthead Station.
Neilston Lower (CR) NS4757.1/1A
A 1TS through road shed, located at NS47355756 and opened in October 1855. No further details are known other than it went out of use in about 1870.

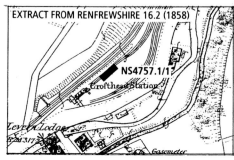

EXTRACT FROM RENFREWSHIRE 16.2 (1858)

BARRHEAD

Site NS4959.1; In the vicinity of Barrhead (G&SWR) Station.
Barrhead (CR/G&SWR) NS4959.1/F1
Some sort of facility, approximately located at NS499594, was opened here. No further details are known.

WEMYSS BAY

Site NS1969.1; On the west side of the line, north of Wemyss Bay Station.
Wemyss Bay (G&WBR) NS1969.1/1A
A stone built 1TS dead ended shed with a slated gable style roof, located at NS19426931 and opened on May 13th, 1865 by the Greenock & Wemyss Bay Railway. The facilities included a water tank and, sited outside of the shed entrance, a turntable. The line was absorbed by the CR in 1893 and the depot was closed by the LMS in 1927, with the shed building being subsequently demolished.

A servicing point was then established ...
Wemyss Bay (LMS) NS1969.1/F1
Locomotives then utilized the turntable, water tank, engine pit and siding until 1937.

The facilities were improved ...
Wemyss Bay (LMS) NS1969.1/F2
The turntable was enlarged and installed on the site of the original shed (NS1969.1/1A) at NS19426931. At the same time the water tank was re-sited and an additional siding installed. It went out of use during BR days.

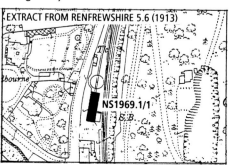

EXTRACT FROM RENFREWSHIRE 5.6 (1913)

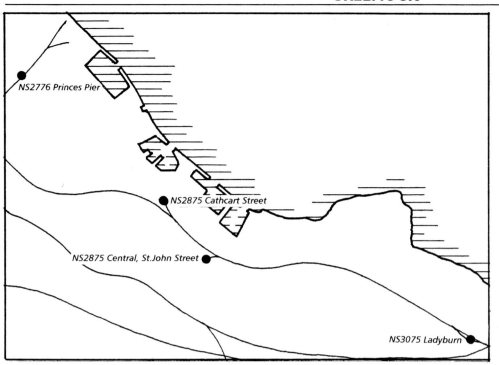

NS2776 Princes Pier

NS2875 Cathcart Street

NS2875 Central, St.John Street

NS3075 Ladyburn

Site NS2875.1; On the west side of Cathcart Street Station.

Cathcart Street (GP&GR) NS2875.1/1A

A works and engine shed were opened here in March 1841 by the Glasgow, Paisley & Greenock Railway and it is assumed to be the building located at NS28187598. No further details are known.

The shed was enlarged ...

Cathcart Street (CR) NS2875.1/1B

The works section was moved out to St.Rollox in 1856 and the running shed then took over all the accommodation within the building. It probably remained in use until the opening of Ladyburn shed (NS3075.1/1) in 1884.

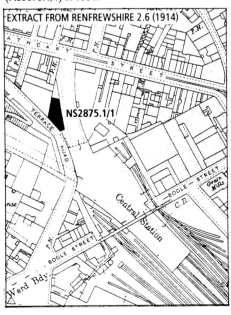

EXTRACT FROM RENFREWSHIRE 2.6 (1914)

NS2875.1/1

Site NS2875.2; On the south side of the line, east of Cathcart Street Station.

Central, St.John Street (CR) NS2875.2/1A

A 2TS dead ended shed, located at NS28737550 and opened in 1854. The building was set at 90° to the main line and the facilities included a turntable by which locomotives gained access to the depot. The depot probably closed in the 1860s, with the shed being subsequently demolished.

A servicing point was then established ...

Central, St.John Street (CR) NS2875.2/F1

The turntable, spurs and engine pits were then utilized for locomotive servicing until the opening of Ladyburn shed (NS3075.1/1) in 1884.

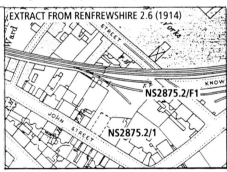

EXTRACT FROM RENFREWSHIRE 2.6 (1914)

NS2875.2/F1

NS2875.2/1

Replaced by ...

Site NS3075.1; On the south side of the line between Cartsdyke and Bogston Stations.

Ladyburn (CR) NS3075.1/1A

A brick built 10TS through road shed with a northlight pattern roof, located at NS30157504 and opened in 1884. The facilities included a ramped coal stage, water tank and turntable. The buildings were severely damaged during air raids in World War II and by nationalization the southernmost five roads were uncovered.

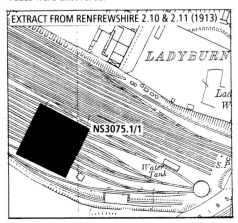

EXTRACT FROM RENFREWSHIRE 2.10 & 2.11 (1913)

NS3075.1/1

The shed was rebuilt in 1958 ...

Ladyburn (BR) NS3075.1/1B

The remaining roof was removed, a new single gable style pitched roof in corrugated sheeting was installed over the southernmost five tracks and a new brick partitioning wall constructed. The depot closed on November 26th, 1966 and was later demolished.

Site NS2776.1; On the west side of the line, south of Princes Pier Station.

Princes Pier (G&AR) NS2776.1/1A

A brick built 3TS dead ended shed with a slated gable style roof*, located at NS27217684 and opened in November 1869 by the Greenock & Ayrshire Railway. The facilities included a water tank, coal stage and turntable.

The shed was re-roofed ...

Princes Pier (BR) NS2776.1/1B

The roof was renewed and a new brick gable with steel lintel installed by the Scottish Region in 1952. The depot closed in May 1959 and it was demolished in the 1960s to make way for sidings.

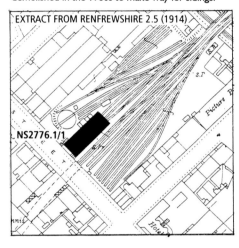

EXTRACT FROM RENFREWSHIRE 2.5 (1914)

NS2776.1/1

*In attempts to reduce the nuisance caused by smoke to local residents, during its existence a variety of high roof ventilators were constructed.

EDINBURGH

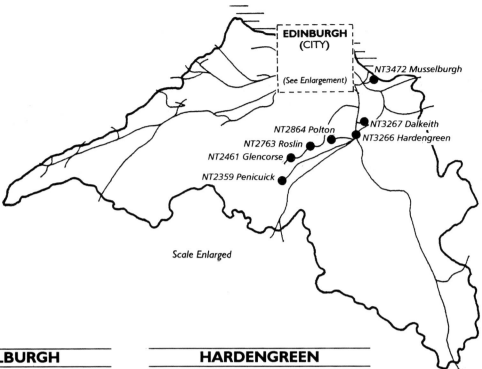

EDINBURGH (CITY) (See Enlargement)

NT3472 Musselburgh

NT2864 Polton
NT2763 Roslin
NT2461 Glencorse
NT2359 Penicuick

NT3267 Dalkeith
NT3266 Hardengreen

Scale Enlarged

MUSSELBURGH

Site NT3472.1; On the east side of Musselburgh Station.
Musselburgh (NB) NT3472.1/1A
A ITS dead ended shed, located at NT34027242 and opened on July 16th, 1847. No further details are known other than it was closed by the LNER in 1930 and later demolished.

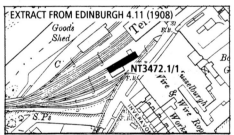

EXTRACT FROM EDINBURGH 4.11 (1908)

POLTON

Site NT2864.1; On the east side of Polton Station.
Polton (EVR) NT2864.1/F1
A servicing area consisting of an engine pit and siding, located at NT28886479 and opened on April 15th, 1867 by the Esk Valley Railway. The facility was closed by BR on September 10th, 1951.

EXTRACT FROM EDINBURGH 8.13 (1907)

GLENCORSE

Site NT2461.1; In the vicinity of Glencorse Station.
Glencorse (NB) NT2461.1/F1
A servicing point consisting of a siding and approximately located at NT246619. No further details are known.

HARDENGREEN

Site NT3266.1; On the west side of Hardengreen Junction, south of Eskbank & Dalkeith Station.
Hardengreen (NB) NT3266.1/F1
A servicing area consisting of coal stage, engine pit and siding located at NT32346621. No further details are known other than it was closed by BR in c1962.

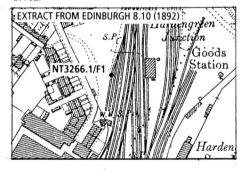

EXTRACT FROM EDINBURGH 8.10 (1892)

ROSLIN

Site NT2763.1; On the north side of the line, west of Roslin Station.
Roslin (EL&RR) NT2763.1/1A
A ITS dead ended shed, located at NT27026361 and opened on July 23rd, 1874 by the Edinburgh, Loanhead & Roslin Railway. The facilities included a water tank and turntable, sited outside of the shed entrance. The depot was closed by the LNER in May 1933 and subsequently demolished.

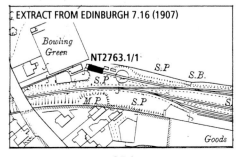

EXTRACT FROM EDINBURGH 7.16 (1907)

DALKEITH

Site NT3267.1; On the east side of Dalkeith Station.
Dalkeith (NB) NT3267.1/1A
A stone built ITS dead ended shed with a slated hipped roof, located at NT32986713 and opened on July 7th, 1847. No further details are known other than it closed in 1915.

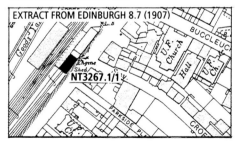

EXTRACT FROM EDINBURGH 8.7 (1907)

PENICUICK

Site NT2359.1; At the west end of Penicuick Station.
Penicuick (EVR) NT2359.1/1A
A brick built ITS dead ended shed with a slated gable style roof, located at NT23635964 and opened on April 15th, 1867 by the Esk Valley Railway. The facilities included a water tank and turntable, sited outside of the shed entrance. The depot was closed by BR on September 10th, 1951 and subsequently demolished.

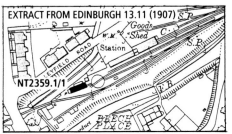

EXTRACT FROM EDINBURGH 13.11 (1907)

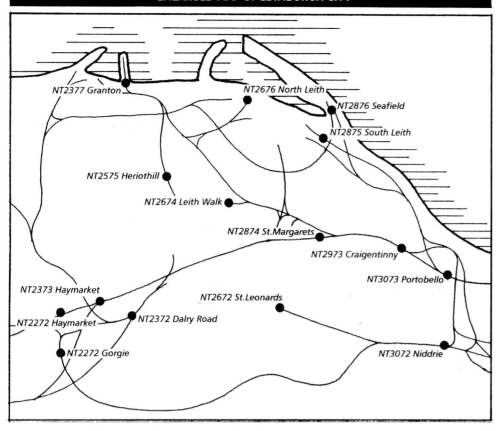

HAYMARKET

Site NT2373.1; On the north side of the line, at the west end of Haymarket Station.
Haymarket (E&GR) NT2373.1/1A
A through road shed, possibly 3TS, located at NT23577302 and opened on February 21st, 1848 by the Edinburgh & Glasgow Railway. No further details are known except that it closed in 1894.

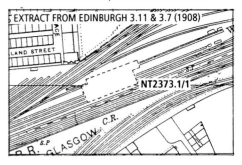

Replaced by ...
Site NT2272.1; On the north side of the line, west of Haymarket Station.
Haymarket (NB) NT2272.1/1A
A brick built 8TS through road shed with a transverse slated multi-pitched roof, located at NT22947281 and opened in 1894. The facilities included a water tank, turntable and ramped coaling stage, replaced later by a mechanical coaling plant. The shed was closed to steam by BR on September 9th, 1963 and a purpose-built diesel depot (NT2272.1/1B) constructed on the same site.

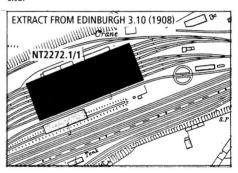

ST.MARGARETS

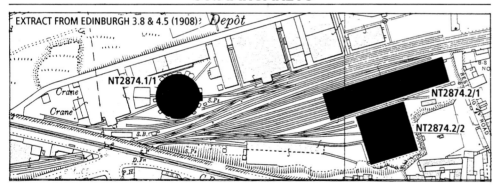

Site NT2874.1; On the north side of the line, east of Waverley Station.
St.Margarets (NB) NT2874.1/1A
A stone built circular IRH shed with a slated continuous pitched roof, located at NT28037426 and opened on June 18th, 1846. Details of the facilities are not known. By 1944, following a fire, the building was largely derelict so the LNER demolished it and utilized the spurs for stabling tank engines. By the time that the depot closed, diesel shunters utilized the site.

Site NT2874.2; On the south side of the line, east of Waverley Station.
St.Margarets (NB) NT2874.2/1A
A brick built 6TS dead ended shed with a slated twin gable style roof, located at NT28227426 and opened in 1866.

St.Margarets (NER) NT2874.2/2A
A brick built square IRH shed with a slated triple pitched roof, located at NT28237420 and opened in 1871. The building was constructed by the NBR (which took over in 1902), closed by the LNER in 1942 and demolished to make way for additional sidings and a new turntable.

The facilities also included a water tank and a ramped coaling stage which remained in use right through until closure and probably made this shed the largest never to receive modernized coaling facilities. The depot was closed by BR on May 1st, 1967 and subsequently demolished, with part of the site being utilized for the Meadowbank Stadium.

HERIOTHILL

Site NT2575.1; On the east side of the line, north of Scotland Street Station.
Heriothill (E&GR) NT2575.1/1A
A 2TS through road shed, located at NT25367520 and opened in c1850 by the Edinburgh & Glasgow Railway. It adjoined the works and the facilities included a water tank and turntable. No further details are known.

Replaced, at some stage, by ...
Site NT2575.2; On the west side of the line, north of Scotland Street Station.
Heriothill (LNER) NT2575.2/F1
A stabling point consisting of a siding located at NT25387518. No further details are known except that it was closed by BR in c1964.

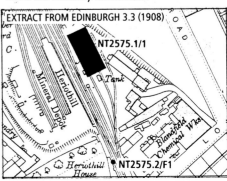

CRAIGENTINNY

Site NT2973.1; In Craigentinny Sidings, on the south side of the line, west of Portobello Station.
Craigentinny (NB) NT2973.1/F1
A facility, consisting of a siding and approximately located at NT298738. No further details are known.

NIDDRIE

Site NT3072.1; In the vicinity of Niddrie Junction West.
Niddrie (NB) NT3072.1/F1
A servicing area, consisting of a siding and approximately located at NT307721. It opened on July 7th, 1847. No further details are known.

NORTH LEITH

Site NT2676.1; On the east side of the line, at the south end of North Leith Station.
North Leith (NB) NT2676.1/F1
A servicing area consisting of a siding and engine pit located at NT26657658 and opened in March 1868. The facility was closed by BR in 1951.

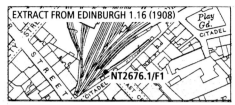
EXTRACT FROM EDINBURGH 1.16 (1908)

SOUTH LEITH

Site NT2875.1; On the north side of the NB South Leith Docks Branch.
South Leith (NB) NT2875.1/F1
A servicing area consisting of a turntable, located at NT28457592, and siding, it opened on July 7th, 1847 and was closed to steam by BR in c1960.

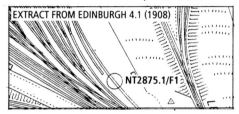
EXTRACT FROM EDINBURGH 4.1 (1908)

ST.LEONARDS

Site NT2672.1; On the north side of St.Leonards Coal Depot.
St.Leonards (E&DR) NT2672.1/1A
A brick built 1TS dead ended shed, located at NT26627290 and opened on July 7th, 1847 by the Edinburgh & Dalkeith Railway. No further details are known other than it was closed by the NBR in 1921 and, following demolition, locomotives utilized the engine pit and shed road until BR days.

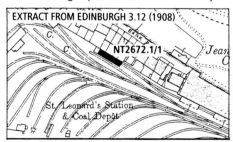
EXTRACT FROM EDINBURGH 3.12 (1908)

SEAFIELD

Site NT2876.1; On the east side of the CR South Leith Docks Branch, at the northern end.
Seafield (CR) NT2876.1/1A
A brick built 2TS through road shed with a slated gable style roof, located at NT28417645 and opened in 1902. The facilities included a ramped coaling stage and 60ft turntable. The depot was leased to the NBR in 1916, closed by BR on October 13th, 1962 and subsequently demolished.

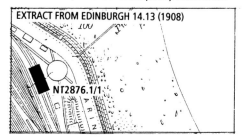
EXTRACT FROM EDINBURGH 14.13 (1908)

GRANTON

Site NT2377.1; At the south end of Middle Pier in Granton Harbour.
Granton (EL&GR) NT2377.1/F1
A servicing area consisting of a coal stage, engine pit and siding, located at NT23757715 and opened on July 17th, 1847 by the Edinburgh, Leith & Granton Railway. It was closed by BR in c1964.

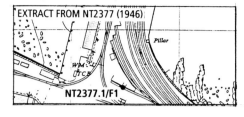
EXTRACT FROM NT2377 (1946)

PORTOBELLO

Site NT3073.1; On the north side of the line, east of Portobello Station.
Portobello (NB) NT3073.1/F1
A servicing area consisting of an engine pit, water column and sidings, located at NT30687343. No further details are known except that it was closed by BR in c1964.

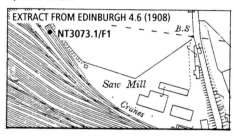
EXTRACT FROM EDINBURGH 4.6 (1908)

LEITH WALK

Site NT2674.1; On the south side of the line, at the east end of Leith Walk Goods Station.
Leith Walk (NB) NT2674.1/F1
A facility consisting of engine pits and sidings, located at NT26967488, and a water tank. It opened on July 2nd, 1868 and was closed by BR in c1964.

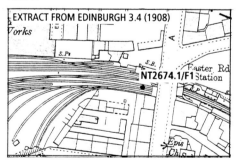
EXTRACT FROM EDINBURGH 3.4 (1908)

GORGIE

Site NT2272.1; On the west side of the line, north of Gorgie Station.
Gorgie (ES&SSJR) NT2272.1/F1
A servicing point consisting of a siding, located at NT22807216 and opened on December 1st, 1884 by the Edinburgh Suburban & South Side Junction Railway. It was closed by BR in c1964.

EXTRACT FROM EDINBURGH 3.10 (1908)

DALRY ROAD

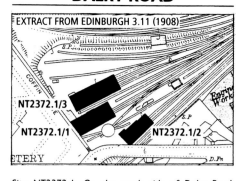
EXTRACT FROM EDINBURGH 3.11 (1908)

Site NT2372.1; On the south side of Dalry Road Station.
Dalry Road (CR) NT2372.1/1A
A timber built 2TS dead ended shed with a gable style pitched roof, located at NT23737257 and opened in 1848. It may have been originally utilized as both a running shed and repair shop but from some point, possibly upon the opening of NT2372.1/2A, it was used solely as a repair shop. Later, and probably in LMS days, it became part of the running shed.

Dalry Road (CR) NT2372.1/2A
A 2TS dead ended shed, located at NT23777255 and opened in 1874. No further details are known other than it was converted to a wagon shop and demolished in c1930.

Dalry Road (CR) NT2372.1/3A
A 4TS dead ended shed, located at NT23737260 and opened in 1895. The facilities initially included a ramped coaling stage, water tank, repair shop and 42ft turntable.

The shed was rebuilt ...
Dalry Road (CR) NT2372.1/3B
A brick built 4TS dead ended shed with a slated transverse multi-pitched roof was erected on the same site in 1911.

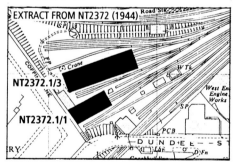
EXTRACT FROM NT2372 (1944)

The depot was closed by BR on October 3rd, 1965 and demolished the following year.

NB: A shed, approximately located at NT247734, may have existed at Lothian Rd Station (as NT2473.1/1A).

LINLITHGOW

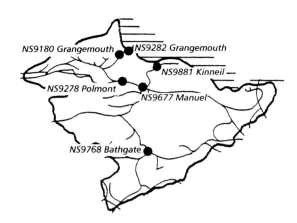

GRANGEMOUTH

Site NS9282.1; On the west side of the line, at the south end of Grangemouth Station.
Grangemouth (CR)[NS9282.1/1A]
A 1TS through road shed, located at NS92488201 and opened in 1870. The facilities included a water tank, coal stage and turntable. No further details are known other than it closed in 1907 upon the opening of Grangemouth shed (NS9180.1/1).

EXTRACT FROM STIRLINGSHIRE N24.16 (1915)
NS9282.1/1
R BASIN

Site NS9282.2; Adjacent to Grangemouth Dock, north of Grangemouth Station.
Grangemouth (CR)[NS9282.2/1A]
A 1TS shed, approximately located at NS927823, opened here in 1875. No further details are known.

Site NS9180.1; On the west side of the line, south of Grangemouth Station.
Grangemouth (CR)[NS9180.1/1A]
A brick built 6TS dead ended shed with a transverse slated multi-pitched roof, located at NS91278076 and opened in 1908. The facilities included a repair shop, ramped coaling stage, water tank and 70ft turntable. The depot was closed to steam by BR on October 12th, 1965 and saw further use as a diesel depot until total closure in March 1993.

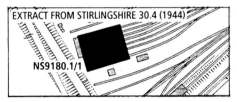
EXTRACT FROM STIRLINGSHIRE 30.4 (1944)
NS9180.1/1

BATHGATE

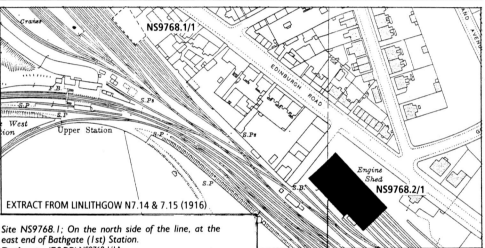
NS9768.1/1
EXTRACT FROM LINLITHGOW N7.14 & 7.15 (1916)
Engine Shed
NS9768.2/1
Upper Station
West ation

Site NS9768.1; On the north side of the line, at the east end of Bathgate (1st) Station.
Bathgate (E&BR)[NS9768.1/1A]
A 2TS shed with one through road, located at NS97536857 and opened on November 12th, 1849 by the Edinburgh & Bathgate Railway. The facilities included a turntable sited outside of the shed entrance. No further details are known other than it closed in 1902.

NS9768.1/1
EXTRACT FROM LINLITHGOW N7.14 (1896)

Replaced by ...
Site NS9768.2; On the north side of the line, east of Bathgate (Upper) Station.
Bathgate (NB)[NS9768.2/1A]
A brick built 6TS dead ended shed with a transverse slated multi-pitched roof, located at NS97736841 and opened in 1902. The facilities included a ramped coaling stage, water tank and 50ft turntable.

The shed was rebuilt in 1954 ...
Bathgate (BR)[NS9768.2/1B]
Owing to subsidence, the building was reduced to a 3TS dead ended shed with a corrugated sheeting clad roof and corrugated sheeting screen. At the same time a new 1TS repair shop was constructed along the northern side. The depot closed in August 1966 and was let out for private use as a commercial vehicle garage, surviving until at least 1996.

KINNEIL

Site NS9881.1; On the west side of the line, at the north end of Kinneil Station.
Kinneil (S&BR)[NS9881.1/1A]
A stone built 2TS shed with one through road and a slated hipped roof, located at NS98428113 and opened by the Slammannan & Borrowstounness Railway in 1851. There were no facilities. The line was absorbed by the NBR in 1865 and the depot was closed by BR in September 1952 and subsequently demolished.

EXTRACT FROM LINLITHGOW 1.6 (1895)
Engine Shed
NS9881.1/1

MANUEL

Site NS9677.1; On the south side of the line, west of Manuel Station.
Manuel, Bo'ness Junction (S&BR)[NS9677.1/1A]
A 3TS dead ended shed located at NS96547726 and opened in 1851. The facilities included a coal stage, water tank and turntable. The line was absorbed by the NBR in 1865 and the depot closed in 1914 upon the opening of Polmont shed (NS9278.1/1A). It was subsequently demolished.

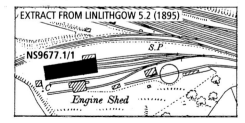
EXTRACT FROM LINLITHGOW 5.2 (1895)
NS9677.1/1
Engine Shed

POLMONT

Site NS9278.1; On the south side of the line, west of Polmont Station.
Polmont (NB)[NS9278.1/1A]
A timber built 5TS through road shed with a transverse slated multi-pitched roof located at NS92387826 and opened in 1914. The facilities included a 51ft 6in turntable, water tank and ramped coaling stage. The depot was closed by BR in May 1964 and later demolished.

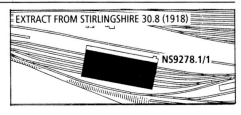
EXTRACT FROM STIRLINGSHIRE 30.8 (1918)
NS9278.1/1

ROXBURGHSHIRE

NT7535 Sprouston
NT7333 Kelso
NT5731 St.Boswells
NT6521 Jedburgh
NT5015 Hawick
NY5397 Riccarton Junction (NB)
NY5497 Riccarton Junction (LNER)

RICCARTON JUNCTION

Site NY5397.1; On the west side of Riccarton Junction Station.
Riccarton Junction (NB/BUR)^{NY5397.1/1A} NY5397.1/1A
A 3TS through road shed located at NY53949764 and opened by the Border Union Railway on July 1st, 1862. The facilities included a ramped coaling stage and turntable. No further details are known other than it burned down in 1900.

A servicing point was then established ...
Riccarton Junction (NB/BUR)^{NY5397.1/F1} NY5397.1/F1
A facility, including the turntable, ramped coaling stage and the former shed roads was established in 1900. The stabling area was dispensed with in 1945.

Replaced by ...
Site NY5497.1; On the east side of the Reedsmouth line, south of Riccarton Junction Station.
Riccarton Junction (LNER)^{NY5497.1/1A} NY5497.1/1A
A lean-to style steel framed corrugated asbestos 1TS through road shed located at NY54109750. It was constructed against the western side of the coaling stage and opened in 1945. The depot was closed by BR in October 1958 and subsequently demolished.

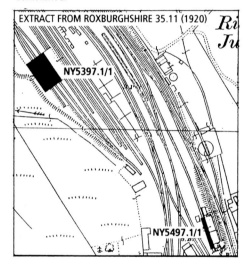

EXTRACT FROM ROXBURGHSHIRE 35.11 (1920)
NY5397.1/1
NY5497.1/1

KELSO

Site NT7333.1; On the north side of the line, at the east end of Kelso Station.
Kelso (NB)^{NT7333.1/1A} NT7333.1/1A
A stone built 2TS dead ended shed with a slated gable style roof, located at NT73203323 and opened on June 1st, 1851. The facilities included a turntable, sited outside of the shed entrance, and water column.

One track was removed ...
Kelso (LNER)^{NT7333.1/1B} NT7333.1/1B
At some stage, probably in LNER days, the northernmost track was removed. The depot was closed by BR in July 1955 and later demolished.

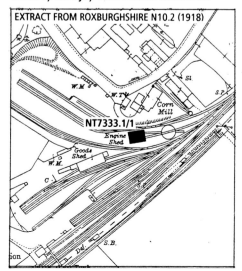

EXTRACT FROM ROXBURGHSHIRE N10.2 (1918)
NT7333.1/1
Engine Shed

HAWICK

Site NT5015.1; On the west side of Hawick Station.
Hawick (E&HR)^{NT5015.1/1A} NT5015.1/1A
A stone built 2TS shed with one through road and a slated gable style roof, located at NT50501531 and opened on November 1st, 1849 by the Edinburgh & Hawick Railway. The facilities included a water column and, sited north of the station, a turntable. At a later date a ramped coaling stage was installed adjacent to the turntable.

The shed was re-roofed ...
Hawick (BR)^{NT5015.1/1B} NT5015.1/1B
A new single pitched roof was installed by the Scottish Region in 1955 and at the same time the shed entrances were rebuilt with steel lintels. The depot closed on January 3rd, 1966 and was later demolished.

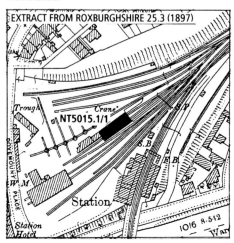

EXTRACT FROM ROXBURGHSHIRE 25.3 (1897)
NT5015.1/1

JEDBURGH

Site NT6521.1; On the east side of Jedburgh Station.
Jedburgh (Jedburgh)^{NT6521.1/1A} NT6521.1/1A
A stone built 1TS dead ended shed with a slated gable style roof incorporating a water tank at the rear. It was located at NT65672153 and was opened by the Jedburgh Railway on July 17th, 1856. The line was worked from the outset by the NBR which absorbed it on July 3rd, 1860.

The shed was re-roofed ...
Jedburgh (LNER)^{NT6521.1/1B} NT6521.1/1B
Following removal of the station overall roof a flat roof with a longitudinal smoke trough was installed. The depot was closed by BR on April 2nd, 1949 and utilized as a garage until the 1960s.

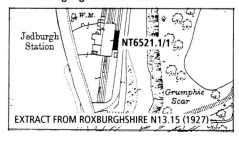

Jedburgh Station
NT6521.1/1
Grumphie Scar
EXTRACT FROM ROXBURGHSHIRE N13.15 (1927)

ST.BOSWELLS

Site NT5731.1: On the east side of St.Boswells Station
St.Boswells (NB) NT5731.1/1A
A stone built 2TS dead ended shed with a slated gable style roof, located at NT57753157 and opened on June 17th, 1850. The facilities included a water tank, coal stage and turntable. The depot was closed by BR on November 16th, 1959 and still stood in 1998 having been let out for private use.

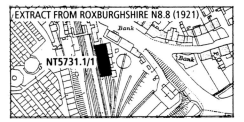

SPROUSTON

Site NT7535.1; On the north side of the line, at the east end of Sprouston Station.
Sprouston (NER) NT7535.1/1A
A timber built 1TS dead ended shed, located at NT75973531 and opened in 1863. It had originally been utilized at another site, as yet unknown, on the Newcastle & Carlisle Railway. No further details are known other than it was destroyed in a gale on October 14th, 1881.

Replaced, on the same site, by ...
Sprouston (NER) NT7535.1/1B
A brick built 1TS dead ended shed with a slated gable style roof and opened in 1882. The facilities included a water tank. Although the depot was closed on July 14th, 1916 it still stood until the 1960s and was utilized during World War II as a store for *City of Truro* from York Railway Museum.

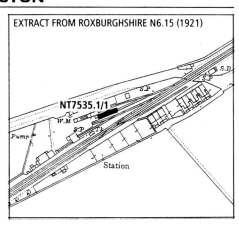

HADDINGTON

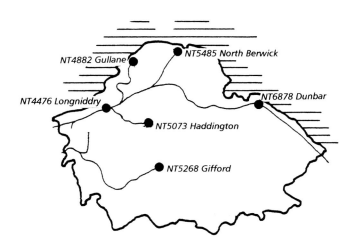

DUNBAR

Site NT6878.1; On the south side of Dunbar Station.
Dunbar (NB) NT6878.1/1A
A brick built 2TS shed with one through road and a slated gable style roof, located at NT68107843 and opened on June 18th, 1846. The facilities included a coal stage, water tank and turntable.

The shed was partially rebuilt ...
Dunbar (BR) NT6878.1/1B
At some stage, probably in early BR days, part of the roof was removed by the Scottish Region, with the remainder being renewed, and the through road was switched from the northernmost track to the southernmost. The depot closed in 1963 and was later demolished.

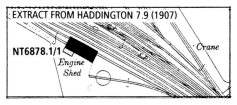

NORTH BERWICK

Site NT5485.1; On the west side of the line, at the south end of North Berwick Station.
North Berwick (NB) NT5485.1/1A
A brick built 2TS dead ended shed with a slated hipped roof, located at NT54498503 and opened on June 17th, 1850. The facilities included a water column. The depot was closed by BR in February 1958 and demolished.

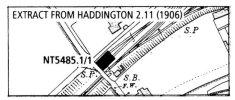

LONGNIDDRY

Site NT4476.1; On the south side of the line, at the east end of Longniddry Station.
Longniddry (NB) NT4476.1/1A
A stone built 2TS shed with one through road and a slated gable style roof, located at NT44827635 and opened on June 18th, 1846. There were no facilities.

The shed was partially rebuilt ...
Longniddry (LNER) NT4476.1/1B
At some stage the arches on the through road section were enlarged and rebuilt with steel lintels. The depot was closed by BR in June 1959 and later demolished.

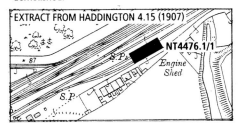

GULLANE

Site NT4882.1; At the east end of Gullane Station.
Gullane (AG&NBR) NT4882.1/1A
A 1TS dead ended shed, located at NT48848289 and opened by the Aberlady, Gullane & North Berwick Railway on April 1st, 1898. No further details are known other than the facilities included a water tank. The line was absorbed by the NBR on August 1st, 1900 and the LNER closed the depot on September 12th, 1932.

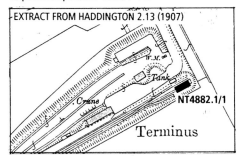

HADDINGTON

Site NT5073.1; In the vicinity of Haddington Station.
Haddington (NB) NT5073.1/1A
A facility consisting of a siding and approximately located at NT507739, was opened here on June 18th, 1846. No further details are known.

GIFFORD

Site NT5268.1; At the north end of Gifford Station.
Gifford (G&GLR) NT5268.1/F1
A servicing area consisting of an engine pit, located at NT52986849, and water tank was opened here by the Gifford & Garvald Light Railway on October 14th, 1901. The line was worked by the NBR and the LNER closed the facility on April 3rd, 1933.

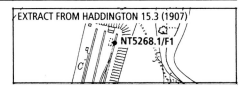

PEEBLES-SHIRE

PEEBLES

Site NT2541.1; On the east side of the line, at the north end of Peebles (1st) Station.
Peebles (Peebles)^{NT2541.1/1A}
A stone built 1TS dead ended shed with a slated gable style roof, located at NT25084104 and opened on July 4th, 1855 by the Peebles Railway. The facilities included a water tank and, installed in c1857, a turntable.

The shed was rebuilt ...
Peebles (NB)^{NT2541.1/1B}
The depot was altered in October 1864, to a 2TS shed with one through road, entrance now being effected from the opposite end of the building. The depot was closed by BR in October 1955 and later demolished.

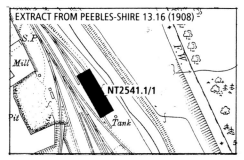
EXTRACT FROM PEEBLES-SHIRE 13.16 (1908)
NT2541.1/1

Site NT2440.1; On the north side of the line, at the west end of Peebles (SB&BR) Station.
Peebles (SB&BR)^{NT2440.1/1A}
A stone built 2TS dead ended shed with a slated gable style roof, located at NT24704029 and opened in January 1864 by the Symington, Biggar & Broughton Railway. The facilities included a water tank, coal stage and a turntable, enlarged to 60ft in 1906. The line was worked from the outset by the CR and the LMS closed the depot in 1940 with demolition following later.

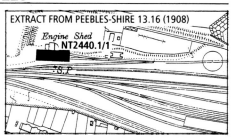
EXTRACT FROM PEEBLES-SHIRE 13.16 (1908)
Engine Shed
NT2440.1/1

BROUGHTON

Site NT1136.1; In the vicinity of Broughton Station.
Broughton (SB&BR)^{NT1136.1/1A}
A temporary shed, approximately located at NT111366, was opened here on November 5th, 1860 by the Symington, Biggar & Broughton Railway and closed on February 1st, 1864 upon the opening of the line through to Peebles.

NT2541 Peebles (NB)
NT2440 Peebles (CR)
NT1136 Broughton

SELKIRKSHIRE

NT4936 Galashiels
NT4628 Selkirk
Remainder of county omitted

SELKIRK

Site NT4628.1; On the east side of the line, at the north end of Selkirk Station.
Selkirk (NB)^{NT4628.1/1A}
A 1TS through road shed located at NT46732896 and opened on April 5th, 1856. No further details are known other than it was closed by the LNER in 1931 and demolished.

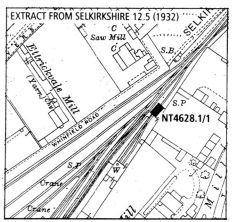
EXTRACT FROM SELKIRKSHIRE 12.5 (1932)
NT4628.1/1

GALASHIELS

Site NT4936.1; On the east side of the line, at the south end of Galashiels Station.
Galashiels (NB)^{NT4936.1/1A}
A brick built 2TS dead ended shed with a slated gable style roof and located at NT49633601. Although the adjacent station came into use on February 20th, 1849, the opening date is not known. The facilities included a turntable and the depot was closed by BR in April 1962 and subsequently demolished.

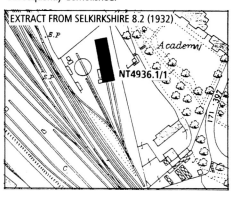
EXTRACT FROM SELKIRKSHIRE 8.2 (1932)
NT4936.1/1

BERWICKSHIRE

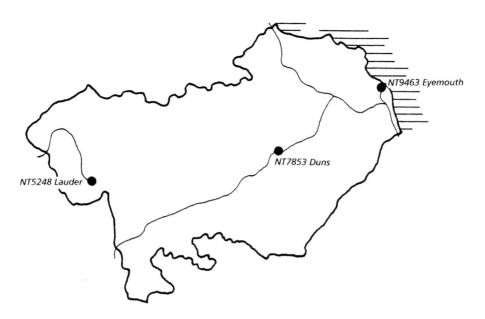

DUNS

Site NT7853.1; On the north side of the line, at the east end of Duns Station.
Duns (NB) NT7853.1/1A
A stone built 2TS dead ended shed with a slated gable style roof incorporating a water tank in the rear, it was located at NT78935321 and opened on August 15th, 1849. The facilities also included a turntable sited outside of the shed entrance. The depot was closed by BR on December 19th, 1949 and demolished in the late 1970s.

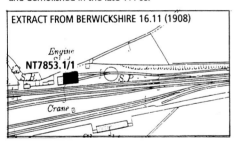

Known as Dunse when opened by the NBR in August 1849, this 2TS shed (NT7853.1/1A) at **Duns** had an operational life of 100 years and 4 months but the building remained standing for many years after 1949. Already looking closed in this picture of about 1936, Mr Camwell has, once again, persuaded a locomotive crew to conform to his "trademark" view and pose their engine in front of the building!
WA Camwell

EYEMOUTH

Site NT9463.1; On the east side of the line, at the south end of Eyemouth Station.
Eyemouth (Eyemouth) NT9463.1/F1
A stabling point consisting of a water tank and a siding, located at NT94386386, was opened here on April 13th, 1891 by the Eyemouth Railway. No further details are known.

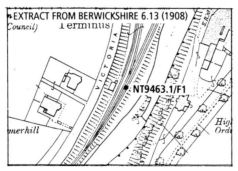

LAUDER

Site NT5248.1; At the west end of Lauder Station.
Lauder (LLR) NT5248.1/1A
A 1TS dead ended shed located at NT52354810 and opened on July 2nd, 1901 by the Lauder Light Railway. The facilities included a water tank. The line was worked by the NBR and the LNER closed the depot on September 12th, 1932. No further details are known.

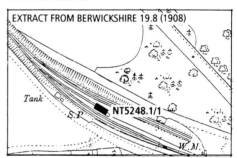

FIFE

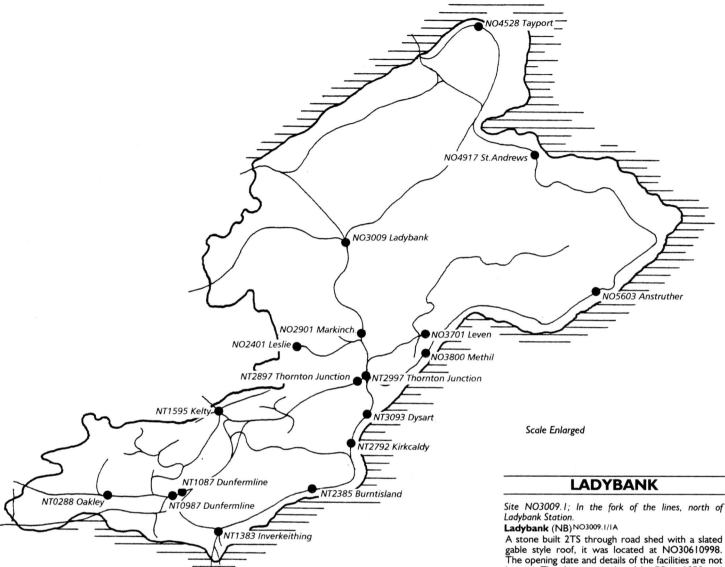

NO4528 Tayport

NO4917 St.Andrews

NO3009 Ladybank

NO5603 Anstruther

NO2901 Markinch
NO3701 Leven
NO2401 Leslie
NO3800 Methil

NT2897 Thornton Junction
NT2997 Thornton Junction

NT1595 Kelty
NT3093 Dysart

NT2792 Kirkcaldy

NT1087 Dunfermline
NT0288 Oakley
NT0987 Dunfermline
NT2385 Burntisland

NT1383 Inverkeithing

Scale Enlarged

KELTY

Site NT1595.1; In the vicinity of Kelty Station.
Kelty (NB) NT1595.1/F1
A facility was established here on January 20th, 1860. No further details are known.

Site NT1595.2; On the west side of the line, north of Kelty Station.
Kelty (BR) NT1595.2/F1
A servicing area consisting of an engine pit and siding. It was located at NT15019530 and probably fell out of use in c1964.

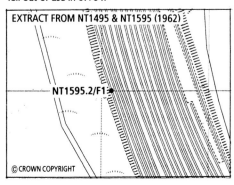

EXTRACT FROM NT1495 & NT1595 (1962)

NT1595.2/F1

© CROWN COPYRIGHT

KIRKCALDY

Site NT2792.1; On the east side of the line, north of Kirkcaldy Station.
Kirkcaldy (NB) NT2792.1/F1
A servicing area consisting of an engine pit, siding and water column located at NT27859219. The opening date is not known but it was closed by BR in c1959.

EXTRACT FROM FIFESHIRE 35.12 (1914)

NT2792.1/F1

MARKINCH

Site NO2901.1; In the vicinity of Markinch Station.
Markinch (NB) NO2901.1/F1
At some stage a facility was established here. No further details are known.

LADYBANK

Site NO3009.1; In the fork of the lines, north of Ladybank Station.
Ladybank (NB) NO3009.1/1A
A stone built 2TS through road shed with a slated gable style roof, it was located at NO30610998. The opening date and details of the facilities are not known. The depot was closed by BR in 1958 and demolished in 1967.

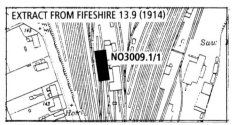

EXTRACT FROM FIFESHIRE 13.9 (1914)

NO3009.1/1

OAKLEY

Site NT0288.1; On the north side of the line, at the west end of Oakley Station.
Oakley (NB) NT0288.1/F1
A facility consisting of a turntable and siding, located at NT02318884 and opened at some time after 1915. No further details are known.

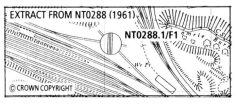

EXTRACT FROM NT0288 (1961)

NT0288.1/F1

© CROWN COPYRIGHT

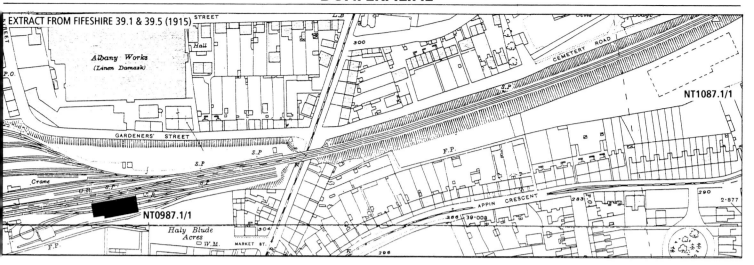

EXTRACT FROM FIFESHIRE 39.1 & 39.5 (1915)

NT0987.1/1

NT1087.1/1

Site NT0987.1; On the south side of the line, at the east end of Dunfermline Upper Station.
Dunfermline (E&NR) NT0987.1/1A
A 2TS dead ended shed, located at NT09558771 and opened on December 13th, 1849 by the Edinburgh & Northern Railway. The facilities included a turntable. No further details are known.

At some stage the shed was enlarged ...
Dunfermline (NB) NT0987.1/1B
It was rebuilt as a 3TS shed with two through roads and the facilities included a turntable and coal stage. It was closed in c1920 and demolished.

Replaced by ...
Site NT1087.1; On the south side of the line, east of Dunfermline Upper Station.
Dunfermline (NB) NT1087.1/1A
A brick built 4TS through road shed with a slated transverse multi-pitched roof, it was located at NT10078783 and was opened in c1920. The facilities included a ramped coaling stage, 50ft turntable and water columns.

The shed was re-roofed ...
Dunfermline (BR) NT1087.1/1B
A new roof with brick screen was installed by the Scottish Region in c1954. The depot closed on May 1st, 1967 and was subsequently demolished.

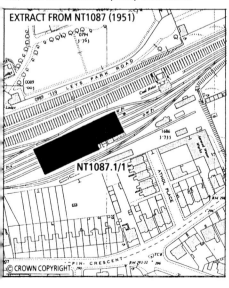

EXTRACT FROM NT1087 (1951)

NT1087.1/1

© CROWN COPYRIGHT

LEVEN

Site NO3701.1; In the vicinity of Leven Station.
Leven (Leven) NO3701.1/1A
A shed was opened here in c1855 by the Leven Railway. No further details are known.

BURNTISLAND

Site NT2385.1; On the south side of the line, east of Burntisland Station.
Burntisland (E&NR) NT2385.1/1A
A stone built circular 1RH shed with a slated conical style roof incorporating a water tank bridging the access road into the building. It was located at NT23688583 and was opened on September 20th, 1847 by the Edinburgh & Northern Railway. The other facilities included a ramped coaling stage. The depot was closed by the LNER in 1933, upon the opening of Thornton Junction shed (NT2897.1/1), and the roundhouse was subsequently demolished.

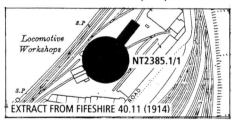

Locomotive Workshops

NT2385.1/1

EXTRACT FROM FIFESHIRE 40.11 (1914)

Replaced by ...
Burntisland (LNER) NT2385.1/1B
The remaining former water tank building was then utilized as a 1TS through road shed. It was closed to steam by BR in 1958 and housed a diesel shunter until total closure and demolition came in 1966.

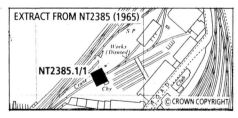

EXTRACT FROM NT2385 (1965)

NT2385.1/1

© CROWN COPYRIGHT

METHIL

Site NO3800.1; In Methil Docks.
Methil Dock (W&BR) NO3800.1/F1
A servicing area consisting of a siding and engine pit, located at NO38070016 and opened on May 5th, 1887 by the Wemyss & Buckhaven Railway. The line was absorbed by the NBR in 1889 and the facility was closed by BR in 1958.

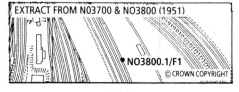

EXTRACT FROM NO3700 & NO3800 (1951)

NO3800.1/F1

© CROWN COPYRIGHT

ANSTRUTHER

Site NO5603.0; In the vicinity of Anstruther Station.
Anstruther (L&EofFR) NO5603.0/1A
A shed was opened here on September 1st, 1863 by the Leven & East of Fife Railway. The line was worked by the Edinburgh, Perth & Dundee Railway which was taken over by the NBR in 1877. No further details are known other than the depot closed on September 1st, 1883.

Replaced by ...
Site NO5603.1; On the south side of the line, at the west end of Anstruther Station.
Anstruther (NB) NO5603.1/1A
A brick built 2TS through road shed with a slated gable style roof, located at NO56110347 and opened on September 1st, 1883. The facilities included a water tank and turntable. The depot was closed by BR in December 1960 and later demolished.

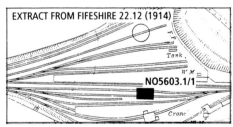

EXTRACT FROM FIFESHIRE 22.12 (1914)

Tank

NO5603.1/1

Crane

St.ANDREWS

Site NO4917.1; On the east side of the line, north of St.Andrews Station.
St.Andrews (St.Andrews) NO4917.1/1A
A timber built 1TS dead ended shed with a slated hipped roof, located at NO49881731 and opened on July 1st, 1852 by the St.Andrews Railway. Details of the facilities are not known. The depot was closed by BR in September 1960 and later demolished.

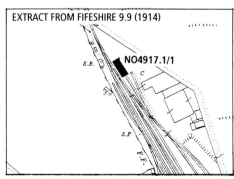

EXTRACT FROM FIFESHIRE 9.9 (1914)

NO4917.1/1

THORNTON JUNCTION

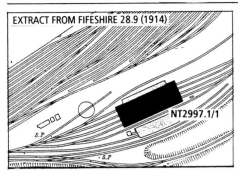

EXTRACT FROM FIFESHIRE 28.9 (1914)

NT2997.1/1

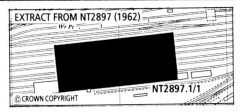

EXTRACT FROM NT2897 (1962)
© CROWN COPYRIGHT
NT2897.1/1

Site NT2997.0; In the vicinity of Thornton Junction.
Thornton Junction (NB) NT2997.0/1A
A shed was opened here on September 4th, 1848. No further details are known.

Replaced by ...
Site NT2997.1; In the triangle of lines at Thornton Junction.
Thornton Junction (NB) NT2997.1/1A
A brick built 4TS through road shed with a slated transverse multi-pitched roof, it was located at NT29769740 and opened in 1896. The facilities included a turntable and ramped coaling stage. The depot was closed by the LNER in 1933 and subsequently demolished.

Replaced by ...
Site NT2897.1; On the south side of the Thornton to Dunfermline line, west of Thornton Junction.
Thornton Junction (LNER) NT2897.1/1A
A corrugated iron built 6TS through road shed with a corrugated iron clad transverse multi-pitched roof, it was located at NT28309706 and opened in 1933. The facilities included a repair shop, coaling plant, water columns, and 70ft turntable. The depot was closed by BR in April 1967 and demolished in the 1970s.

LESLIE

Site NO2401.1; On the south side of Leslie Station.
Leslie (NB) NO2401.1/1A
A 1TS through road shed, located at NO24610127 and opened in 1857. The facilities included a water tank. No further details are known other than it was closed by the LNER in January 1932 and later demolished.

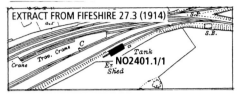

EXTRACT FROM FIFESHIRE 27.3 (1914)
NO2401.1/1

DYSART

Site NT3093.1; In the vicinity of Dysart Station.
Dysart (NB) NT3093.1/1A
A 1TS shed, approximately located at NT302934, was opened here. No further details are known.

TAYPORT

Site NO4528.1; On the west side of the line, south of Tayport Station.
Tayport (NB) NO4528.1/1A
A stone built 1TS dead ended shed with a slated hipped roof, located at NO45952886 and opened on May 17th, 1850. The facilities included a turntable. The depot was closed by BR on October 1st, 1951 but was not demolished until the 1960s.

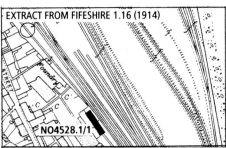

EXTRACT FROM FIFESHIRE 1.16 (1914)
NO4528.1/1

INVERKEITHING

Site NT1383.1; In the fork of the lines, north of Inverkeithing Station.
Inverkeithing (NB) NT1383.1/F1
A servicing area consisting of a coal stage, engine pit water columns and sidings, located at NT13118372 and opened on November 1st, 1877. The facility was closed by BR in 1966.

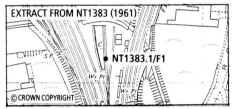

EXTRACT FROM NT1383 (1961)
NT1383.1/F1
© CROWN COPYRIGHT

CLACKMANNANSHIRE

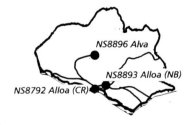

NS8896 Alva
NS8893 Alloa (NB)
NS8792 Alloa (CR)

ALLOA

Site NS8792.1; On the south side of the line, west of Alloa (CR) Goods Station.
Alloa (CR) NS8792.1/1A
A timber built 1TS through road shed with a gable style roof, located at NS87649262 and opened in 1903. No further details are known other than it was closed by the LMS in 1930.

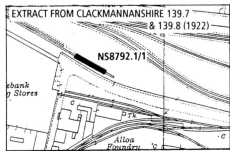

EXTRACT FROM CLACKMANNANSHIRE 139.7 & 139.8 (1922)
NS8792.1/1

Site NS8893.1; On the north side of the line, east of Alloa Station.
Alloa (NB) NS8893.1/1A
A stone built 2TS through road shed* with a slated gable style roof, located at NS88839314 and opened in 1885. The facilities included a coal stage. The depot was closed by BR in January 1967 and later demolished.

EXTRACT FROM CLACKMANNANSHIRE 139.4 (1922)
NS8893.1/1

The building may have been originally built as a 2TS dead ended structure (as NS8893.1/1B).

ALVA

Site NS8896.1; On the south side of the line, at the west end of Alva Station.
Alva (S&DR) NS8896.1/1A
A 1TS dead ended shed located at NS88029675 and opened on June 3rd, 1863 by the Stirling & Dunfermline Railway. No further details are known other than the facilities included a water tank and it was closed by the LNER in 1931.

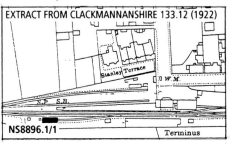

EXTRACT FROM CLACKMANNANSHIRE 133.12 (1922)
NS8896.1/1

STIRLINGSHIRE

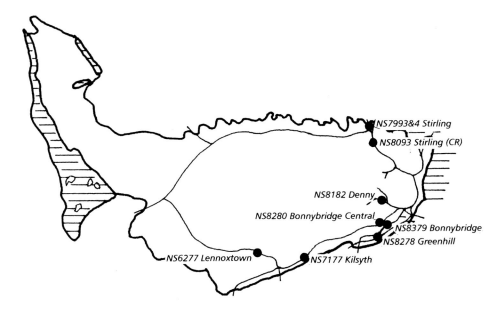

NS7993&4 Stirling
NS8093 Stirling (CR)
NS8182 Denny
NS8280 Bonnybridge Central
NS8379 Bonnybridge
NS8278 Greenhill
NS6277 Lennoxtown
NS7177 Kilsyth

STIRLING

EXTRACT FROM STIRLINGSHIRE 17.3 (1918)

NS7994.1/1

NS7993&4.1/1

NS7993&4.1/2

Site NS7994.1; On the west side of the line, north of Stirling Station.

Stirling (F&CJR) NS7994.1/1A

A brick built 4TS dead ended shed with a slated twin gable roof, it was located at NS79749433 and was opened in February 1861 by the Forth & Clyde Junction Railway. The facilities included a coal stage, water tank and turntable. The depot was closed by BR on September 16th, 1957 and later demolished.

Site NS7993&4.1; On the east side of the line, north of Stirling Station.

Stirling Shore Road (S&DR) NS7993&4.1/2A

A goods shed, located at NS79779393, was utilized as a 1TS through road shed by the Stirling & Dunfermline Railway between July 1st, 1852 and August 1853.

Stirling Shore Road (NB) NS7993&4.1/1A

A stone built 2TS shed with one through road and a slated gable style roof, located at NS79759401 and opened prior to 1864. The facilities included a ramped coaling stage, turntable and water tank. The depot was closed by BR on September 16th, 1957 and subsequently demolished.

EXTRACT FROM STIRLINGSHIRE 17.3 (1918)

Signal Bridge
Timber Yard
Forthbank Carpet Works
Saw Mill
NS8093.1/1
Football
UPPER CRAIGS
SPRINGFIELD PLACE

Site NS7993.1; At the south end of Stirling Station.

Stirling (SCR) NS7993.1/1A

A timber built shed, approximately located at NS799935 was opened here on March 3rd, 1848 by the Scottish Central Railway and closed in 1850. No further details are known.

Replaced by ...
Site NS8093.1; On the east side of the line, south of Stirling Station.

Stirling (CR) NS8093.1/1A

A stone built 4TS dead ended shed with a slated twin gable style roof, located at NS80089310 and opened in 1850. The facilities included a turntable, coke/coal stage and water tank.

The building was modified ...
Stirling (CR) NS8093.1/1B

The structure was converted to a 4TS through road shed in 1898 and a ramped coaling stage was installed in 1909.

The shed was re-roofed ...
Stirling (BR) NS8093.1/1C

The roof was re-clad in c1950 by the Scottish Region and the brick arches at the southern end were demolished and replaced with wooden gables. The depot closed on June 13th, 1966 and stabled diesel shunters for a short while prior to demolition.

DENNY

Site NS8182.1; On the north side of the line, at the east end of Denny Station.

Denny (SCR) NS8182.1/1A

A 2TS shed with one through road, it was located at NS81488250 and was opened on April 1st, 1858 by the Scottish Central Railway. The facilities included a water column. The depot was closed by the LMS on July 28th, 1930 and demolished.

EXTRACT FROM STIRLINGSHIRE 23.16 (1918)

Crane
Engine Shed
NS8182.1/1

BONNYBRIDGE

Site NS8379.1; On the north side of the line, at the east end of Bonnybridge Station.
Bonnybridge (CR) NS8379.1/1A
A 1TS dead ended shed located at NS83117929 and opened on August 2nd, 1886. No further details are known other than it closed in 1921.

EXTRACT FROM STIRLINGSHIRE N29.8 (1918)
NS8379.1/1

Site NS8280.1; On the east side of the line, north of Bonnybridge Central Station.
Bonnybridge Central (K&BR) NS8280.1/1A
A timber built 1TS dead ended shed with a slated gable style roof, located at NS82438060 and opened on July 2nd, 1888 by the Kilsyth & Bonnybridge Railway, a line worked by both the NB and CR. The facilities included a turntable, sited outside of the shed entrance, and a water tank. The Caledonian Railway vacated the shed in 1921 and it was finally closed by the LNER in January 1932. The building survived into BR days before being demolished.

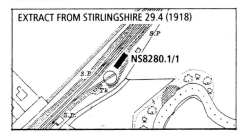
EXTRACT FROM STIRLINGSHIRE 29.4 (1918)
NS8280.1/1

GREENHILL

Site NS8278.1; In the fork of the lines at Greenhill Junction.
Greenhill (SCR) NS8278.1/1A
A 2TS dead ended shed, located at NS82157891 and opened on May 22nd, 1848. No further details are known other than it closed in 1900.

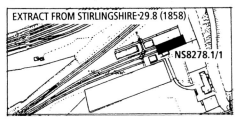
EXTRACT FROM STIRLINGSHIRE 29.8 (1858)
NS8278.1/1

Replaced by ...
Greenhill (CR) NS8278.1/2A
A timber built 2TS shed with one through road and a slated gable style roof, it was sited slightly west of its predecessor (NS8278.1/1A) at NS82107889. The facilities included a 60ft turntable and water was available from the adjacent reservoir. The depot was closed by the LMS in 1935 and later demolished.

EXTRACT FROM STIRLINGSHIRE 29.8 (1918)
NS8278.1/1
NS8278.1/2
Reservoir

LENNOXTOWN

Site NS6277.1; On the west side of the line, at the south end of Lennoxtown (1st) Station.
Lennoxtown (E&GR) NS6277.1/1A
A 1TS dead ended shed located at NS62757768 and opened on July 5th, 1848 by the Edinburgh & Glasgow Railway. No further details are known.

EXTRACT FROM STIRLINGSHIRE 28.9 (1863)
NS6277.1/1
Haugh
U.P.Chu

Replaced, at some stage, by ...
Site NS6277.2; On the north side of Lennoxtown (1st) Station.
Lennoxtown (NB) NS6277.2/1A
A timber built 1TS through road shed with a slated gable style roof and located at NS62707781. Details of the facilities are not known.

At some stage, probably in LNER days, the shed was rebuilt on the same site ...
Lennoxtown (LNER) NS6277.2/1B
A brick built 1TS through road shed with a corrugated asbestos pitched roof and brick gables. The depot was closed by BR on October 1st, 1951 and later demolished.

EXTRACT FROM STIRLINGSHIRE 27.12 (1918)
Engine Shed
NS6277.2/1
Goods Shed
Station
NS6277.1/1

KILSYTH

Site NS7177.1; On the north side of the line, west of Kilsyth Station.
Kilsyth (KVR) NS7177.1/1A
A 1TS dead ended shed, located at NS71147793 and opened on June 1st, 1878 by the Kilsyth Valley Railway. The facilities included a turntable and a water tank.

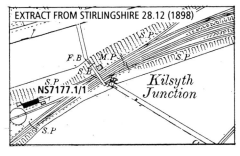
EXTRACT FROM STIRLINGSHIRE 28.12 (1898)
NS7177.1/1
Kilsyth Junction

The shed was rebuilt after 1898 ...
Kilsyth (NB) NS7177.1/2A
At some stage a brick built 1TS dead ended shed with a slated gable style roof was constructed. This was twice the length, and was partially built on the site of its predecessor (NS7177.1/1A). The depot was closed by BR on August 4th, 1951 but did not suffer demolition until the 1960s.

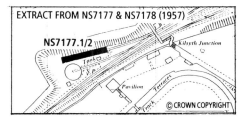
EXTRACT FROM NS7177 & NS7178 (1957)
NS7177.1/2
Kilsyth Junction
Pavilion
© CROWN COPYRIGHT

Pictured here *(below)* on August 2nd, 1937 is the second depot (NS6277.2/1A) at **Lennoxtown**, a North British Railway timber built structure of an, as yet, unknown building date which had replaced an Edinburgh & Glasgow Railway shed of July 1848 (NS6277.1/1A).

Mysterious dates continued to be associated with this site because, by its closure in October 1951, the shed was of brick build (as NS6277.2/1B), a reconstruction that has yet to be fixed in time, but possibly had something to do with World War II.
WA Camwell

DUNBARTONSHIRE

BALLOCH

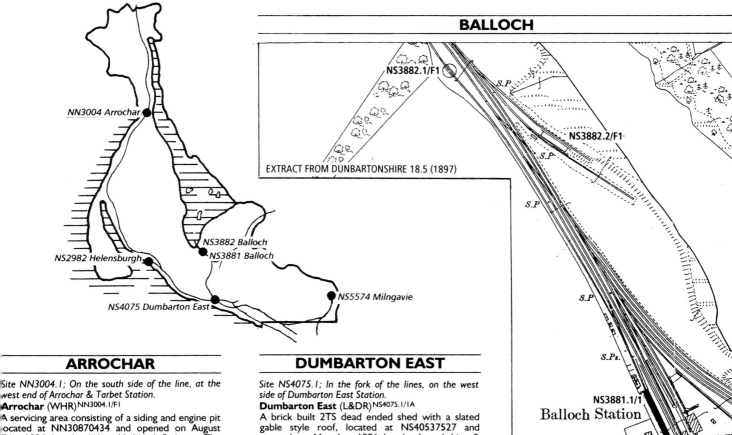

EXTRACT FROM DUNBARTONSHIRE 18.5 (1897)

NS3882.1/F1

NS3882.2/F1

NS3881.1/1

Balloch Station

ARROCHAR

Site NN3004.1; On the south side of the line, at the west end of Arrochar & Tarbet Station.

Arrochar (WHR)^{NN3004.1/F1}
A servicing area consisting of a siding and engine pit located at NN30870434 and opened on August 7th, 1894 by the West Highland Railway. The facility was closed by BR in October 1959.

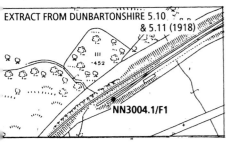

EXTRACT FROM DUNBARTONSHIRE 5.10 & 5.11 (1918)

NN3004.1/F1

HELENSBURGH

Site NS2982.1; On the north side of Helensburgh Station.

Helensburgh (NB) ^{NS2982.1/1A}
A brick built 2TS dead ended shed with a slated gable style roof, located at NS29788243 and opened on August 11th, 1894. The facilities included a turntable and water tank. The depot was closed by BR on November 7th, 1960 but re-opened as an emergency measure on December 18th, 1960 following the failure of the Glasgow Suburban Electric Trains. It finally closed on September 30th, 1961 and was later demolished.

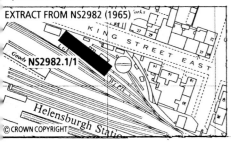

EXTRACT FROM NS2982 (1965)

NS2982.1/1

Helensburgh Sta...

© CROWN COPYRIGHT

DUMBARTON EAST

Site NS4075.1; In the fork of the lines, on the west side of Dumbarton East Station.

Dumbarton East (L&DR)^{NS4075.1/1A}
A brick built 2TS dead ended shed with a slated gable style roof, located at NS40537527 and opened on May 1st, 1896 by the Lanarkshire & Dunbartonshire Railway. The facilities included a turntable, coal stage and water tank. The depot was closed by BR on October 5th, 1964 and later demolished.

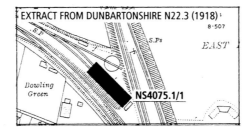

EXTRACT FROM DUNBARTONSHIRE N22.3 (1918)

NS4075.1/1

MILNGAVIE

Site NS5574.1; On the east side of Milngavie Station.

Milngavie (NB) ^{NS5574.1/1A}
A stone built 1TS dead ended shed with a slated gable style roof, located at NS55567441 and opened on July 28th, 1863. The facilities included a water column and turntable. The depot was closed by the LNER in 1928 but the shed, being an integral part of the station buildings, survived until at least 1952. It was later demolished, although part of the shed building still remained in 1996, in use as a partition wall.

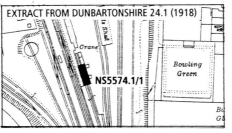

EXTRACT FROM DUNBARTONSHIRE 24.1 (1918)

NS5574.1/1

Site NS3882.1; On the west side of the line, north of Balloch Station.

Balloch (CR)^{NS3882.1/F1}
A servicing area consisting of a turntable and siding located at NS38768230 and opened on October 1st, 1896.

The facility was expanded ...
Site NS3882.2; On the east side of the line, north of Balloch Station.

Balloch (CR)^{NS3882.2/F1}
At some stage a coal stage, sidings and water column were installed on the opposite side of the line at NS38858223. The closure date is not known.

Site NS3881.1; On the west side of Balloch Station.

Balloch (C&DR)^{NS3881.1/1A}
A 1TS dead ended shed located at NS38948196 and opened on July 15th, 1850 by the Caledonian & Dunbartonshire Railway. The facilities included a water tank. No further details are known other than prior to 1936 the building was destroyed by a fire.

A servicing point was then established ...
Balloch (LNER)^{NS3881.1/F1}
The shed road, engine pit and water tank were utilized as a stabling point.

Replaced, on the original site, by ...
Balloch (BR)^{NS3881.1/1B}
A steel framed corrugated iron 1TS through road shed with a corrugated iron pitched roof was constructed on the original shed site by the Scottish Region in 1948. The depot closed on November 7th, 1960 but was re-opened as an emergency measure on December 18th, 1960 following the failure of the Glasgow Suburban Electric Trains. It finally closed on September 30th, 1961 and was later demolished.

PERTHSHIRE

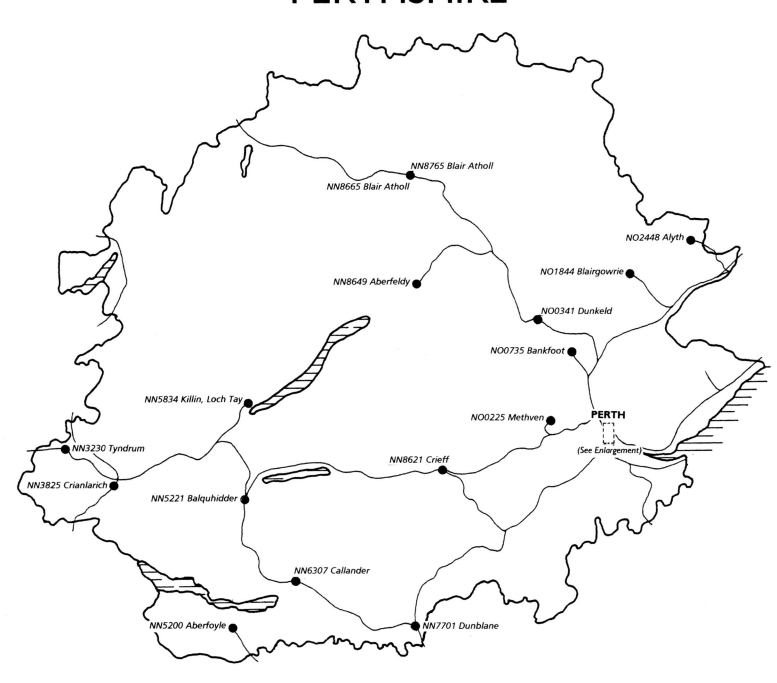

NN8765 Blair Atholl
NN8665 Blair Atholl
NO2448 Alyth
NO1844 Blairgowrie
NN8649 Aberfeldy
NO0341 Dunkeld
NO0735 Bankfoot
NN5834 Killin, Loch Tay
NO0225 Methven
PERTH
(See Enlargement)
NN3230 Tyndrum
NN8621 Crieff
NN3825 Crianlarich
NN5221 Balquhidder
NN6307 Callander
NN5200 Aberfoyle
NN7701 Dunblane

CALLANDER

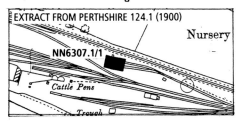

Site NN6307.1; On the south side of the line, east of Callander Station.
Callander (DD&CR) NN6307.1/1A
A stone built 2TS dead ended shed with a slated gable style roof, located at NN63490768 and opened on July 1st, 1858 by the Dunblane, Doune & Callander Railway. The facilities included a turntable. The depot was closed by the LMS in 1924 and remained standing until the 1970s.

EXTRACT FROM PERTHSHIRE 124.1 (1900)
Nursery
NN6307.1/1
Cattle Pens
Trough

ABERFOYLE

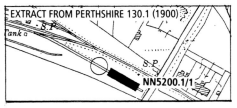

Site NN5200.1; On the south side of the line, at the east end of Aberfoyle Station.
Aberfoyle (S&AR) NN5200.1/1A
A brick built 1TS through road shed with a slated gable style roof, located at NN52350086 and opened on August 1st, 1882 by the Strathendrick & Aberfoyle Railway. The facilities included a water tank and a turntable, sited outside of the shed entrance. The depot was closed by BR on October 1st, 1951 and later demolished.

EXTRACT FROM PERTHSHIRE 130.1 (1900)
Tank
S.P.
S.P.
NN5200.1/1

TYNDRUM

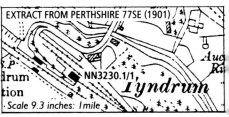

Site NN3230.1; On the north side of the line, at the east end of Tyndrum Lower Station.
Tyndrum (C&OR) NN3230.1/1A
A stone built 1TS dead ended shed, located at NN32833011 and opened in August 1873 by the Callander & Oban Railway. The facilities included a 42ft turntable, sited outside of the shed entrance, and a water tank. The depot was closed by the CR on December 31st, 1915 and later demolished.

EXTRACT FROM PERTHSHIRE 77SE (1901)
S.P.
drum
tion
NN3230.1/1
Tyndrum
Auc
R
Scale 9.3 inches: 1mile

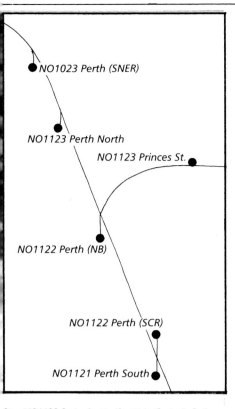

NO1023 Perth (SNER)

NO1123 Perth North

NO1123 Princes St.

NO1122 Perth (NB)

NO1122 Perth (SCR)

NO1121 Perth South

Site NO1122.2; In Perth (Scottish Central) Railway Works, east of the line, south of Perth (General) Station.

Perth (SCR) NO1122.2/1A

A timber built 4TS dead ended shed, located at NO11552232, and opened by the Scottish Central Railway on May 22nd, 1848. It closed when Perth South shed (NO1121.1/1) was built in 1854 and the building was absorbed into the works. No further details are known.

EXTRACT FROM PERTHSHIRE 98.9 (1901)

NO1122.2/1A

Site NO1122.1; On the west side of the line, at the south end of Perth (General) Station.

Perth (EP&DR) NO1122.1/1A

A 2TS through road shed, located at NO11312281 and opened on July 18th, 1848 by the Edinburgh, Perth & Dundee Railway. The facilities included a turntable. The line was absorbed by the NB in 1862 and the depot closed at some point prior to 1899. No further details are known.

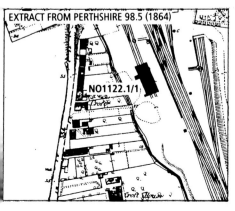

EXTRACT FROM PERTHSHIRE 98.5 (1864)

NO1122.1/1

Replaced by ...
Perth (NB) NO1122.1/2A

A brick built 3TS dead ended shed with a slated transverse multi-hipped roof, it was sited slightly north west of its predecessor (NO1121.1/1A) at NO11282285. The facilities included a turntable and coal stage. The depot was closed by BR on January 7th, 1950 and the building was utilized by the Signals Department prior to demolition in the late 1980s.

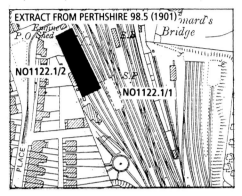

EXTRACT FROM PERTHSHIRE 98.5 (1901)

NO1122.1/2

NO1122.1/1

Site NO1123.1;On the north side of the line, at the west end of Perth (Princes St) Station.

Perth, Princes St (DP&AJR) NO1123.1/1A

A brick built 3TS dead ended shed, located at NO11882318 and opened on March 24th, 1847 by the Dundee, Perth & Aberdeen Junction Railway. It formed part of a very unusual and larger structure which also spanned the three running tracks along the southern side. The facilities included a 34ft turntable. The line was absorbed by the Scottish Central Railway in 1862 and the depot was closed and demolished in 1863.

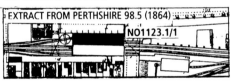

EXTRACT FROM PERTHSHIRE 98.5 (1864)

NO1123.1/1

Site NO1123.2; On the east side of the line, north of Perth (General) Station.

Perth (SNER) NO1123.2/1A

A 6TS dead ended shed, located at NO11062388 and opened in 1854 by the Scottish North Eastern Railway. Details of the facilities are not known but the accommodation was shared with the goods department. It closed for locomotive purposes in 1866 and saw further use as a wagon works as well as as a goods shed, surviving until at least 1965.

Site NO1023.1; On the west side of the line, north of Perth (General) Station.

Perth (SNER) NO1023.1/1A

A 6TS dead ended shed, located at NO10982389 and opened in 1854 by the Scottish North Eastern Railway. Details of the facilities are not known but the accommodation was shared with the goods department. It closed, for locomotive purposes, in 1866 and saw further use as a wagon works as well as as a goods shed and survived until at least 1965.

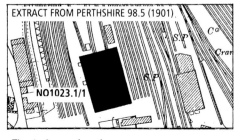

EXTRACT FROM PERTHSHIRE 98.5 (1901)

NO1023.1/1

The shed was enlarged ...
Perth North (HR) NO1123.3/1B

The building was extended in 1865. No further details are known other than it closed in 1875.

Replaced, on the same site, by ...
Perth North (HR) NO1123.3/1C

A stone built 8TS dead ended shed with twin slated gable style roofs. It opened in 1875 and the facilities included a ramped coaling stage, water tank and 45ft turntable.

The shed was rebuilt ...
Perth North (HR) NO1123.3/1D

The original arched entrances, probably in 1897, were replaced with wooden gables and the depot was closed by the LMS on May 29th, 1938, the locomotives transferring to the newly enlarged Perth South shed (NO1121.1/2A). The building was subsequently utilized for locomotive storage and later the most westerly four-bay section was demolished. The remaining portion still stood in 1998, in private use as an antiques warehouse.

EXTRACT FROM PERTHSHIRE 98.5 (1901)

NO1123.3/1

Site NO1121.1; On the west side of the line, south of Perth (General) Station.

Perth South (CR) NO1121.1/1A

A stone built 7TS dead ended shed with three slated gable style pitched roofs, located at NO11622192 and opened in 1854. The facilities included a coal stage and 45ft turntable.

The building was modified ...
Perth South (CR) NO1121.1/1B

Prior to 1900, four of the tracks were extended through the rear wall. At the same time a new ramped coaling stage was installed in the yard and the turntable was repositioned and increased in size to 50ft. By 1937 the building and yard had become too small and the shed was progressively demolished.

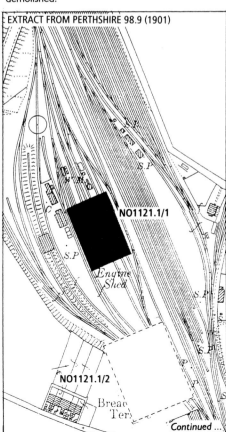

EXTRACT FROM PERTHSHIRE 98.9 (1901)

NO1121.1/1

NO1121.1/2

Continued ...

Replaced by ...

Perth South (LMS) NO1121.1/2A

A brick built 8TS through road shed with a corrugated sheeted multi-pitched roof and corrugated sheet clad gables. It was sited south of its predecessor, NO1121.1/1A, at NO11662179 and officially opened on May 14th, 1938. The facilities included a repair shop, mechanical coaling plant, water tank and 70ft turntable. The depot was closed to steam by BR on May 14th, 1967, totally on October 5th, 1969 and demolished in 1972.

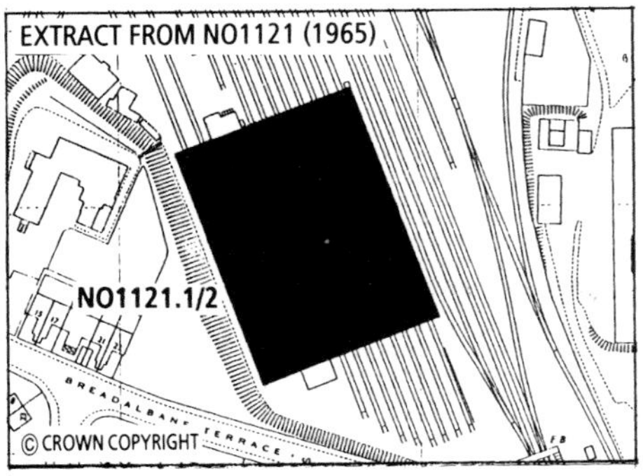

EXTRACT FROM NO1121 (1965)

© CROWN COPYRIGHT

CRIEFF

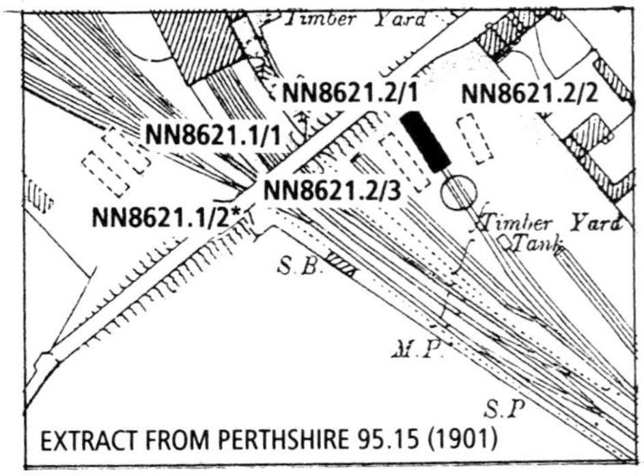

EXTRACT FROM PERTHSHIRE 95.15 (1901)

Site NN8621.1; On the west side of the line, at the south end of Crieff (1st) Station.

Crieff (CJR) NN8621.1/1A

A brick built 1TS dead ended shed, located at NN86262120 and opened on March 16th, 1856 by the Crieff Junction Railway.

Crieff (SNER) NN8621.1/2A

A 1TS shed, probably located at NN86252119 and opened on May 21st, 1866 by the Scottish North Eastern Railway.

No further details are known other than they both closed in 1892 upon the opening of NN8621.2/1A nearby.

Site NN8621.2; On the east side of the line, at the south end of Crieff Station.

Crieff (CR) NN8621.2/1A

A brick built 1TS dead ended shed with a slated gable style roof, located at NN86362120 and opened on May 21st, 1896. The facilities included a 45ft turntable which was sited outside of the shed entrance and removed in c1910.

Crieff (CR) NN8621.2/2A

A timber built 1TS dead ended shed with a slated gable style roof, located at NN86382120 and opened in 1899.

Crieff (CR) NN8621.2/3A

A timber built 1TS dead ended shed with a slated gable style roof, located at NN86352119 and opened in 1899.

The facilities included a turntable, installed outside of the shed entrance of NN8621.2/2A in 1910 and a water tank. NN8621.2/3A was closed by the LMS in 1943 and the other two lasted into BR days, not closing until September 13th, 1958.

BLAIR ATHOLL

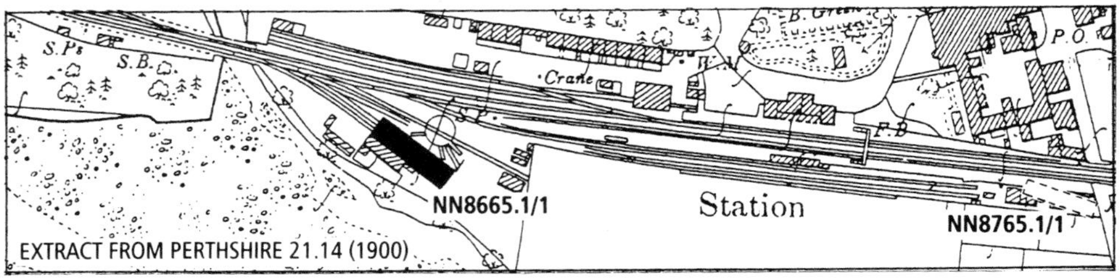

EXTRACT FROM PERTHSHIRE 21.14 (1900)

Site NN8765.1; On the south side of the line, at the east end of Blair Atholl Station.

Blair Atholl (HR) NN8765.1/1A

A timber built 1TS dead ended shed, located at NN87146524 and opened on September 9th, 1863. The facilities included a 20ft turntable, sited outside of the shed entrance. The depot was closed in 1868.

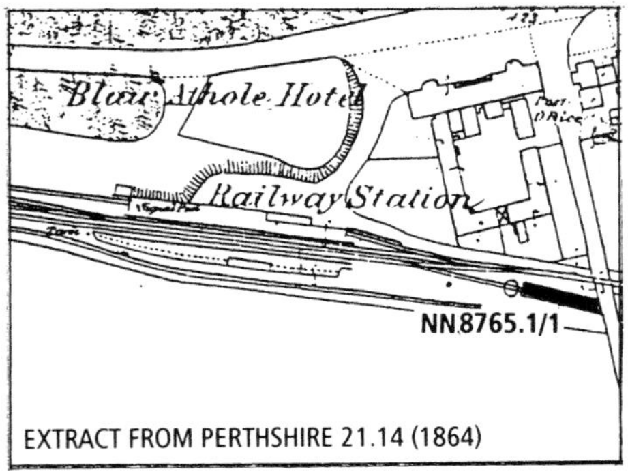

EXTRACT FROM PERTHSHIRE 21.14 (1864)

Replaced by ...

Site NN8665.1; On the south side of the line, at the west end of Blair Atholl Station.

Blair Atholl (HR) NN8665.1/1A

A stone built 2TS dead ended shed with a slated gable style roof, located at NN86876527 and opened in August 1868. The building had, in the main, been constructed out of stone blocks salvaged from Keith shed (NJ4251.1/1) and the facilities included a water tank and a 42ft turntable, later enlarged to 55ft 3in.

The shed was modified ...

Blair Atholl (LMS) NN8665.1/1B

At some stage, possibly after grouping, the building was modified to a 2TS through road shed with a timber gable surmounting the new rear entrance.

The shed was re-roofed ...

Blair Atholl (BR) NN8665.1/1C

A corrugated sheeting clad single pitched roof with corrugated sheeting gables was installed by the Scottish Region in c1948. The depot closed in c1962 and remained standing in a derelict condition until at least 1999.

BLAIRGOWRIE

Site NO1844.1; On the east side of the line, at the south end of Blairgowrie Station.

Blairgowrie (CR) NO1844.1/1A

A timber built 1TS dead ended shed located at NO18194495 and opened in August 1855. No further details are known.

The shed may have been enlarged ...

Blairgowrie (CR) NO1844.1/1B

At some stage after 1863 the shed may have been enlarged to a timber built 2TS structure. The depot was closed in 1887 and demolished.

EXTRACT FROM PERTHSHIRE 52.16 (1863)

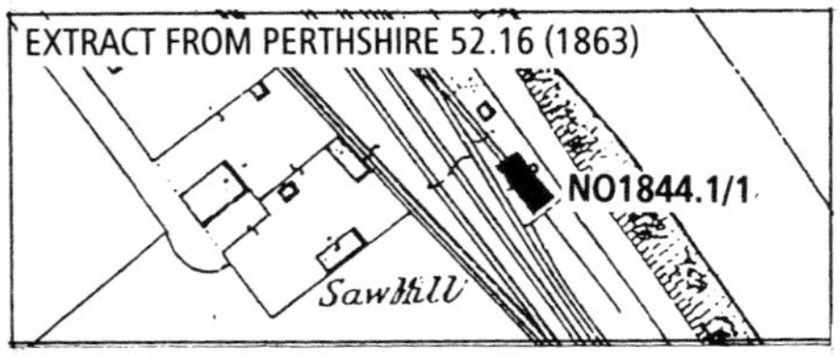

Replaced by ...

Site NO1844.2; On the west side of the line, at the south end of Blairgowrie Station.

Blairgowrie (CR) NO1844.2/1A

A stone built 2TS through road shed with a slated gable style roof, located at NO18194491 and opened in 1887. The facilities included a water tank and 42ft turntable. The depot was closed by the LMS on January 3rd, 1942 and let out for private use, surviving into the 1990s.

EXTRACT FROM PERTHSHIRE 63.4 (1901)

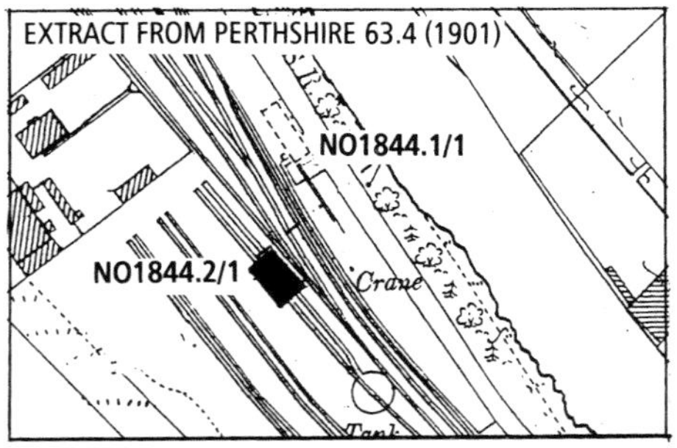

ALYTH

Site NO2448.1; On the south side of Alyth Station.

Alyth (CR) NO2448.1/1A

A 1TS through road shed located at NO24914823 and opened on August 12th, 1861. The facilities included a turntable. No further details are known other than it closed in 1913.

Replaced by ...

Site NO2448.2; On the north side of Alyth Station.

Alyth (CR) NO2448.2/1A

A brick built 1TS dead ended shed with a slated gable style roof, located at NO24854828 and opened in 1913. The facilities included a water tank. Although the depot was closed by the LMS on February 23rd, 1943 and survived until the 1960s, locomotives utilized the shed yard until passenger services were withdrawn by BR on July 2nd, 1951.

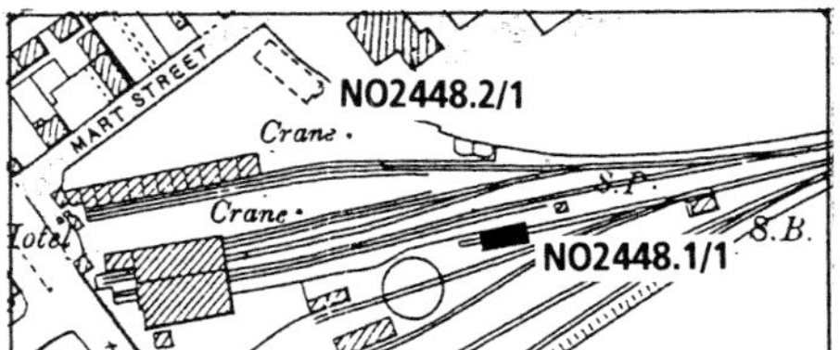

EXTRACT FROM PERTHSHIRE 53.6 (1900)

KILLIN

Site NN5834.1; At the end of the line, at the north end of Loch Tay Station.
Killin, Loch Tay (Killin)^{NN5834.1/1A}
A timber built 1TS dead ended shed with a slated gable style roof, located at NN58483451 and opened on March 13th, 1886 by the Killin Railway. The facilities included a water column. The building was destroyed by a fire on October 24th, 1917.

Replaced, on the same site, by ...
Killin, Loch Tay (CR)^{NN5834.1/1B}
A timber built 1TS dead ended shed with a slated gable style roof was constructed on the site in 1918. The depot, along with the Killin branch and Dunblane to Crianlarich line, was due to be closed by BR on November 1st, 1965 but a landslip at Glenogle on September 27th, 1965 damaged the track to such an extent that it was all closed immediately. The shed was partially demolished and the brick base wall incorporated into a house for use as a garage.

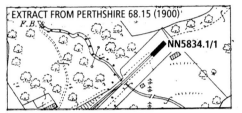
EXTRACT FROM PERTHSHIRE 68.15 (1900)
NN5834.1/1

ABERFELDY

Site NN8649.1; On the east side of the line, at the north end of Aberfeldy Station.
Aberfeldy (HR)^{NN8649.1/1A}
A timber built 1TS dead ended shed with a gable style roof located at NN86054928 and opened on July 3rd, 1865. The facilities included a water tank and turntable sited outside of the shed entrance. The building was destroyed by a fire in 1902.

Replaced, on the same site, by ....
Aberfeldy (HR)^{NN8649.1/1B}
A timber built 1TS dead ended shed with a gable style roof, it opened in 1902. The turntable was removed in c1920 and the depot was closed by BR in c1962 with demolition following in the late 1960s.

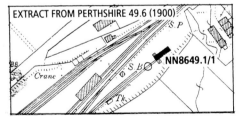
EXTRACT FROM PERTHSHIRE 49.6 (1900)
NN8649.1/1

CRIANLARICH

Site NN3825.1; On the east side of the line, at the south end of Crianlarich Station.
Crianlarich (WHR)^{NN3825.1/1A}
A brick built 1TS dead ended shed with a slated gable style roof, located at NN38482599 and opened on August 7th, 1894 by the West Highland Railway. The facilities included a turntable. The depot was closed by the LNER in 1930 and remained standing until at least 1998, housing pw machines.

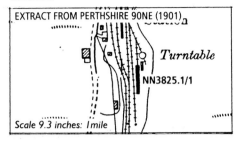
EXTRACT FROM PERTHSHIRE 90NE (1901)
Turntable
NN3825.1/1
Scale 9.3 inches: 1mile

DUNBLANE

Site NN7701.1; In the fork of the lines, north of Dunblane Station.
Dunblane (SCR)^{NN7701.1/1A}
A 1TS dead ended shed, probably built in timber and with a slated gable style roof, it was located at NN77980139 and was opened on May 23rd, 1848 by the Scottish Central Railway. It closed in 1865 and three years later was removed to Dolphinton and re-erected as NT1047.1/1A.

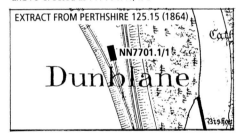
EXTRACT FROM PERTHSHIRE 125.15 (1864)
NN7701.1/1
Dunblane

BANKFOOT

Site NO0735.1; On the east side of the line, at the south end of Bankfoot Station.
Bankfoot (B&SLR)^{NO0735.1/1A}
A timber built 1TS through road shed with a slated gable style roof was opened here on May 1st, 1906 by the Bankfoot & Strathord Light Railway. It was approximately located at NO07083500 and the facilities included a water tank. The line was worked by the CR, which absorbed the line in 1913 and closed the depot in c1920.

DUNKELD

Site NO0341.1; On the south side of the line, at the east end of Dunkeld Station.
Dunkeld (P&DR)^{NO0341.1/1A}
A stone built 1TS dead ended shed with a slated gable style roof, located at NO03244155 and opened on April 7th, 1856 by the Perth & Dunkeld Railway. No further details are known other than it closed in 1866 and was later demolished to accommodate station enlargements.

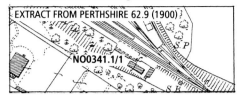
EXTRACT FROM PERTHSHIRE 62.9 (1900)
NO0341.1/1

METHVEN

Site NO0225.1; On the east side of Methven Station.
Methven (PAV&MR)^{NO0225.1/1A}
A brick built 1TS dead ended shed with a slated gable style roof, located at NO02332552 and opened on January 1st, 1858 by the Perth, Almond Valley & Methven Railway. The facilities included a water tank. The depot was closed by the LNER in 1931 and subsequently demolished.

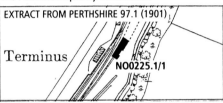
EXTRACT FROM PERTHSHIRE 97.1 (1901)
Terminus
NO0225.1/1

BALQUHIDDER

Site NN5221.1; In the fork of the lines, on the north side of Balquhidder Station.
Balquhidder (CR)^{NN5221.1/1A}
A timber built 1TS dead ended shed with a slated gable style roof, located at NN52752130 and opened on May 1st, 1905. The facilities included a 60ft turntable sited outside of the shed entrance. The depot was closed by the LMS on February 28th, 1942 and subsequently demolished.

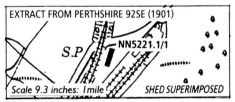
EXTRACT FROM PERTHSHIRE 92SE (1901)
S.P
NN5221.1/1
Scale 9.3 inches: 1mile   SHED SUPERIMPOSED

KINROSS

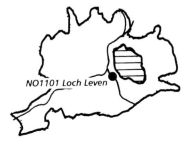
NO1101 Loch Leven

LOCH LEVEN

Site NO1101.1; On the east side of the line, south of Loch Leven Station
Loch Leven (NB)^{NO1101.1/1A}
A stone built 1TS dead ended shed with a slated gable style roof, located at NO11830143 and opened on January 20th, 1860. No further details are known.

The shed was extended ...
Loch Lèven (NB)^{NO1101.1/1B}
At some stage prior to 1913 the building was doubled in length. The depot was closed by BR on April 14th, 1951 and let out for private use prior to demolition.

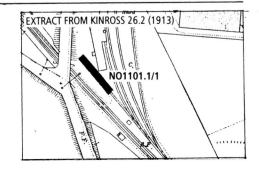
EXTRACT FROM KINROSS 26.2 (1913)
NO1101.1/1

ARGYLL

WESTERN SECTION OF ARGYLL

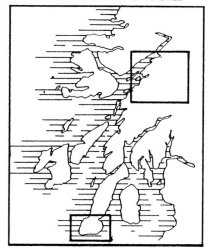

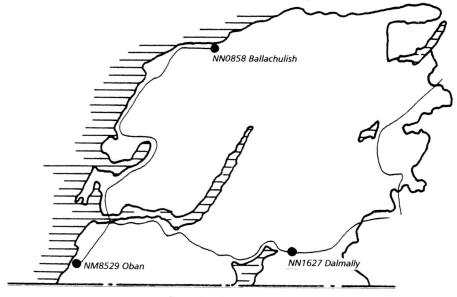

Remainder of county omitted

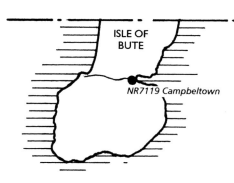

OBAN

Site NM8529.1; In the fork of the Goods Station spur and main line, south of Oban Station.

Oban (C&OR) NM8529.1/1A

A timber built 2TS dead ended shed with a slated gable style roof, located at NM85632943 and opened on June 30th, 1880 by the Callander & Oban Railway. The facilities included a coal stage (later replaced by a small mechanical coaler), 50ft turntable and water tank. The depot was closed by BR on May 6th, 1963 and later demolished.

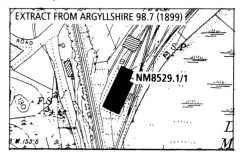

DALMALLY

Site NN1627.1: On the south side of Dalmally Station.

Dalmally (C&OR) NN1627.1/1A

A stone built 1TS dead ended shed with a slated gable style roof, located at NN16082715 and opened in May 1877 by the Callander & Oban Railway. The facilities included a water tank and a turntable, sited outside of the shed entrance. The depot was closed by the LMS in 1930 and later demolished.

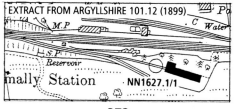

BALLACHULISH

Site NN0858.1; On the north side of Ballachulish Station.

Ballachulish (C&OR) NN0858.1/1A

A timber built 2TS dead ended shed with a slated gable style roof, located at NN08255844 and opened on August 24th, 1903 by the Callander & Oban Railway. The facilities included a water tank, 60ft turntable and coal stage. The depot was closed by BR on March 12th, 1962 and saw subsequent use as a garage until at least 1998.

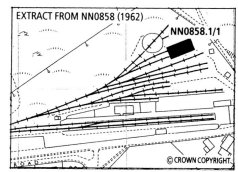

Please Note: The construction and dismantling dates of this line preclude its inclusion in a complete form in OS maps. Some, or all, of the buildings and track have been superimposed.

CAMPBELTOWN

Site NR7119.1; In the fork of the Coal Depot spur and the main line, west of Campbeltown Station.

Campbeltown, Limecraigs (C&MLR) NR7119.1/1A

A 2ft 3in gauge 1TS dead ended shed with a gable style roof, located at NR71901987 and opened on August 16th, 1906* by the Campbeltown & Machrihanish Light Railway. The shed was either constructed in timber or corrugated iron and the facilities included a water column and coal stage. The depot closed in November 1931 and was subsequently demolished.

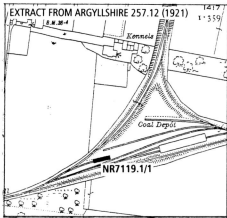

*The depot may have dated from May 23rd, 1877 when the line opened as a mineral railway (Argyll Coal & Canal Co.).

372

ABERDEENSHIRE

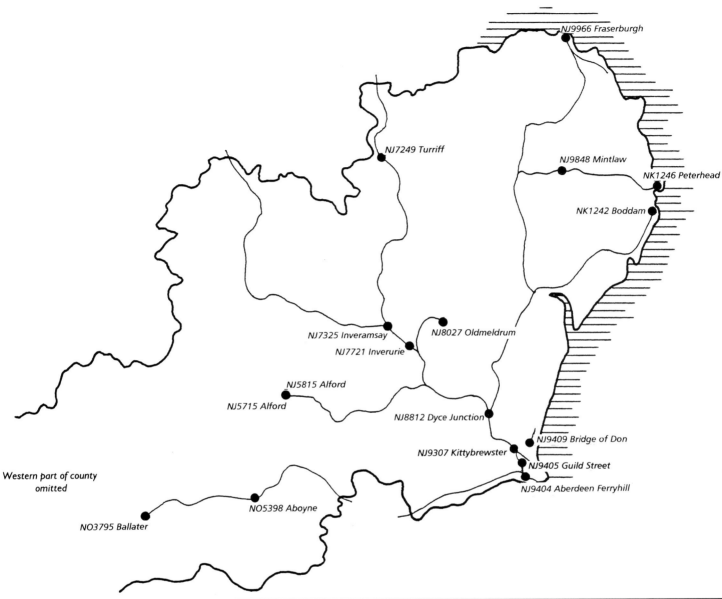

NJ9966 Fraserburgh

NJ7249 Turriff

NJ9848 Mintlaw

NK1246 Peterhead

NK1242 Boddam

NJ7325 Inveramsay

NJ8027 Oldmeldrum

NJ7721 Inverurie

NJ5815 Alford

NJ5715 Alford

NJ8812 Dyce Junction

NJ9409 Bridge of Don

NJ9307 Kittybrewster

NJ9405 Guild Street

NJ9404 Aberdeen Ferryhill

Western part of county
omitted

NO5398 Aboyne

NO3795 Ballater

Built by the Inverury (sic) & Oldmeldrum Railway in 1856, the engine shed (NJ8027.1/1A) at the line's terminus at **Oldmeldrum** housed the GNofSR and, later, LNER engines working the line until passenger services were withdrawn in October 1931.

The shed still stood about four years later though, when this photograph showed how it had been crudely boarded up and, with the somewhat rudimentary water tank having lost its hose, it is evident that no engine servicing of any kind was being carried out. No doubt, demolition was not far away.   WA Camwell

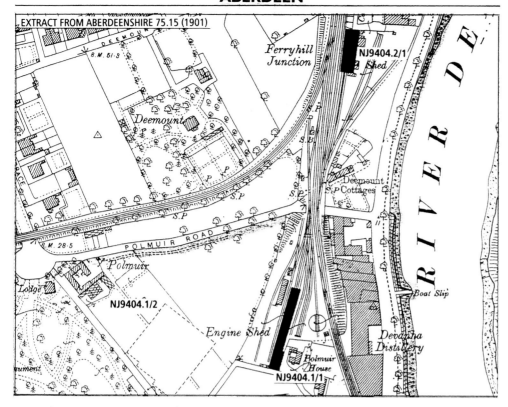

EXTRACT FROM ABERDEENSHIRE 75.15 (1901)

NJ9404.2/1

NJ9404.1/2

NJ9404.1/1

Site NJ9404.2; On the east side of Ferryhill Junction, south of Aberdeen Station.

Aberdeen (CR/NB) NJ9404.2/1A

A 2TS dead ended shed located at NJ94190482 and opened in 1896. No further details are known other than it closed in 1908 upon the opening of Ferryhill shed (NJ9404.1/2) and was later demolished.

Site NJ9404.1; In the fork of the Ballater and Perth lines, south of Aberdeen Station.

Aberdeen (Aberdeen) NJ9404.1/1A

A 2TS dead ended shed located at NJ94130456 and opened on April 1st, 1850 by the Aberdeen Railway. The facilities included a turntable and a water tank.

The shed was enlarged ...

Aberdeen (CR) NJ9404.1/1B

At some stage prior to 1900 the building was extended and a 50ft turntable installed. The depot was closed in 1908 and then utilized as a wagon repair shop, surviving until at least 1996.

Replaced by ....

Ferryhill (CR/NB) NJ9404.1/2A

A brick built 10TS dead ended shed with a slated gable style roof, located at NJ94020454 and opened in 1908. The facilities included a water tank, 70ft turntable, ramped coaling stage and 2TS repair shop.

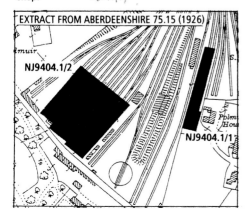

EXTRACT FROM ABERDEENSHIRE 75.15 (1926)

NJ9404.1/2

NJ9404.1/1

The shed was re-roofed ...

Ferryhill (BR) NJ9404.1/2B

The roof was re-slated by the Scottish Region in c1949 and the depot closed to steam on March 18th, 1967. It was closed totally on December 6th, 1987 and given over to private use, surviving until at least 1990.

Site NJ9405.1; On the east side of the line, at the south end of Guild Street Station.

Guild Street (Deeside) NJ9405.1/1A

A 2TS through road shed with a single gable style roof, located at NJ94290584 and opened by the Deeside Railway. No further details are known other than it was in existence here in 1869.

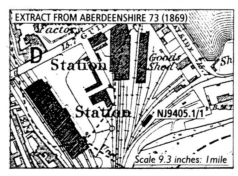

EXTRACT FROM ABERDEENSHIRE 73 (1869)

NJ9405.1/1

Scale 9.3 inches: 1mile

TURRIFF

Site NJ7249.1; On the north side of the line, at the east end of Turriff Station.

Turriff (GNofSR) NJ7249.1/F1

A servicing area consisting of a turntable and siding located at NJ72584934 was opened here prior to 1869. No further details are known.

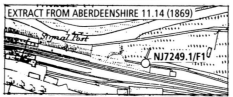

EXTRACT FROM ABERDEENSHIRE 11.14 (1869)

NJ7249.1/F0

Site NJ9307.1; On the west side of Kittybrewster Station.

Kittybrewster (GNofSR) NJ9307.1/1A

A 4TS dead ended shed located at NJ93170783 and opened on September 12th, 1854. The facilities included a coal stage and turntable. At some stage it was closed and absorbed into the adjacent works.

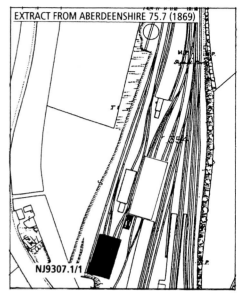

EXTRACT FROM ABERDEENSHIRE 75.7 (1869)

NJ9307.1/1

Replaced by ...

Kittybrewster (GNofSR) NJ9307.1/2A

A stone built semi-roundhouse shed* with a slated continuous hipped roof located at NJ93170793. No further details are known.

The depot was partially rebuilt ...

Kittybrewster (LNER) NJ9307.1/2B

At some stage the building was partially re-roofed with a continuous northlight pattern roof* and some of the original stone entrance arches may have been removed.

The depot was re-roofed ...

Kittybrewster (BR) NJ9307.1/2C

In 1956 the Scottish Region re-roofed eleven stalls and removed the roof over the remaining seven. The depot closed to steam on June 12th, 1961 and was utilized for diesel locomotives for a few years prior to demolition.

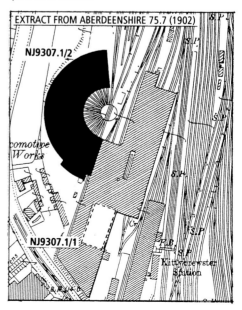

EXTRACT FROM ABERDEENSHIRE 75.7 (1902)

NJ9307.1/2

NJ9307.1/1

The building was probably constructed in two sections at separate dates.

ALFORD

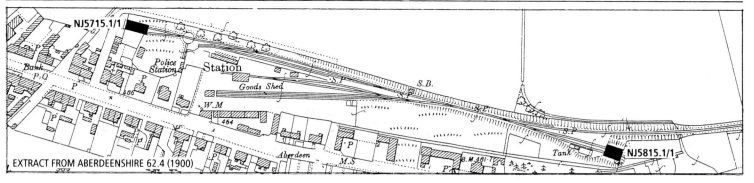

EXTRACT FROM ABERDEENSHIRE 62.4 (1900)

Site NJ5815.1; On the south side of the line, east of Alford Station.
Alford (AVR) NJ5815.1/1A
A stone built 2TS dead ended shed with a slated gable style roof, located at NJ58301581 and opened on March 21st, 1859 by the Alford Valley Railway. The facilities included a water tank. Although the depot was closed by BR on January 2nd, 1950 locomotives continued to utilize the shed yard. The building was later demolished.

Site NJ5715.1; At the end of the line, at the west end of Alford Station.
Alford (AVR) NJ5715.1/1A
A 1TS dead ended shed*, located at NJ57851594, was opened here prior to 1866 by the Alford Valley Railway. No further details are known other than the facilities included a turntable.

At some stage the shed was rebuilt ...
Alford (AVR) NJ5715.1/1B
A stone built 2TS dead ended shed* with a slated gable style roof was constructed on the same site. No further details are known.

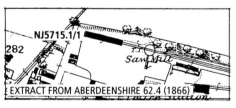

EXTRACT FROM ABERDEENSHIRE 62.4 (1866)

The shed was re-gauged...
Alford (AVR) NJ5715.1/1C
In the 1980s the building was adapted to house the locomotives for the new narrow gauge Alford Valley Railway and still stood in 1999.

It is not known for certain whether these buildings were ever utilized as standard gauge engine sheds.

DYCE JUNCTION

Site NJ8812.1; On the east side of the line, at the south end of Dyce Junction Station.
Dyce Junction (GNofSR) NJ8812.1/1A
A 2TS dead ended shed located at NJ88551260 and opened prior to 1869. The facilities included a turntable.

The shed was modified ...
Dyce Junction (GNofSR) NJ8812.1/1B
At some stage prior to 1900 the shed was altered to a 2TS structure with one through road and the turntable removed. No further details are known.

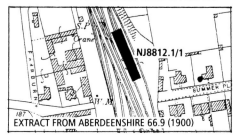

EXTRACT FROM ABERDEENSHIRE 66.9 (1900)

BALLATER

Site NO3795.1; On the north side of the line, at the east end of Ballater Station.
Ballater (A&BR) NO3795.1/1A
A 1TS dead ended shed located at NO37029599.

Adjoined by ...
Ballater (A&BR) NO3795.1/2A
A 1TS dead ended shed located at NO37029598.

One, or both of the sheds were opened in 1866 by the Aboyne & Ballater Railway. The facilities included a turntable and water tank. They were closed in 1893 and demolished at some time prior to 1900.

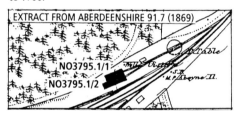

EXTRACT FROM ABERDEENSHIRE 91.7 (1869)

Replaced by ...
Site NO3795.2; On the south side of the line, at the east end of Ballater Station.
Ballater (GNofSR) NO3795.2/1A
A stone built 2TS dead ended shed with a slated pitched roof and timber and glazed gables. It was located at NO37119595 and opened in 1893. The facilities included a 50ft turntable and water tank. The depot was closed to steam by BR in April 1958 and later demolished.

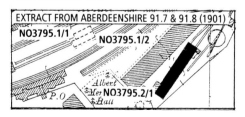

EXTRACT FROM ABERDEENSHIRE 91.7 & 91.8 (1901)

BRIDGE OF DON

Site NJ9409.1; On the north side of Bridge of Don Station.
Bridge of Don (S&BLR) NJ9409.1/1A
A 3ft 0in gauge 1TS dead ended shed located at NJ94700968 and opened in 1899 by the Strabathie & Blackdog Light Railway. No further details are known other than it closed in 1924.

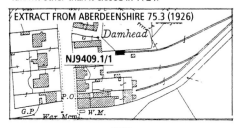

EXTRACT FROM ABERDEENSHIRE 75.3 (1926)

INVERURIE

Site NJ7721.1; At the rear of the main works building.
Inverurie (GNofSR) NJ7721.1/F1
A stabling area consisting of a siding located at NJ77412189 and established in 1901. At some stage the works building was modified necessitating re-siting of the stabling point.

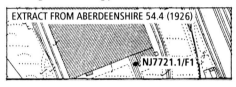

EXTRACT FROM ABERDEENSHIRE 54.4 (1926)

Replaced by ...
Site NJ7721.2; On a spur on the east side of the works yard.
Inverurie (LNER) NJ7721.2/F1
A stabling area consisting of a siding located at NJ77452187. The facility was closed by BR in March 1959 when the duties were taken over by a diesel shunter.

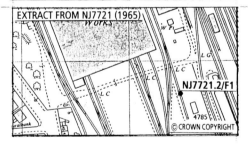

EXTRACT FROM NJ7721 (1965)
© CROWN COPYRIGHT

INVERAMSAY

Site NJ7325.1; On the east side of Inveramsay Junction Station.
Inveramsay (GNofSR) NJ7325.1/1A
A 1TS dead ended shed located at NJ73692532. No further details are known other than the facilities included a turntable.

The shed was enlarged ...
Inveramsay (GNofSR) NJ7325.1/1B
At some stage prior to 1900 the building was modified to a 2TS dead ended shed and the yard was enlarged and the turntable re-sited. No further details are known.

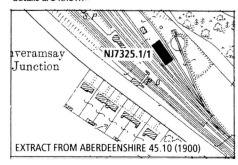

EXTRACT FROM ABERDEENSHIRE 45.10 (1900)

PETERHEAD

Site NK1246.1; On the north side of Peterhead Station.
Peterhead (GNofSR) NK1246.1/1A
A stone built 2TS dead ended shed with a slated gable style roof, located at NK12664662 and opened on July 3rd, 1862. The facilities included a water tank, turntable and coal stage. The depot was closed to steam by BR in June 1961, totally on May 3rd, 1965 and later demolished.

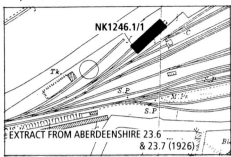

ABOYNE

Site NO5398.1; On the south side of the line, east of Aboyne Station.
Aboyne (GNofSR) NO5398.1/1A
A 1TS dead ended shed located at NO53169868 and opened in 1859. The facilities included a water tank. No further details are known other than it closed in October 1866 and was demolished to accommodate track realignment.

OLDMELDRUM

Site NJ8027.1; On the north side of the line, at the west end of Oldmeldrum Station.
Oldmeldrum (GNofSR) NJ8027.1/1A
A 2TS dead ended shed, located at NJ80192710 and opened on July 1st, 1856. No further details are known other than it was closed by the LNER in November 1931.

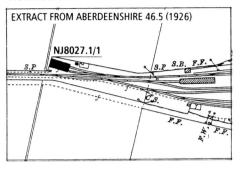

BODDAM

Site NK1242.1; On the east side of the line, south of Boddam Station.
Boddam (GNofSR) NK1242.1/1A
A corrugated sheet built 2TS dead ended shed with a tiled gable style roof, located at NK12984216 and opened on August 2nd, 1897. The facilities included a turntable. The depot was closed by the LNER on October 31st, 1932.

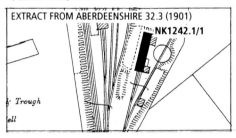

FRASERBURGH

Site NJ9966.1; On the west side of Fraserburgh Station.
Fraserburgh (F&BR) NJ9966.1/1A
A stone built 2TS dead ended shed with a slated gable style roof, located at NJ99896666 and opened on April 24th, 1865 by the Formartine & Buchan Railway. The facilities included a water tank and turntable. The depot was closed by BR in June 1961 and later let out for private use. It was still standing in 1998.

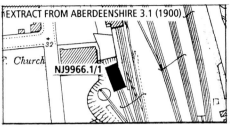

MINTLAW

Site NJ9848.1; On the north side of Old Deer & Mintlaw Station.
Mintlaw (GNofSR) NJ9848.1/F1
A facility consisting of a turntable and siding, located at NJ98944854, was opened here in 1861 and closed in July 1862. No further details are known.

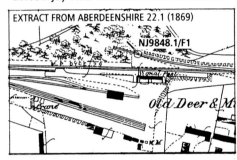

Opened by the Glasgow, Barrhead & Kilmarnock Railway in June 1873, the stone built 1TS engine shed (NS3453.1/1A) at **Beith** was of generous proportions, as may be seen from this photograph which dates from August 1952. Note the wagon for holding coal and the attendant small coaling crane - see also the result of years of ash accumulation.

The CR/G&SWR Joint Committee provided an 0-4-4T engine for the branch service but when this locomotive was withdrawn around 1923 the duties became the responsibility of the former G&SWR shed at Hurlford (NS4536.1/1A) until Beith's closure in 1962.   *J Edgington*

MORAY

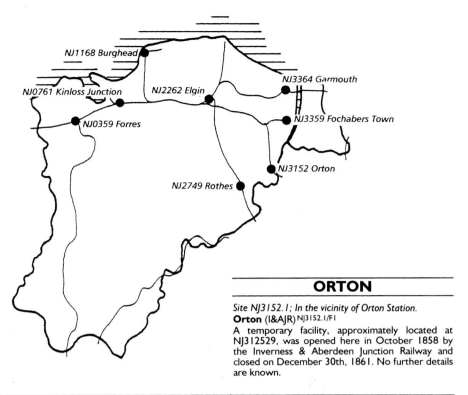

NJ1168 Burghead
NJ0761 Kinloss Junction
NJ2262 Elgin
NJ3364 Garmouth
NJ0359 Forres
NJ3359 Fochabers Town
NJ3152 Orton
NJ2749 Rothes

ORTON

Site NJ3152.1; In the vicinity of Orton Station.
Orton (I&AJR) NJ3152.1/F1
A temporary facility, approximately located at NJ312529, was opened here in October 1858 by the Inverness & Aberdeen Junction Railway and closed on December 30th, 1861. No further details are known.

ELGIN

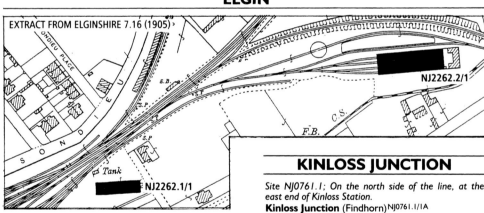

EXTRACT FROM ELGINSHIRE 7.16 (1905)
NJ2262.2/1
NJ2262.1/1

Site NJ2262.1; On the south side of the line, at the east end of Elgin (GNofSR) Station.
Elgin (I&AJR) NJ2262.1/1A
A stone built 2TS dead ended shed with a slated gable style roof, located at NJ22336233 and opened on August 11th, 1852 by the Inverness & Aberdeen Junction Railway. No further details are known other than it still stood in 1998, preserved as a listed building and housing commercial vehicles.

Site NJ2262.2; On the south side of the Craigellachie line, east of Elgin (GNofSR) Station.
Elgin (GNofSR) NJ2262.2/1A
A stone built 4TS dead ended shed with a slated transverse multi-hipped roof it was located at NJ22606245. The opening date is not known and the facilities included a coal stage, water tank and (installed later) a turntable. The shed was closed to steam by BR in June 1961 and after brief use as a diesel depot, during which time one track was removed (becoming NJ2262.2/1B), it was utilized for storing redundant North British Class 21 D6100 locomotives. It still stood in 1999, in use as a lorry depot for Grampian County Council.

KINLOSS JUNCTION

Site NJ0761.1; On the north side of the line, at the east end of Kinloss Station.
Kinloss Junction (Findhorn) NJ0761.1/1A
A 1TS dead ended shed, located at NJ07506135, and opened on April 16th, 1860 by the Findhorn Railway. No further details are known.

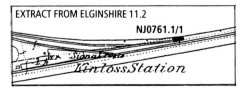

EXTRACT FROM ELGINSHIRE 11.2
NJ0761.1/1
Kinloss Station

NB: A 1TS dead ended building, sited at the end of the branch at Findhorn and located at NJ03906441 may have been used as an engine shed (as NJ0364.1/1A) following the closure of Kinloss Jct (NJ0761.1/1A).

ROTHES

Site NJ2749.1; In the vicinity of Rothes Station.
Rothes (Morayshire) NJ2749.1/F1
Some form of temporary facility, approximately located at NJ278494, was opened here by the Morayshire Railway on August 23rd, 1848 and closed on December 23rd, 1858. No further details are known.

FORRES

Site NJ0359.1; On the north side of Forres Station.
Forres (I&PR) NJ0359.1/1A
A stone built 2TS dead ended shed with a slated gable style roof, located at NJ03055901 and opened on August 3rd, 1863 by the Inverness & Perth Railway. The facilities included a water tank, coal stage and turntable.

The shed was partially rebuilt in c1901 ...
Forres (HR) NJ0359.1/1B
The original stone arched entrances were demolished and replaced by a wooden gable. The depot was closed to steam by BR in May 1959 and saw brief use as a diesel depot before total closure and demolition.

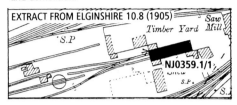

EXTRACT FROM ELGINSHIRE 10.8 (1905)
Saw Mill
Timber Yard
S.P
NJ0359.1/1

FOCHABERS

Site NJ3359.1; On the west side of the line, north of Fochabers Town Station.
Fochabers Town (HR) NJ3359.1/1A
A stone built 1TS dead ended shed with a slated gable style roof, located at NJ33655973 and opened on October 23rd, 1893. The facilities included a water tank. The depot was closed by the LMS in September 1931 and subsequently demolished.

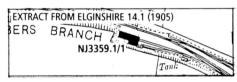

EXTRACT FROM ELGINSHIRE 14.1 (1905)
ERS BRANCH
NJ3359.1/1
Tank

BURGHEAD

Site NJ1168.1; On the north side of the line, at the east end of Burghead (1st) Station.
Burghead (I&AJR) NJ1168.1/1A
A timber built 1TS dead ended shed, located at NJ11406868 and opened on December 22nd, 1862 by the Inverness & Aberdeen Junction Railway. The facilities included a water tank. The building was destroyed by a fire in 1894.

Replaced, on the same site, by ...
Burghead (HR) NJ1168.1/1B
A stone built 2TS dead ended shed with a slated gable style roof was constructed here in 1895. The depot was closed by the LMS in 1938 and survived into the 1950s before being demolished.

EXTRACT FROM ELGINSHIRE 1.15 (1905)
Tank Well
NJ1168.1/1

GARMOUTH

Site NJ3364.1: On the north side of Garmouth Station.
Garmouth (GNofSR) NJ3364.1/F1
A temporary facility, consisting of a siding approximately located at NJ33496408, was opened here in 1884 and closed in April 1886. No further details are known.

KINCARDINE

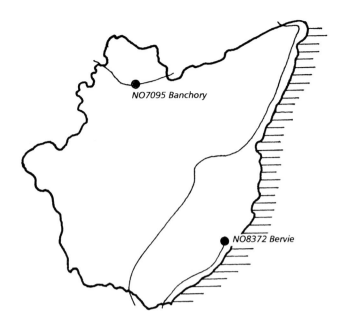

NO7095 Banchory

NO8372 Bervie

BERVIE

Site NO8372.1; On the east side of the line, at the south end of Bervie Station.
Bervie (M&BR) NO8372.1/1A
A 1TS shed, located at NO83277216 and opened on November 1st, 1865 by the Montrose & Bervie Railway. No further details are known other than it was destroyed by a fire.

Replaced, on the same site, by ...
Bervie (NB) NO8372.1/1B
A timber built 1TS through road shed with a slated gable style roof was constructed here at an unknown date. The facilities included a turntable, sited outside of the shed entrance, and water tank. The depot closed in 1919 but remained standing until at least 1939.

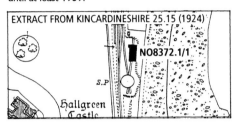

EXTRACT FROM KINCARDINESHIRE 25.15 (1924)

NO8372.1/1

BANCHORY

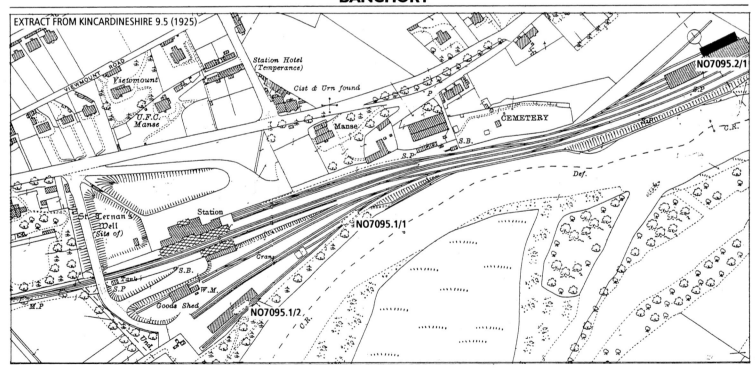

EXTRACT FROM KINCARDINESHIRE 9.5 (1925)

NO7095.2/1

NO7095.1/1

NO7095.1/2

Site NO7095.1; On the south side of Banchory Station.
Banchory (Deeside) NO7095.1/1A
A 1TS through road shed, located at NO70569564 and opened by the Deeside Railway on September 8th, 1853. The facilities included a turntable. No further details are known other than it probably closed in 1893.

Replaced by ...
Banchory (GNofSR) NO7095.1/2A
A 1TS dead ended shed, located at NO70459556 and probably opened in 1893. The facilities included a turntable sited outside of the shed entrance. No further details are known other than it closed prior to 1924.

Replaced by ...
Site NO7095.2; On the north side of the line, east of Banchory Station.
Banchory (GNofSR) NO7095.2/1A
A 1TS dead ended shed, located at NO70919580 and opened prior to 1925. The building was attached to the side of the carriage shed and the facilities included a turntable. The depot was closed by the LNER in 1933 and later demolished.

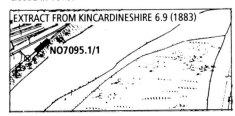

EXTRACT FROM KINCARDINESHIRE 6.9 (1883)

NO7095.1/1

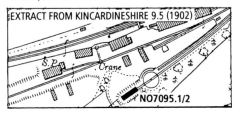

EXTRACT FROM KINCARDINESHIRE 9.5 (1902)

NO7095.1/2

ANGUS

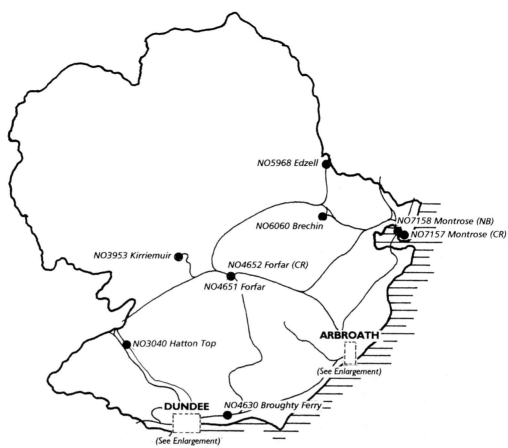

MONTROSE

Site NO7157.1; On the south side of Montrose (CR) Station.
Montrose (Aberdeen)[NO7157.1/1A]
A timber built 2TS dead ended shed with a slated gable style roof, located at NO71755737 and opened in 1849 by the Aberdeen Railway. The facilities included a 15ft turntable originally sited outside of the shed entrance and later enlarged to 45ft and re-sited in 1885. The shed was burned down by a fire in May 1939 at which point the LMS closed the depot and moved the locomotives to Brechin shed (NO6060.2/1).

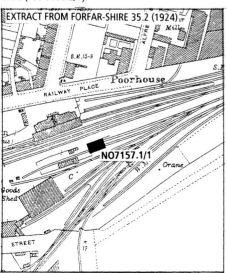

EXTRACT FROM FORFAR-SHIRE 35.2 (1924)

NO7157.1/1

Site NO7158.1; On the east side of Montrose (NB) Station.
Montrose (NB)[NO7158.1/1A]
A timber built 2TS through road shed with a slated gable style roof, located at NO71275803 and opened on March 1st, 1881. The facilities included a water tank, turntable and ramped coaling stage. The depot was closed by BR in May 1966 and subsequently demolished.

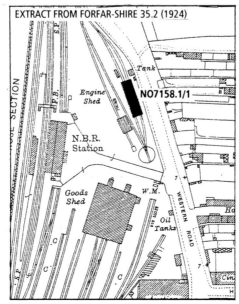

EXTRACT FROM FORFAR-SHIRE 35.2 (1924)

NO7158.1/1

KIRRIEMUIR

Site NO3953.1; On the south side of the line, at the east end of Kirriemuir Station.
Kirriemuir (CR)[NO3953.1/1A]
A 1TS dead ended shed, located at NO39155396 and opened on August 12th, 1861. The facilities included a water tank.

The building was modified ...
Kirriemuir (CR)[NO3953.1/1B]
At some stage the building was altered to a 1TS through road structure, the water tank was re-sited and a turntable installed at the rear of the shed. The depot closed in 1896 and was demolished by 1922.

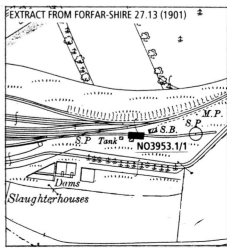

EXTRACT FROM FORFAR-SHIRE 27.13 (1901)

NO3953.1/1

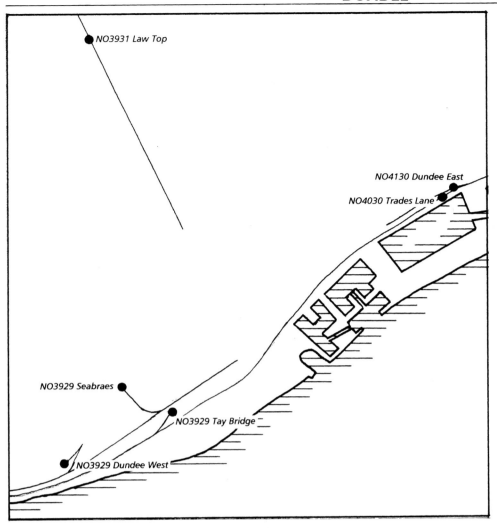

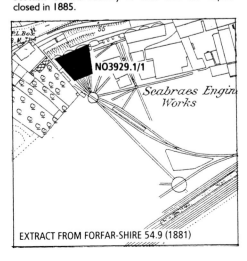

Site NO3929.1; On the north side of the line, at the west end of Dundee West Station.

Seabraes (D&PR) NO3929.1/1A

A timber built 3TS rhomboidal shaped shed with a triple pitched roof, located at NO39662976 and opened on May 24th, 1847 by the Dundee & Perth Railway. The facilities included a water tank, coal stage and turntable from which all the shed roads radiated.

The shed was enlarged ...
Seabraes (D&PR) NO3929.1/1B

At some stage an additional bay was added along the western side. The line was absorbed by the Scottish Central Railway in 1863 and the depot closed in 1885.

EXTRACT FROM FORFAR-SHIRE 54.9 (1881)

Replaced by ...
Site NO3929.2; On the north side of the line, west of Dundee West Station.

Dundee West (CR) NO3929.2/1A

A brick built 8TS through road shed with a slated transverse multi-pitched roof, located at NO39392944 and opened in 1885. The facilities included a 70ft turntable, ramped coaling stage and water tank. Following nationalization the adjacent Tay Bridge shed (NO3929.3/1A) assumed most of the responsibility for servicing locomotives in the area and Dundee West was then mainly utilized as an engine store or stabling area. The shed officially closed in 1958 and the building was completely refurbished, re-opening in 1960 as a dmu maintenance depot. It closed in c1982 and was demolished in 1987.

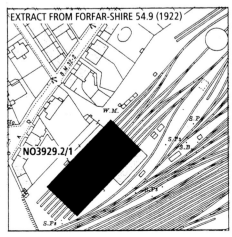

EXTRACT FROM FORFAR-SHIRE 54.9 (1922)

Site NO4030.1; On the south side of the line, at the west end of Dundee Trades Lane Station.

Dundee Trades Lane (D&AR) NO4030.1/1A

A 5ft 6in gauge 2TS shed with one through road, located at NO40973051, was opened here by the Dundee & Arbroath Railway on April 1st, 1840.

The line was re-gauged ...
Dundee Trades Lane (D&AR) NO4030.1/1B

The line was altered to standard gauge in 1846 and leased to the Dundee & Perth Railway in 1848. The depot closed in February 1858 and was later demolished. No further details are known.

Replaced by ...
Site NO4130.1; On the north side of the line, at the east end of Dundee East (Formerly "Trades Lane") Station.

Dundee East (NB) NO4130.1/1A

A 3TS dead ended shed, located at NO41103055 and opened in February 1858. The facilities included a 36ft turntable and a coal stage. No further details are known other than the depot was closed and demolished prior to 1900.

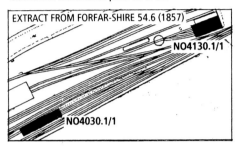

EXTRACT FROM FORFAR-SHIRE 54.6 (1857)

Replaced by ...
Site NO3929.3; On the north side of the line, at the west end of Dundee Tay Bridge Station.

Dundee Tay Bridge (NB) NO3929.3/1A

A brick built 6TS through road shed with a slated transverse multi-pitched roof, located at NO39852960 and probably opened on January 1st, 1878. The facilities included a ramped coaling stage, later replaced by a mechanical coaling plant, water tank and turntable. The depot was closed by BR on May 1st, 1967 and demolished in 1969.

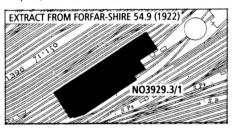

EXTRACT FROM FORFAR-SHIRE 54.9 (1922)

Site NO3931.1; On the east side of the line, north of Dundee Ward Street Station.

Dundee Law Top (D&NR) NO3931.1/1A

A 4ft 6in gauge 2TS shed located at NO39403168 and opened on December 16th, 1831 by the Dundee & Newtyle Railway. It had an unusual layout in which each track entered from opposite ends and terminated within the building. The facilities included a 15ft turntable and coal stage.

The line was re-gauged ...
Dundee Law Top (D&NR) NO3931.1/1B

The line was altered to standard gauge in 1846 and leased to the Dundee & Perth Railway. The depot closed in 1861.

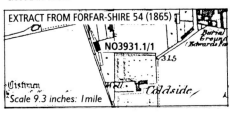

EXTRACT FROM FORFAR-SHIRE 54 (1865)

Scale 9.3 inches: 1mile

ARBROATH

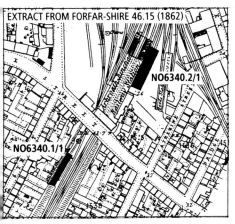

NO6341 Arbroath (CR/NB)

NO6341 Arbroath (SNER)

NO6340 Arbroath (D&AR)
NO6340 Arbroath (A&FR)

Site NO6341.0; In the vicinity of Arbroath Station.
Arbroath (NB) NO6341.0/1A
Some sort of temporary shed was opened here in 1880. No further details are known.

Site NO6340.2; On the east side of Arbroath Station.
Arbroath (A&FR) NO6340.2/1A
A 5ft 6in gauge 2TS dead ended shed located at NO63924099 and opened on December 4th, 1838 by the Arbroath & Forfar Railway. No further details are known.

The line was re-gauged ...
Arbroath (A&FR) NO6340.2/1B
The line was altered to standard gauge in 1846 and leased to the Aberdeen Railway on February 1st, 1848. The depot closed in 1897 and was later demolished.

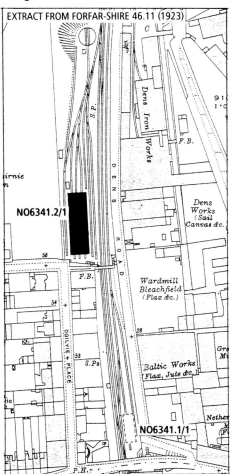

EXTRACT FROM FORFAR-SHIRE 46.15 (1862)

NO6340.2/1

NO6340.1/1

Site NO6340.1; On the west side of the line, south of Arbroath Station.
Arbroath (D&AR) NO6340.1/1A
A 5ft 6in gauge 1TS dead ended shed located at NO63824090 and opened on October 3rd, 1838 by the Dundee & Arbroath Railway. The facilities included a turntable.

The line was re-gauged ...
Arbroath (D&AR) NO6340.1/1B
The line was altered to standard gauge in 1846 and leased to the Dundee & Perth Railway in 1847. The line was absorbed by the SNER in 1862 and the CR closed the depot in 1897.

EXTRACT FROM FORFAR-SHIRE 46.11 (1862)

NO6341.1/1

Site NO6341.1; On the east side of the line, north of Arbroath Station.
Arbroath (SNER) NO6341.1/1A
A 2TS dead ended shed located at NO63904131 and opened by the Scottish North Eastern Railway. The facilities included a turntable. No further details are known.

Site NO6341.2; On the west side of the line, north of Arbroath Station.
Arbroath (CR/NB) NO6341.2/1A
A brick built 3TS dead ended shed with a slated transverse multi-pitched roof, located at NO63854161 and opened in 1897. The facilities included a water tank and turntable. The depot was closed by BR on January 3rd, 1959 and demolished during the 1960s.

EXTRACT FROM FORFAR-SHIRE 46.11 (1923)

NO6341.2/1

NO6341.1/1

HATTON TOP

Site NO3040.1; On the west side of the line, south of Newtyle Station.
Hatton Top (D&NR) NO3040.1/1A
A 4ft 6in gauge 2TS shed located at NO30694061 and opened on December 16th, 1831 by the Dundee & Newtyle Railway. Details of the construction and facilities are not known.

The line was re-gauged ...
Hatton Top (D&NR) NO3040.1/1B
The line was altered to standard gauge in 1846 and leased to the Dundee & Perth Railway. The depot closed in 1861.

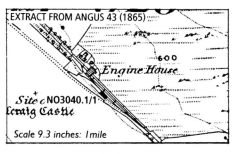

EXTRACT FROM ANGUS 43 (1865)

Engine House

Site NO3040.1/1

Scale 9.3 inches: 1mile

EDZELL

Site NO5968.1; On the west side of the line, at the south end of Edzell Station.
Edzell (B&ER) NO5968.1/1A
A 1TS dead ended shed, located at NO59956844 and opened on June 1st, 1896 by the Brechin & Edzell Railway. No further details are known other than it was closed by the CR in 1910 and demolished by 1922.

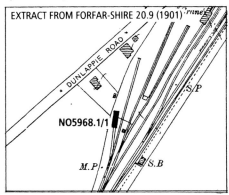

EXTRACT FROM FORFAR-SHIRE 20.9 (1901)

NO5968.1/1

BROUGHTY FERRY

Site NO4630.1; On the south side of the line, east of Broughty Ferry Station.
Broughty Ferry (D&AR) NO4630.1/1A
A 1TS dead ended shed, believed to be the building located at NO46443090, and opened in 1838 by the Dundee & Arbroath Railway. No further details are known other than it closed in 1840.

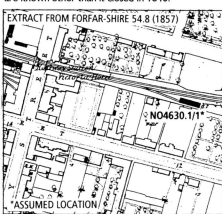

EXTRACT FROM FORFAR-SHIRE 54.8 (1857)

NO4630.1/1*

*ASSUMED LOCATION

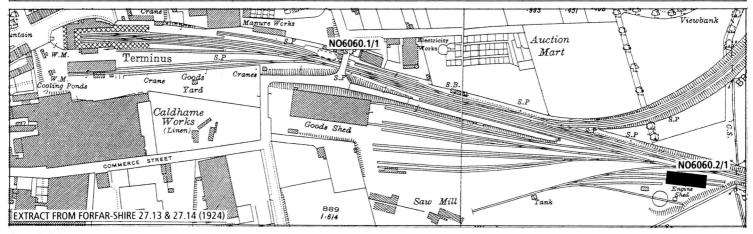

EXTRACT FROM FORFAR-SHIRE 27.13 & 27.14 (1924)

Site NO6060.1; On the north side of the line, at the east end of Brechin Station.
Brechin (SNER)[NO6060.1/1A]
A 1TS dead ended shed located at NO60396016 and opened on February 1st, 1848 by the Scottish North Eastern Railway. The facilities included a water tank. No further details are known other than it closed in 1894.

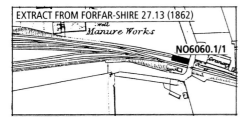

EXTRACT FROM FORFAR-SHIRE 27.13 (1862)

Replaced by ...
Site NO6060.2; On the south side of the line, east of Brechin Station.
Brechin (CR)[NO6060.2/1A]
A brick built 2TS dead ended shed with a slated gable style roof, located at NO60726005 and opened in 1894. The facilities included a water tank and 50ft turntable. The depot was closed by BR on August 2nd, 1952 and was utilized for wagon repairs prior to demolition.

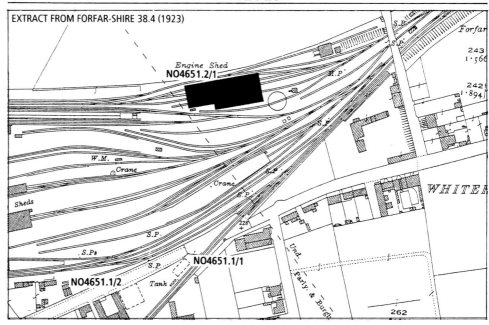

EXTRACT FROM FORFAR-SHIRE 38.4 (1923)

Site NO4651.1; On the south side of the line, at the east end of Forfar Station.
Forfar (A&FR)[NO4651.1/1A]
A 5ft 6in gauge 1TS through road tank shed, it was located at NO46125138 and opened on March 1st, 1839 by the Arbroath & Forfar Railway. The facilities included a 34ft turntable and coal stage.

The line was re-gauged ...
Forfar (A&FR)[NO4651.1/1B]
The line was altered to standard gauge in 1846 and leased to the Aberdeen Railway on January 1st, 1848. The depot closed in 1850.

Replaced by ....
Forfar (CR)[NO4651.1/2A]
A 4TS dead ended shed adjacently sited on the west side of the turntable and located at NO46085135. It was opened in 1850 and closed on December 18th, 1899. No further details are known.

Replaced by ...
Site NO4651.2; On the north side of the line, at the east end of Forfar Station.
Forfar (CR)[NO4651.2/1A]
A brick built 4TS through road shed with a slated transverse multi-pitched roof, it was located at NO46175154 and opened on December 18th, 1899. The facilities included a ramped coaling stage, 54ft turntable and water tank. It was closed by BR on July 18th, 1964 and subsequently let out for private use. It still stood in 1996, being utilized as a vehicle body shop.

EXTRACT FROM FORFAR-SHIRE 38.4 (1860)

SUTHERLAND

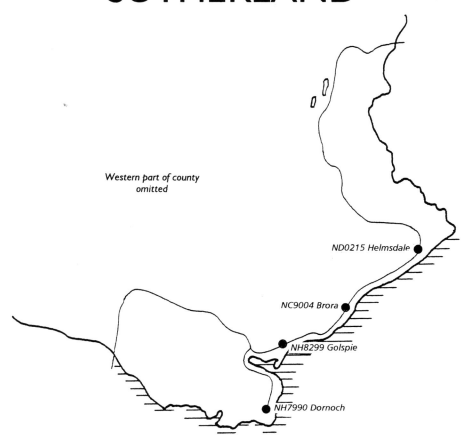

Western part of county omitted

ND0215 Helmsdale

NC9004 Brora

NH8299 Golspie

NH7990 Dornoch

DORNOCH

Site NH7990.1; On the east side of the line, at the north end of Dornoch Station.
Dornoch (DLR)^{NH7990.1/1A}
A timber built 1TS dead ended shed with a slated gable style roof, located at NH79899002 and opened on June 2nd, 1902 by the Dornoch Light Railway. The facilities included a water tank and coal stage. The line was worked by the HR and the depot was closed by BR on June 11th, 1960 and later demolished.

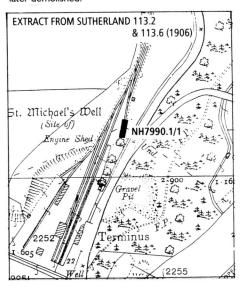

EXTRACT FROM SUTHERLAND 113.2 & 113.6 (1906)

NH7990.1/1

GOLSPIE

Site NH8299.1; On the east side of the line, at the south end of Golspie Station.
Golspie (DofS)^{NH8299.1/1A}
A timber built 1TS dead ended shed with a corrugated iron clad gable style roof, located at NH82549967 and opened by the Duke of Sutherland in 1896. The facilities included a coal stage and a turntable. The depot closed in 1948 and remained standing until the 1950s.

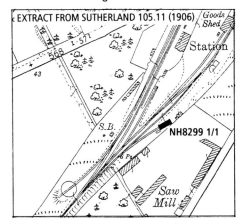

EXTRACT FROM SUTHERLAND 105.11 (1906)

NH8299 1/1

BRORA

Site NC9004.1; In the vicinity of Brora Station.
Brora (DofS)^{NC9004.1/1A}
A 1TS shed, approximately located at NC906042, was opened here by the Duke of Sutherland in 1870 and closed in 1896. No further details are known.

HELMSDALE

Site ND0215.1; On the west side of the line, at the north end of Helmsdale Station.
Helmsdale (HR)^{ND0215.1/1A}
A timber built 2TS dead ended shed with a twin slated gable style roof, located at ND02321554 and opened on June 19th, 1871. The facilities included a 40ft turntable, enlarged to 50ft in 1889. By 1899 the building had become totally derelict.

Replaced in 1899 by ...
Helmsdale (HR)^{ND0215.1/1B}
A timber built 2TS dead ended structure with a slated gable style roof was built on the same site, utilizing some of the original framework and cladding. It was destroyed in a gale in February 1921.

Replaced by ...
Helmsdale (HR)^{ND0215.1/1C}
A timber built 2TS dead ended shed with a dutch barn style roof was constructed on the same site in 1921. The facilities included a 55ft turntable, coal stage and water columns. The depot was closed by BR in July 1961 and subsequently demolished.

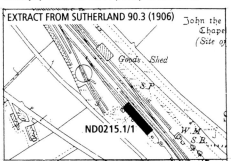

EXTRACT FROM SUTHERLAND 90.3 (1906)

ND0215.1/1

ROSS & CROMARTY

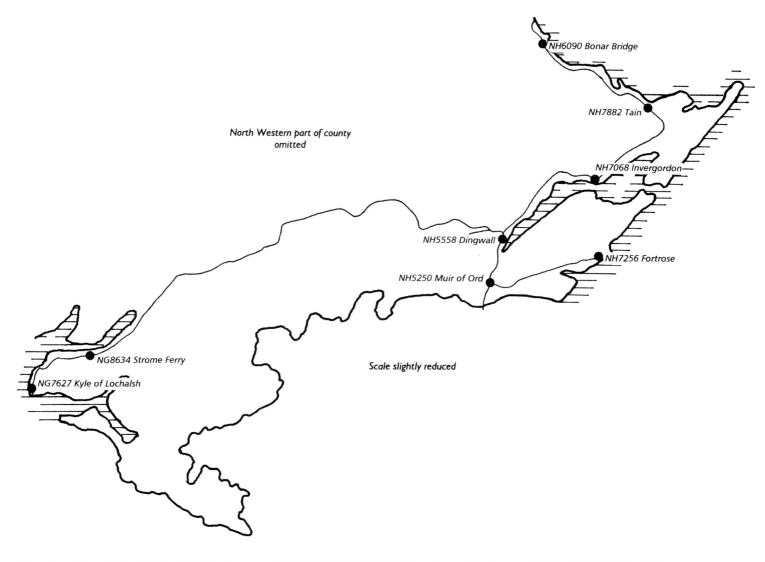

NH6090 Bonar Bridge

NH7882 Tain

NH7068 Invergordon

North Western part of county
omitted

NH5558 Dingwall

NH7256 Fortrose

NH5250 Muir of Ord

NG8634 Strome Ferry

NG7627 Kyle of Lochalsh

Scale slightly reduced

DINGWALL

Site NH5558.1; On the west side of the line, at the south end of Dingwall Station.
Dingwall (HR) NH5558.1/1A
A timber built 2TS dead ended shed with a slated gable style roof, located at NH55235830 and opened in 1870. The facilities included a turntable which was removed in c1930. The depot was closed by BR in December 1961 and subsequently demolished.

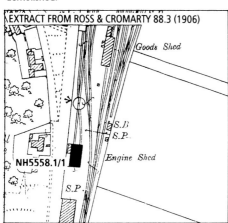

EXTRACT FROM ROSS & CROMARTY 88.3 (1906)

Good's Shed

S.B
S.P.

Engine Shed

NH5558.1/1

S.P.

STROME FERRY

Site NG8634.1; On the south side of the line. east of Strome Ferry Station.
Strome Ferry (D&SR) NG8634.1/1A
A timber built 2TS dead ended shed with a slated gable style roof, located at NG86803459 and opened on August 19th, 1870 by the Dingwall & Skye Railway. The facilities included a 43ft 7in turntable and a water tank. The line was worked by the HR and absorbed in 1877. The depot closed in 1897 and was subsequently demolished.

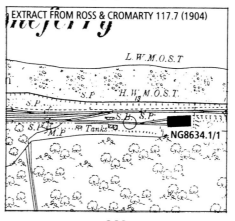

EXTRACT FROM ROSS & CROMARTY 117.7 (1904)

L.W.M.O.S.T.

H.W.M.O.S.T.

S.P.

S.P.

S.P.

M.P.   Tanks

NG8634.1/1

MUIR OF ORD

Site NH5250.1; On the east side of the line, at the north end of Muir of Ord Station.
Muir of Ord (HR) NH5250.1/1A
A 1TS dead ended building located at NH52805023 may have been utilized as an engine shed from an unknown date until 1920. The facilities would have included a turntable.

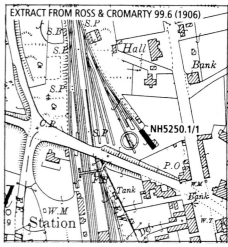

EXTRACT FROM ROSS & CROMARTY 99.6 (1906)

S.B
S.P.

Hall

Bank

S.P.

NH5250.1/1

P.O.

Tank   Bank

Station

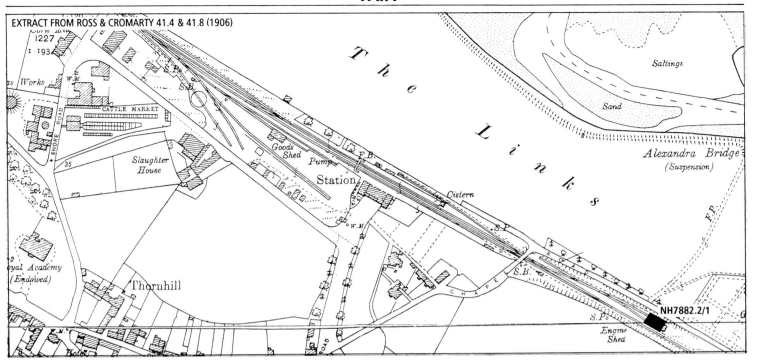

EXTRACT FROM ROSS & CROMARTY 41.4 & 41.8 (1906)

TAIN

Site NH7882.1; In the vicinity of Tain Station.
Tain (HR) NH7882.1/1A
The timber built 2TS former Invergordon shed (NH7068.0/1A) was re-erected and opened here in June 1864. It was approximately located at NH781823 and the facilities included a turntable. No further details are known other than it burned down on April 20th, 1877.

Replaced by ...
Site NH7882.2; On the north side of the line, east of Tain Station.
Tain (HR) NH7882.2/1A
A stone built 2TS dead ended shed with a slated gable style roof, located at NH78448224 and opened in 1877. There were no facilities at the shed but a water column and turntable were sited at the nearby station. The depot was closed by BR on June 18th, 1962 and later demolished.

BONAR BRIDGE

Site NH6090.1; In the vicinity of Bonar Bridge Station.
Bonar Bridge (HR) NH6090.1/F1
A shed, approximately located at NH601903, was opened here in May 1863. No further details are known other than the facilities included a turntable and it closed in 1871.

INVERGORDON

Site NH7068.0; In the vicinity of Invergordon Station.
Invergordon (HR) NH7068.0/1A
A temporary timber built 2TS shed, approximately located at NH704686 opened here on March 25th, 1863. It closed prior to June 1864 and was removed to Tain where it was re-erected as the engine shed there (NH7882.1/1A). No further details are known.

Invergordon (HR) NH7068.0/2A
A 1TS shed was opened here in 1915 and damaged by fire on August 12th, 1916. The depot* closed in 1919. No further details are known.

*Following the fire the shed may have been rebuilt (as NH7068.0/2B).

FORTROSE

Site NH7256.1; On the north side of Fortrose Station.
Fortrose (HR) NH7256.1/1A
A timber built 1TS dead ended shed with a slated gable style roof, located at NH72495663 and opened on February 1st, 1894. The facilities included a turntable and water tank. The building was destroyed by a fire in 1943.

Replaced, on the same site, by ...
Fortrose (LMS) NH7256.1/1B
A corrugated iron built 1TS dead ended shed with a corrugated iron clad gable style roof was constructed in 1943. The depot was closed by BR in October 1950 and subsequently demolished.

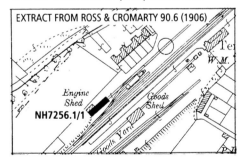

EXTRACT FROM ROSS & CROMARTY 90.6 (1906)

KYLE OF LOCHALSH

Site NG7627.1; On the west side of the line, north of Kyle of Lochalsh Station.
Kyle of Lochalsh (HR) NG7627.1/1A
A stone built 2TS dead ended shed with a slated gable style roof, located at NG76182744 and opened in 1897. The facilities included a water tank, coal stage and 50ft turntable, enlarged to 54ft in 1946. The depot was closed to steam by BR on June 10th, 1961 and totally on June 18th, 1962. The building was later demolished.

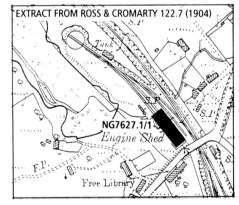

EXTRACT FROM ROSS & CROMARTY 122.7 (1904)

CAITHNESS

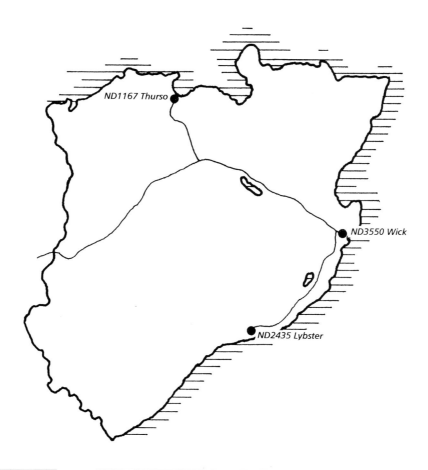

ND1167 Thurso

ND3550 Wick

ND2435 Lybster

LYBSTER

Site ND2435.1; On the south side of the line, at the east end of Lybster Station.
Lybster (W&LLR)^{ND2435.1/1A}
A timber built 1TS through road shed with a slated gable style roof, located at ND24963584 and opened on July 1st, 1903 by the Wick & Lybster Light Railway. The facilities included a 43ft 6in turntable. The line was worked from the outset by the HR and the depot was closed by the LMS on April 3rd, 1944 and subsequently demolished.

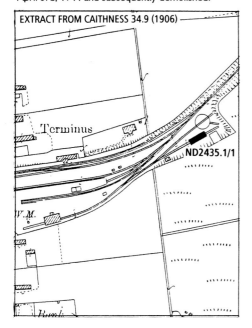

EXTRACT FROM CAITHNESS 34.9 (1906)

Terminus

ND2435.1/1

W.M.

THURSO

Site ND1167.1; On the east side of the line, at the south end of Thurso Station.
Thurso (HR)^{ND1167.1/1A}
A stone built 1TS dead ended shed with a slated gable style roof, located at ND11276775 and opened on July 28th, 1874. The facilities included a 45ft turntable, sited outside of the shed entrance, water tank and coal stage. The depot was closed by BR in 1962 and the building still stood in 1998, in use as a carpet warehouse.

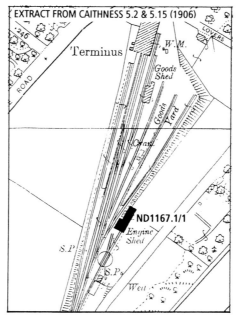

EXTRACT FROM CAITHNESS 5.2 & 5.15 (1906)

Terminus

Goods Shed

Goods Yard

ND1167.1/1

Engine Shed

WICK

Site ND3550.1; On the south side of Wick Station.
Wick (HR)^{ND3550.1/1A}
A stone built 2TS through road shed with a slated gable style roof, located at ND35965081 and opened on July 28th, 1874. The facilities included a 45ft turntable (enlarged to 55ft in 1901), coal stage and water tank.

The shed was re-roofed ...
Wick (BR)^{ND3550.1/1B}
A new roof with longitudinal smoke vents was installed by the Scottish Region in c1959. The depot closed to steam in July 1962 and then stabled diesel locomotives for a short time before being abandoned. It was later let out for private use and the building still stood in 1998, in use as a supermarket.

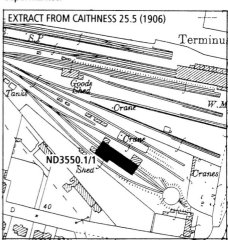

EXTRACT FROM CAITHNESS 25.5 (1906)

S.P.

Terminus

Goods Shed

Tanks

Crane

W.M.

Crane

ND3550.1/1

Shed

Cranes

An outpost of the Cleator & Workington Railway, the stone built shed at **Distington** (NY0123.1/1A) opened in 1879 and served, little known and unremarked, until closure by the LMS in April 1931. The robust little building was then turned over to other use and is seen here standing proud on an embankment, on September 20th, 1966. When the shed was finally removed is not known.

WT Stubbs

(See Page 328)

Destined to serve for 97 years, 1856-1953, was the Carlisle & Silloth Railway and Dock Company's 2TS shed (NY1053.1/1A) at **Silloth**. It was utilized by the locomotives of the operating company, the NBR, and the neat stone built depot is seen here on July 4th, 1937. Apart from No.9213 being parked outside, Mr Camwell notes on his photograph that No.9763 was housed inside the securely closed shed. *WA Camwell*

(See Page 328)

Erected at **Cockermouth** by the Cockermouth & Workington Railway in April 1847, the 2TS stone built engine shed (NY1130.1/1A) was extended in 1858 (as NY1130.1/1B) and absorbed in 1866 by the L&NWR. It closed 10 years later and found further use as a goods shed, surviving into the 1990s before being demolished.

Bernard Matthews Collection

(See Page 329)

Famous for its horse-drawn passenger service, the Port Carlisle Railway also used steam locomotives between 1855 and 1899. However the NBR re-introduced steam power in 1914 and built a 1TS timber shed (NY2462.1/1B) at the end of the line at **Port Carlisle** which was destined to last until closure in July 1928.

Taken only a few years later, this view clearly shows the lifted line's rapid progress back to nature. The demolition date for the engine shed is not known. *WA Camwell*

(See Page 330)

When the Newcastle & Carlisle Railway opened through to Carlisle, in July 1836, it provided a 2TS shed (NY4154&5.1/1A) at **Carlisle London Road**. This was replaced in 1864 by what is believed to have been a small roundhouse (NY4154&5.1/2A). This, in turn, was superseded by a larger roundhouse (NY4154&5.1/3A) with the last extension being the erection of a second turntable shed in 1890 (as NY4154&5.1/3B).

This 1961 side view shows that although it had been closed in 1933, the coaling stage and yard turntable were still being utilized into BR days by locomotives working in from Tyneside. Above the mineral wagon to the left, the different colouring of the shed's brickwork indicates where the 1890 extension was made. At some stage the shed building was let out for private use and still stood in 1999. *Authors' Collection*

(See Page 333)

Positioned to service locomotive working over the gruelling Stainmore Summit, **Kirkby Stephen** shed opened in 1861 as a 1TS structure (NY7707.1/1A). After only four years, increasing traffic caused an expansion to two roads (as NY7707.1/1B) and, almost immediately, it was doubled in size again when a 2TS shed was constructed alongside, but at a slight angle (as NY7707.1/2A). As such the shed served until closure late in 1961; this view dates from 10 years prior to closure. *J Edgington*

(See Page 336)

Despite standing for many years, until 1904, the NBR engine shed at **Cowlairs** (NS6067.1/1A) has proven to be photographically shy. Hence the inclusion of this less than perfect print which does, however, convey a good impression of the depot's massiveness; 15 roads in seven stone built, separately gabled sections, of which six are visible.

Following closure of the depot, the shed was utilized for extensions to the NBR's adjacent Cowlairs Works, part of which are seen to the shed's right and rear.   *Authors' Collection*

(See Page 339)

The replacement depot for Cowlairs *(see above)* was a brick built 14TS shed (NS6068.1/1A) constructed at **Eastfield** and opened in 1904. This was the NBR's largest depot and is viewed here shortly after coming into service. BR closed it in 1966 and it was progressively rebuilt as a diesel depot which, however, has itself since been closed and demolished.   *Authors' Collection*

(See Page 338)

Ex-LNER Class K1 2-6-0 No.62005 is today's sole survivor of its type, but in this 1949 picture the engine is fresh from its builders, the North British Locomotive Company, and had been "borrowed" by Eastfield for a running-in duty to **Clydebank East**.

The small engine shed (NS5069.1/1A), which was built with the terminus in 1882, is seen at left, still standing, although closed in about 1925.

WA Camwell

(See Page 339)

Opening in 1864, the line to **Langholm** branched off the Border Counties Railway at Riddings, immediately crossed from England into Scotland and terminated at this delightful station complex. The integral engine shed (NY3684.1/1A) closed in 1932, some three years before this picture was taken.

It would shortly lose its roof as, apparently, roofless buildings in Scotland did not attract payment into the General Rate! The station, too, was destined to lose its attractive overall roof but continued to serve until passenger services were withdrawn in June 1964. *H Garrett Collection*

(See Page 342)

Both the Wishaw & Coltness and North British Railways had sheds at **Morningside** in the years up to 1896, from when a simple stabling point was maintained to hold and service engines and provide a signing-on point for the crews (NS8355.1/F1).

A quiet Sunday in the 1930s finds two 0-6-0s slumbering between duties, but coaled-up ready for the new week ahead. Apart from a water tank, behind the camera, all of Morningside's facilities may be seen. Stabling ceased in 1960.

WA Camwell

(See Page 344)

The town of Coatbridge was the site of an early shed, that of the Monklands & Kirkintilloch Railway (NS7365.1/1A) which later came into the NBR. In 1890 that venerable depot was irreparably damaged by fire so the NBR made what was probably a cost-effective replacement - relocation of the engine shed utilized by the contractors building the Forth Bridge, where work had relatively recently finished.

This 3TS timber built structure (NS7365.1/2A), located at **Kipps**, served until closure early in 1963. This scene dates from the 1930s. *AG Ellis*

(See Page 346)

The short branch line to **Dalkeith** had an on-off history. Opened by the Edinburgh & Dalkeith Railway in June 1832, the line was 4ft 6in gauge and haulage was by horse. In 1846 the NBR purchased the railway, closed and upgraded it for locomotive working, with re-opening in 1847.

The line closed again to passengers in January 1917, with a second re-opening in October 1919. Final closure to passengers came in January 1942. The NBR provided a ITS shed (NT3267.1/1A) at the terminus in 1847 and closed it again 70 years later, with the building serving other purposes for many years after that. The hipped roof stone built shed is shown here in about 1935.   *WA Camwell*

(See Page 354)

Edinburgh St.Margarets engine shed was renowned for its large allocation of engines, many of which were housed at the depot's host of sub-sheds. Even so, at weekends, space was at such a premium that a so-called sub-shed was formally created amongst the sidings at **Craigentinny** (NT2973.1/F1).

There was no covered accommodation for either locomotives or crew and the siding is seen here on August 31st, 1958 with a dozen engines coaled-up and in light steam, in readiness for Monday's return to work.   *WT Stubbs*

(See Page 355)

Local interests caused the Jedburgh Railway to be promoted, to bring the rails to this remote corner of Roxburghshire. Opening of the line was in July 1856, with services being worked by the NBR, whose locomotives had access to the small shed (NT6521.1/1A) at the **Jedburgh** terminus. Some time after this mid-1930s picture was taken the station lost its overall roof and the shed received a singularly unattractive flat roof with a longitudinal smoke trough (as NT6521.1/1B). The depot closed in April 1949, but served afterwards as a garage for the BR lorry that undertook local goods deliveries.

WA Camwell

(See Page 358)

The important coal mining centre of **Bathgate** was served by an Edinburgh & Bathgate Railway shed from 1849, with that 2TS building (NS9768.1/1A) being replaced in about 1902 by the substantial 6TS structure (NS9768.2/1A) seen *(top)* in 1947.

However, the mining of the area led to a subsidence problem which British Railways were forced to deal with in 1953/4, when the shed was replaced by the 3TS structure (NS9768.2/1B) seen *(below)* in 1959; the fourth road was utilized for repairs and, on their arrival, for Bathgate's diesel shunters.

Closed in August 1966 the building saw further use and still stood, abandoned, in 1999.

H Garrett Collection & Authors' Collection

(See Page 357)

Opened during the Light Railway "mania" of the 1890s, the Aberlady, Gullane & North Berwick Railway was operated by the NBR from the outset (April 1898), but whether the engine shed provided at the **Gullane** terminus (NT4882.1/1A) ever saw much use is open to conjecture. Passenger services over the line were withdrawn in September 1932 - however Mr Camwell's visit of 1935 found the depot looking as if it had been out of use for somewhat more than just three years.

WA Camwell

(See Page 359)

The 2TS stone shed at **Longniddry** (NT4476.1/1A) is said to have opened in June 1846 and the style of building does not belie this. At some time the original arched entrance portals at each end of the building and over one of the tracks were remodelled (as NT4476.1/1B). Quite why this was done is uncertain but a close inspection of this 1952 photograph reveals what appears to be an internal wall, so it is possible that half of the building had been given over to a use other than locomotive servicing. Whatever, the engine shed closed in June 1959 and was later demolished.

AG Ellis

(See Page 359)

The border country between England and Scotland rejoiced in a number of isolated railway outposts, including the North Eastern's only venture into Caledonia, at **Sprouston**, where a timber built shed (NT7535.1/1A) was provided at the opening in 1863. According to some records, this structure was a redundant and re-located ex-Newcastle & Carlisle Railway engine shed - if so the authors have not yet determined from whence it came.

Whatever - the building had the misfortune to be blown down on October 14th, 1881, to be replaced in the next year by the brick built shed seen here on August 18th, 1964 (NT7535.1/1B). This second depot had, in fact, closed in July 1916 but still retained its tracks when World War II came, and GWR 4-4-0 *City of Truro* was housed in this out-of-the-way safe place for the duration.

AG Ellis

(See Page 359)

Predecessors of the Caledonian and North British Railways made an end-on junction at **Peebles**, with each company building an engine shed. The building depicted here, in an undated photograph, is the 2TS shed (NT2541.1/1B) rebuilt by the NBR in 1864 from the original 1TS shed (NT2541.1/1A) which had been constructed by the Peebles Railway in 1855. The NBR depot survived until closure in 1955. *H Garrett Collection*

(See Page 360)

To serve the busy crossroads at **Ladybank**, the NBR provided a 2TS shed (NO3009.1/1A) which is seen here on June 17th, 1936. The opening date of this stone built depot still eludes the authors, but what is known is that it closed in 1958 with, according to some informants, continued use by diesels for some while after. The building was subsequently demolished in 1967.

Bernard Matthews Collection

(See Page 362)

Forth & Clyde Junction Railway services to Stirling opened in March 1856, being worked by the Scottish Central Railway until February 1860 and then the Scottish North Eastern Railway for about a year, until the arrival of the F&CJR's own locomotives.

Thus the **Stirling (F&CJR)** shed (NS7994.1/1A) was then opened and served for an, as yet, undetermined number of years, latterly forming an annexe to the adjacent NBR shed across the tracks at Shore Road (NS7993&4.1/1A). After locomotive utilization ceased, it saw other uses, the building standing well into BR days. The disused shed is seen here in the mid-1930s and, with characteristic persuasiveness, Mr Camwell has arranged for a locomotive to be present to add an air of active authenticity! *WA Camwell*

(See Page 365)

Opened by the Strathendrick & Aberfoyle Railway in August 1882, the branch from Buchlyvie to Aberfoyle was worked by the NBR and its successors until closure on October 1st, 1951.

Probably because of its "small company" origins **Aberfoyle** shed (NN5200.1/1A), viewed here in about 1950, was built in brick rather than the more usual normal Scottish material of stone.

H Garrett Collection

(See Page 368)

Another long-surviving, but obscure, depot was opened by the Scottish North Eastern Railway in 1854. **Perth (SNER)** shed (NO1023.1/1A) only serviced locomotives until 1866 before being turned over to a wagon works, in which guise it stood into the 1960s. This picture dates from September 3rd, 1959 and Bill Stubbs confirmed that men working at the site knew of its engine shed origins, but thought perhaps that only part of this large building had been utilized for locomotive servicing in those far off years.

WT Stubbs

(See Page 369)

Another long-surviving, but obscure, depot was opened by the Scottish North Eastern Railway in 1854. **Perth (SNER)** shed (NO1123.2/1A) only serviced locomotives until 1866 before being turned over to a wagon works, in which guise it stood into the 1960s. This picture dates from September 3rd, 1959 and Bill Stubbs confirmed that men working at the site knew of its engine shed origins, but thought perhaps that only part of this large building had been utilized for locomotive servicing in those far off years. *WT Stubbs*

(See Page 369)

The Inverness & Aberdeen Junction Railway reached **Elgin** in 1852, providing a 2TS stone built shed (NJ2262.1/1A) at the station. This served until about the turn of the century, after which the building became a works for Messrs Campbell - wording depicting this may just be discerned in this picture of June 5th, 1958. The building still stood in 1999, having had a variety of uses including that as a whisky store. Coincidently, the nearby 4TS replacement (NJ2262.2/1B), itself closed in 1961, also still existed, in use as a council depot.

WT Stubbs

(See Page 377)

The small Deeside town of **Banchory** was the site of no fewer than three engine sheds over the years from the opening, in September 1853. Dates are uncertain but contemporary maps show the three buildings, with that illustrated here (NO7095.2/1A) in about 1936, being the third and dating from the early 1900s.

The branch line, famous for its royal trains to Ballater, was operated in turn by the Deeside Railway, GNofSR and, finally, the LNER, with the latter closing Banchory shed in about 1933.

Authors' Collection

(See Page 378)

Known as Inverbervie in LNER days, the branch terminus at **Bervie** was provided with a shed from the opening in November 1865. At a date, yet to be confirmed, this shed (NO8372.1/1A) burned down, to be replaced by NO8372.1/1B, a timber building, sited at the sea's edge. That white painted edifice is seen here in about 1935, still in remarkably good condition, following its closure in 1919. The date of the final removal is not known.

WA Camwell

(See Page 378)

The remote branch line terminus at **Banff** was opened in July 1859, by the Banff, Portsoy & Strathisla Railway, later to become part of the Great North of Scotland Railway. The sturdy, stone built engine shed (NJ6864.1/1A) is seen here in 1937, the depot continuing to serve until closure in July 1964.

At one time, just out of picture to the left, was a turntable and off that, at a right angle to the engine shed, the 1909 OS Map shows another single road building. What purpose this structure may have served has yet to be determined.

H Garrett Collection

(See Page 383)

Banff Bridge, on the outskirts of Macduff, was the railhead of the Banff, Macduff & Turriff Jct Railway from 1860 to 1872. A 2TS shed (NJ6963.1/1A) was provided at the "temporary" station. In July 1872 the BM&TJR's successor, the GNofSR, completed the line into **Macduff** proper and erected a 2TS shed (NJ6964.1/1A), substantially built in stone, at the new terminus. That building and Macduff's station signal box are seen in this view dating from 1937; the locomotive depot served until closure in October 1951 and still stood in 1999. *H Garrett Collection*

(See Page 383)

The GNofSR had a history of the fragmented development of lines, with that from Craigellachie to Aviemore being a prime example. Complete with a 2TS shed (NJ0020.1/1A), the western railhead between the years 1863 and 1866 was at Nethy Bridge, before extension in the latter year to **Boat of Garten** where this attractive stone built depot (NH9419.1/1A) was erected. The depot closed with the relatively early dieselization of the Speyside line in 1958. This view was taken in about 1936. *WA Camwell*

(See Page 386)

There is a strong feeling amongst *aficionados* that the confused history of the branch line to Fort Augustus resulted in the depot at **Spean Bridge** (NN2181.1/1A) never actually being used. Opened in 1901, the Fort Augustus & Invergarry Railway was worked - somewhat bizarrely - by the Highland Railway between June 1903 and April 1907, then by the NBR and LNER until closure of the hopelessly uneconomic line in November 1933.

Being little, or never, used the compact little shed at Spean Bridge would have remained in good condition and it stood into the 1990s. This picture, taken from a moving train, comes from July 1931. *Authors' Collection*

(See Page 386)

INDEX

ADDENDA
TO
VOLUME I

PLEASE NOTE
This section includes additional information received up to January 2000.

CORNWALL
P.10 **Calstock** (SX4269.1/1A). It still stood in 1997.
P.14 **Wadebridge** (SW9972.2/1C). The building was demolished in 1969.

DORSET
P.15 **Bridport** (SY4973.1/1A). The building was demolished at some stage between 1963 & 1975.

SOMERSET
P.20 **Bridgwater North** (ST3037.2/1A). The shed was demolished in 1985.
P.23 **Radstock** (ST6954.3/1A). Demolished in 1980.

Additional Depot ...

SALTFORD
Site ST6867.1; At the east end of Saltford Tunnel, west of Saltford Station.
Saltford Tunnel (GWR) ST6867.1/1A
The tunnel was utilized as a temporary engine shed and erecting shop in c1841. No further details are known other than it was located at ST68376730.

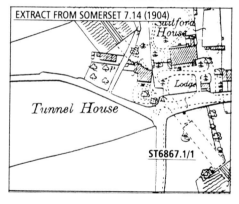

DEVON
P.33 **Exmouth Junction** (SX9393.1/2A). The depot was demolished in 1970.
P.35 **Plymouth Laira**. The 1RH shed (SX5055.2/1A) was demolished during 1967 and the 4TS building (SX5055.2/2A) during 1979.
P.36 **Princetown** (SX5873.1/1A). The building was demolished at some time during 1959 and 1960.

WILTSHIRE
P.43 **Salisbury** (SU1230.1/1B). The building was demolished at some stage between 1967 and 1969.
P.46 **Swindon Town** (SU1682.1/1A). The shed was demolished during the 1970s.

HAMPSHIRE
P.53 **Southampton Docks** (SU4210.1/1D). It was demolished at some stage between 1976 & 1980.

KENT
P.64 **Hythe** (TR1534.1/1A). The depot had closed by 1963 but the turntable and water tank still remained in use (as TR1534.1/F1). In 1995 the shed building was in commercial use by Crowhurst Engineering.

SUSSEX
P.69 **Brighton** (TQ3005.2/1B). The shed closed on June 15th, 1964.
P.70 **Horsham** (TQ1831.1/1B). Demolished in 1969.

SURREY
P.78 **Redhill** (TQ2850.1/1B). The shed building, apart from the offices, was demolished in 1969. The offices, which were then employed for the diesel stabling point, were not pulled down until 1991/2.

GREATER LONDON
P.87 **Stewarts Lane** (TQ2976.1/1C). The depot was finally closed on September 28th, 1997 and a ballast store established in the shed yard.
P.91 **Neasden** (TQ2184.1/1A). Demolished in 1967.
P.92 **Cricklewood** (TQ2386.1/1B & 2/1B). The shed was demolished in 1969.
P.98 **Plaistow** (TQ3983.2/1A). The building was demolished at some stage between 1963 & 1965.

Additional Depot ...

WHITE CITY
Site TQ2380.1; On the south side of Wood Lane (Central London Rly) Station
White City (CLR) TQ2380.1/1A
A 1TS dead ended shed located at TQ23538012 and opened by the Central London Railway in 1900, it was utilized by two oil-fired Hunslet tank engines until their duties were taken over by electric locomotives in 1923. No further details are known.

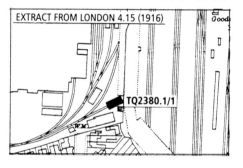

HERTFORDSHIRE
P.104 **Hatfield** (TL2308.1/1C). Demolished in 1966.
P.106 **Hitchin** (TL1929.3/1B). Demolished in 1989.
P.106 **St.Albans** (TL1506.2/1A). Demolished in 1968.

OXFORDSHIRE
P.108 **Banbury** (SP4639.1/1A). The building was demolished at some stage between 1969 & 1972.
P.108 **Henley on Thames** (SU7682.1/1A). The shed was demolished in 1964.
P.109 **Oxford** (SP5006.2/1C). The building was demolished during March and April 1964.

GLOUCESTERSHIRE
P.116 **Barrow Road** (ST6073.1/1A). The shed was demolished in 1967.
P.113 **Cheltenham Malvern Rd** (SO9322.1/1A & 2A). Both portions of the shed still stood in 1998.

BUCKINGHAMSHIRE
P.118 **Aylesbury** (SP8113.1/1C). At some stage the shed was modified to a 2TS shed with one through road (as SP8113.1/1D). This was possibly undertaken at the same time as the shed was re-roofed and the turntable removed.
P.118 **Aylesbury** (SP8213.1/1C). The building was demolished at some point between 1964 & 1966.
P.119 **Slough** (SU9780.2/1B & 2A). The buildings were demolished in 1970.

ESSEX
P.124 **Clacton**. The shed closed totally in 1981 and the original building (TM1715.2/1A) was subsequently demolished. The extension (TM1715.2/1B) still stood in 1989.

NORFOLK
P.130 **Cromer Beach** (TG2142.1/1A). The shed was demolished in 1991.
P.132 **Lowestoft** (TM5392.1/1B). The building was demolished at some stage between 1979 & 1986.
P.134 **Hunstanton** (TF6740.2/1B). The building was demolished in 1964.
P.135 **Vauxhall** (TG5108.1/1A). The shed building was demolished in April 1988.

SUFFOLK
P.139 **Ipswich** (TM1643.1/2C). The building was demolished in 1991.

WORCESTERSHIRE
P.144 **Bromsgrove** (SO9669.1/1C). The building was demolished in 1982.

SHROPSHIRE
P.149 **Snailbeach** (SJ3702.1/1A). The building, a 2TS dead ended stone built shed with a corrugated sheeting clad twin gable style roof, was restored by Shropshire County Council in 1991 and still stood, as part of a lead mine museum, in 1999.
P.149 **Kinnerley Junction** (SJ3319.1/1A). The shed was probably rebuilt in c1941 by the War Department (as SJ3319.1/1B) and was demolished in 1998.

WARWICKSHIRE
P.154 **Leamington Spa** (SP3264.1/1A). The building was demolished at some stage between 1967 & 1969.
P.154 **Rugby No.1** (SP5176.1/1B). The building was demolished in 1968.

WEST MIDLANDS
P.163 **Coventry** (SP3378.1/1C). Demolished at some stage between 1969 & 1972.
P.163 **Hampton in Arden** (SP2081.1/1A). The shed was destroyed by a fire in 1975.
P.164 **Pleck** (SP0097.1/1A). Demolished in 1971.
P.164 **Stourbridge Junction** (SO9084.1/1B & 2A). The buildings were demolished in 1969.

MONMOUTHSHIRE
P.167 **Severn Tunnel Junction** (ST4687.2/1B). The shed was demolished in 1983.
P.170 **Newport Pill** (ST3186.1/1A). The depot was closed to steam on June 17th, 1963 and totally on November 2nd, 1964. It was demolished at some point between 1965 & 1971.

SOUTH WALES
P.172 **Aberdare** (SO0003.1/1A). The building was demolished in 1969.
P.174 **Dowlais Central** (SO0608.2/1B). The depot closed in May 1960.
P.175 **Neath Riverside** (SS7598.1/2B). The building was demolished in March 1998.
P.176 **Merthyr** (SO0505.2/1C). The building was demolished at some stage between 1992 & 1995.
P.183 **Cardiff East Dock** (ST1974.2/3A). Between 1958 and 1962 the shed was utilized as a diesel stabling point for the docks shunters.
P.xiv The works at **Machen**, which may have been used as an engine shed until 1922, were of Merthyr & Brecon Railway origin.

Continued ...

CARDIGANSHIRE

P.187 **Aberystwyth** (SN5881.1/D). *The depot was re-gauged during 1967/8.*
P.187 **Aberystwyth** (SN5881.2/3A). *The shed closed in 1968.*

MONTGOMERYSHIRE

P.189 **Llanidloes** (SN9584.2/2A). *The building was demolished at some point during 1985/6.*

MERIONETHSHIRE

P.194 **Dinas Mawddwy** (SH8513.1/1B). *The building was destroyed by a fire in c1996/7.*
P.195 **Penmaenpool** (SH6918.1/1B). *The shed was demolished at some stage between 1980 & 1982.*

DENBIGH

P.201 **Croes Newydd** (SJ3250.1/1B). *The shed was demolished in 1975.*

ANGLESEY

P.202 **Holyhead** (SH2481.2/1B). *The building was demolished in 1989 and replaced by a small 1TS diesel servicing shed (SH2482.2A) at the north end of the yard.*

APPENDIX

Throughout this volume the more well known railway companies are identified merely by initials that are not expanded upon in the text. In order to assist those readers not totally familiar with these, a short list is reproduced below;

MR; *Midland Railway*
GNR; *Great Northern Railway*
LNWR or L&NWR; *London & North Western Railway*
LMS; *London Midland & Scottish Railway*
NSR; *North Staffordshire Railway*
MSLR or MS&LR; *Manchester, Sheffield & Lincolnshire Railway*
GCR; *Great Central Railway*
CLC; *Cheshire Lines Committee*
GWR; *Great Western Railway*
LNER; *London & North Eastern Railway*
LYR or L&YR; *Lancashire & Yorkshire Railway*
FR; *Furness Railway*
NER; *North Eastern Railway*
NBR; *North British Railway*
CR; *Caledonian Railway*
G&SWR; *Glasgow & South Western Railway*
HR; *Highland Railway*
GNofS; *Great North of Scotland Railway*

Abbreviations utilized occasionally and not expanded upon in the text are;
S&BR; *Slamannan & Borrowstounness Railway*
GP&GR; *Glasgow, Paisley & Greenock Railway*
SCR; *Scottish Central Railway*
EP&DR; *Edinburgh, Perth & Dundee Railway*

ERRATA
TO
VOLUME I

PLEASE NOTE
This section includes additional information received up to January 2000.

WILTSHIRE

Copy for **Grafton** *(P.44) should read ...*
A temporary shed was opened here by the Swindon, Marlborough & Andover Railway on May 2nd, 1882. It closed on February 5th, 1883.

HAMPSHIRE

Caption on map for **Lee on Solent** *(P.47) should read ..*
SU5600 Lee on Solent
Caption for **Ryde**, *3rd shed (P.57) should read ...*
Ryde (SR) SZ5991.2/2A

KENT

Site caption for **Slade Green** *(P.66) should read ...*
Site TQ5276.1; At Crayford Creek Junction, on the east side of the Dartford line, south of Slade Green Station.

SUSSEX

Caption on map for **Petworth** *(P.68) should read ...*
SU9719 Petworth

GREATER LONDON

Captions for **Victoria Station** *(P.87) should read ...*
Victoria Station (LCDR/GWR/SER) TQ2878.1/F1
Victoria Station (LB&SCR) TQ2878.2/F1
Victoria Station (LB&SCR) TQ2878.2/F2

Copy for **Kentish Town No.2** *(P.92) should read ...*
The building was modified in 1898 ...
Kentish Town No.2 (MR) TQ2885.1/2B
The south western corner of the shed was removed to allow for track reorganization and, following the removal of TQ2885.1/1A, it became known as No.1 Shed.

Captions for the **Westbourne Park** *depots on the map (P.93) should be interchanged.*

Captions for **Blackwall** *(P.99) should read ...*
Site TQ3880.1; On the south side of the line, west of Blackwall Station.
Blackwall (London & Blackwall) TQ3880.1/1A
Replaced by ...
Blackwall (GER) TQ3880.1/F1

Site caption for **Farringdon Street** *(P.99) should read .*
Site TQ3181.1; On the east side of the line, at the north end of Farringdon Street Station.

Caption for **Silvertown Goods** *(P.103) should read ...*
Site TQ4180.1; On the north side of the goods branch, at the west end of Silvertown Station.
Silvertown Goods Yard (GER) TQ4180.1/F1

P.84 **Feltham** (TQ1273.1/1A). *The repair shop was a 1TS building and not 2TS.*
P.94 **Norwood Junction** (TQ3468.1/1A). *The shed was 5TS not 6TS.*

GLOUCESTERSHIRE

Caption for **Chalford** *(P.111) should read ...*
Chalford (GWR) SO9002.1/1A

Site caption for **Cirencester Watermoor** *(P.112) should read ...*
Site SP0201.2; On the west side of Cirencester Watermoor Station.

NORFOLK

Site caption for **Foulsham** *(P.132) should read ...*
Site TG0224.1; On the south side of the line, west of Foulsham Station.

SHROPSHIRE

Site caption for **Snailbeach** *(P.149) should read ...*
Site SJ3702.1; At the Snailbeach Mine on the east side of the line, north of Snailbeach Station.

WEST MIDLANDS

Caption on map for **Bordesley** *(P.160) should read ...*
SP0985 Bordesley

BRECKNOCK

Captions for the **Brecon** *sheds on the map (P.192) should be interchanged.*

ADDENDA
TO
VOLUME 2

PLEASE NOTE
This section includes additional information received up to January 2000. Amendments and alterations are listed in county order and by page numbers.

NB. There was no additional information at hand prior to going to press.

UPDATE

As additional information comes to hand it will be published in

RAILWAY ·WORLD·

The new details will be printed in the same format as this publication and, in order to keep this volume up to date, readers are invited to cut out or photocopy the appropriate section and paste it on to this and subsequent pages:

Knott End Railway services commenced in December 1870 and had chequered fortunes up to the 1923 Grouping, when the little line came into the empire of the LMS. The new owners kept the passenger service going until March 31st, 1930 at which time the engine shed at **Garstang Town** (SD4945.1/1A) was closed. Six months after Grouping, 0-6-0ST *New Century* (HC1900), poses outside of the timber building.   *K. Hartley*

BIBLIOGRAPHY

To assist us in the compilation of this directory the following in-depth shed history books were consulted:

AN HISTORICAL SURVEY OF GREAT WESTERN ENGINE SHEDS 1947 by ET Lyons (ISBN 902888 16 1).
Oxford Publishing Company 1972.

AN HISTORICAL SURVEY OF GREAT WESTERN ENGINE SHEDS 1837-1947 by ET Lyons and E Mountford
(ISBN 86093 019X). Oxford Publishing Company 1979.

AN HISTORICAL SURVEY OF SOUTHERN SHEDS by Chris Hawkins & George Reeve (ISBN 86093 020 3).
Oxford Publishing Company 1979.

GREAT EASTERN RAILWAY ENGINE SHEDS by Chris Hawkins & George Reeve. Wild Swan Publications.
Part One: Stratford, Peterborough & Norwich Districts (ISBN 0 906867 40 1) 1986.
Part Two: Ipswich and Cambridge Districts (ISBN 0 906867 48 7) 1987.

GREAT NORTHERN RAILWAY ENGINE SHEDS by Roger Griffiths & John Hooper.
Volume 1: Southern Area (ISBN 1 871 608 07 4). Irwell Press 1989.
Volume 2: The Lincolnshire Loop, Nottinghamshire & Derbyshire (ISBN 1 899624 08 2). Challenger Publications 1996.

LMS ENGINE SHEDS by Chris Hawkins and George Reeve. Wild Swan Publications.
Volume 1: The L&NWR (ISBN 0 90687 02 9) 1981.
Volume 2: The Midland Railway (ISBN 0 90687 05 3) 1981.
Volume 3: The Lancashire & Yorkshire Railway (ISBN 0 90687 07 X) 1982.
Volume 4: The Smaller English Constituents (ISBN 0 90687 20 7) 1984.
Volume 5: The Caledonian Railway (ISBN 0 90687 56 8) 1987.

LMS ENGINE SHEDS by Chris Hawkins, George Reeve and James Stevenson. Irwell Press.
Volume 6: The Highland Railway (ISBN 1 871608 04 X) 1989.
Volume 7: The Glasgow & South Western Railway (ISBN 1 871608 10 4) 1990.

LONDON & SOUTH WESTERN RAILWAY ENGINE SHEDS by Chris Hawkins & George Reeve. Irwell Press.
Western District (ISBN 1 871608 11 2) 1990.

NORTH EASTERN LOCOMOTIVE SHEDS by Ken Hoole (ISBN 0 7153 5323 3) 1972. David & Charles.

Additional Information was gleaned from:
THE DIRECTORY OF BRITISH TRAMWAYS by Keith Turner (ISBN 1 85260 549 9) 1996. Patrick Stephens Ltd.

BR STEAM MOTIVE POWER DEPOTS by Paul Bolger. Ian Allan Ltd 1982-3
LMR (ISBN 0 7110 1019 6), ER (ISBN 0 7110 1193 1), SR, ScR (ISBN 0 7110 1248 2), NER (ISBN 0 7110 1362 4), WR (ISBN 0 7110 1311 X).

SHEDS IN CAMERA. Oxford Publishing Company 1983-89
LNER: by John Hooper (ISBN 0 86093 324 5).
LMS: by John Hooper (ISBN 0 86093 274 5).
GWR: by Roger Griffiths (ISBN 0 86093 385 7).
SR: by Roger Griffiths (ISBN 0 86093 415 2).

THE HANDBOOK OF BRITISH RAILWAYS STEAM MOTIVE POWER DEPOTS by Paul Smith. Platform 5.
Volume 1: Southern England (ISBN 0 906579 99 6) 1989.
Volume 2: Central England, East Anglia & Wales (ISBN 0 906579 95 3) 1989.
Volume 3: North Midlands, Lancashire & Yorkshire (ISBN 1 872524 05 2) 1990.
Volume 4: Northern England & Scotland (ISBN 1 872524 14 1) 1990.

BURTON DIESEL DEPOT [SK2322.1/3A] Abandoned and derelict on September 24th, 1987   *P Smith*

EPILOGUE

The 1960s saw the end of steam and the gradual provision of new or modernized and refurbished buildings to accommodate diesel and electric locomotives. Although this fleet was considerably smaller than that formerly required, a large number of depots remained throughout the system.

Almost immediately, a change in railway operations that was even more enormous than that that engulfed steam ensured that not only the smaller depots, such as at Burton were quickly closed but huge sheds like Eastfield, steeped in railway history and almost regarded as pivotal to locomotive working in Scotland, had by 2000 just vanished!